STUDY GUIDE
to accompany

Raven and Johnson

BIOLOGY

THIRD EDITION

Margaret Gould Burke
University of Mary

Ronald M. Taylor
Lansing Community College

 Mosby
Year Book

St. Louis   Baltimore   Boston   Chicago   London   Philadelphia   Sydney   Toronto

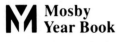

Mosby
Year Book

Dedicated to Publishing Excellence

Editor: Robert J. Callanan
Developmental Editor: Rhonda Lauck

Copyright © 1992 by Mosby-Year Book, Inc.
11830 Westline Industrial Drive
St. Louis, Missouri 63146

Printed in the United States of America

ISBN: 0-8016-6601-5

PREFACE

GETTING THE MOST OUT OF THIS STUDY GUIDE
AND YOUR STUDYING

Welcome to the world of introductory biology. It is a fascinating and exciting world, but one that can also seem overwhelming at times. This Study Guide is designed to help you appreciate the fascination and excitement, without being overwhelmed. By reading this preface you are taking a first and very important step toward helping yourself do as well as possible in your biological endeavors. In the next few pages we (the authors) will explain the philosophy behind the way we have written this Study Guide; will tell you (the student) what is in this Study Guide; and will tell you the best way to use the Study Guide.

This Study Guide was written specifically to accompany the third edition of Raven and Johnson's BIOLOGY. Just as the textbook has changed between the second and third editions, so too has the Study Guide. It has been rewritten and incorporates a format that uses the latest in learning techniques. We believe that working through this Study Guide will help you truly understand and master the material in each chapter, rather than having you memorize seemingly random facts.

Each chapter in the Raven and Johnson textbook has an accompanying chapter in this Study Guide. To help you organize and learn the new material, and relate it to what you have already learned and to the real world, each of our chapters follows a consistent format. We start off with a section called **In the Grand Scheme**. This sets the scene for you. It not only introduces the major concepts of the chapter, but also places them in perspective. It gives you the "big picture," and shows how the material in the chapter is a part of the entire world of biology and the life of living organisms.

In the Grand Scheme is followed by the section **For Review**. Each chapter in the Raven and Johnson textbook lists terms that have been introduced earlier and that are important for understanding the material presented in the new chapter. Our for Review section provides definitions and explanations for each of the terms listed in the textbook. It should help you appreciate the importance and applicability of these terms. It is also a good review to make sure you remember the definitions of the terms. The farther you go in your studies of biology, the more you will realize that the complexities of life and biology are built upon fundamental principles. The For Review section will help make sure that you have a strong foundation on which to build your increasing knowledge.

Next comes the **Chapter Outline**. Our outline of the textbook chapter has four tiers or levels. The first three tiers match the different levels of headings in the textbook chapter. The fourth tier is a "memory jogger" for you. It lists important concepts that are not covered in the first three tiers. it is designed to help the outline stand on its own as a complete reminder of the major emphases of the chapter. We have used the fourth tier sparingly so as not to overload the outline. Each of the four tiers of the outline is set apart by its indentation and pattern of capitalization. We have listed the textbook page numbers for each first tier, to help you more easily refer to these sections in the textbook.

After you have organized your thoughts and the material in the chapter by looking at the Chapter Outline, it is time to focus on the new vocabulary. This is done in the **Key Terms** section. Studying introductory biology is in many ways similar to studying a foreign language. You must know the vocabulary to be able to communicate. Before you can hope to understand all the concepts and how they relate to one another, you must first know what the words mean. We have listed the key terms in the sequence in which they are presented in the textbook to maintain the coherency of the material and the flow of ideas. This should help you remember the development of the various concepts much more easily than if the list of key terms was alphabetized. We have included in our Key Terms every word in the chapter that is in bold face type, as well as any others that we feel may be new and important to you. These words are taken from the figure captions and boxed essays as well as the text. We have provided the textbook page number for each term to help you in your studying.

The remaining four sections of the Study Guide chapter are designed to have you actively do something to help you test yourself and make sure you have mastered the material in the chapter. Active, rather than passive, learning is one of the guiding philosophies behind the way we have written this Study Guide. The more actively you are involved with this Study Guide the more likely you are to learn and retain the information. That is why we have you fill in charts, make drawings, label drawings, make lists, answer questions, and fill in the blanks. That is why we don't have you just passively read text summaries to yourself.

The first of these active sections is the **Topic Exercises**. These are two or three things to do that reinforce important concepts or topics in the chapter. The exact nature of each exercise varies with the different chapters, but they are all designed for you to actively draw, write, or match items; to use the knowledge you have acquired in the chapter. We have provided space in the Study Guide for many of these exercises; some will have to be done on separate sheets of paper.

The knowledge that we have of biology today, as represented in the pages of your textbook, exists because of the research conducted by scientists over the centuries. To help you remember the important people behind the science, many of the chapters have a section called **Who's Who**. This section requires you to complete the chart that is given by filling in names of the scientists or their contributions to biology.

The next active participation section in each chapter is the **Learning Checklist**. Here we ask you to answer specific questions or name specific items. This section focuses on the major concepts presented in the chapter and makes sure you can formulate a correct and complete response to short-answer type questions about the material. By asking you to write answers to questions, we are again asking you to actively participate in the learning process. This should help you much more than passively reading a list of open-ended learning objectives.

The final active section is the **Mini Exam**. This is your chance to test yourself to see if you have learned the material in the chapter. It provides excellent practice for your by presenting different types of questions that you are likely to encounter on your biology class exams. Practicing with the Mini Exam will not only let you know if you have learned the material thoroughly, but will also help you overcome test anxiety by practicing at your own speed and as often as you wish. Each Mini Exam begins with a selection of multiple choice questions. For each multiple choice question we have provided four or five answer choices; only one of them is correct. One of the most effective ways to study is to go through each question very carefully, asking yourself not only which is the correct answer, but also why is it right and the other choices wrong. This will help ensure that you really understand the material rather than just making a lucky guess. Each Mini Exam also has a group of fill-in-the-blank questions where you are asked to provide the appropriate term to complete each statement. The fill-ins require you to be able to recall and provide proper terminology, rather than simply recognizing the right term in a multiple choice format.

Many of the chapter Mini Exams also ask you to briefly answer one or a few short answer questions. These questions allow you to put the newly learned concepts into your own words and to apply your "textbook learning" to the "real world". They also serve as good practice for essay and written exams. We do not have separate true-false questions in the Mini Exam because we feel that the other question formats are more beneficial to you. If you can answer the Mini Exam questions you should not have trouble handling any true-false questions your biology instructor may give you on exams. Remember, each multiple choice question is essentially four or five true-false questions; you have to decide if each choice is true or false.

We close each chapter with the **Answers** for each of the questions asked in the Topic Exercises, Who's Who, Learning Checklist, and Mini Exam. This way you get immediate feedback on whether your answer is correct. We have also provided the textbook page references for the Learning Checklist and Short Answer answers in case you want to reread the appropriate material in the text.

Beside using this Study Guide, there are many other things you can do to help yourself do well in your biology course. First, go to class. Your instructor will help guide you and help you focus on what he or she considers to be the most important aspects of the material. If you could master everything on your own just by reading the textbook, colleges and universities wouldn't schedule lectures.

Second, keep up with the reading. Leaving it all until the weekend or night before the exam is foolish. It will prevent you from getting the most from the weekly lectures; it will put tremendous stress on you right before the exam; and it will probably result in poor grades.

Third, ask questions. Ask your instructor, your graduate teaching assistant, your classmates. If you have questions, ask. It is better to clear up any confusion as you go along. Remember, you are trying to build a solid foundation from the very beginning. A point you don't understand early in the semester may come back to haunt you later. You may not want to interrupt the instructor in the middle of the class to ask your question, but instructors and teaching assistants almost always have office hours. And they are usually thrilled to help students who have taken the initiative to help themselves.

Fourth, study actively, not passively. Don't just sit and read your textbook and lecture notes; do something active. Study with your classmates; make up and ask each other questions. Pretend you are the instructor and write your own exam to cover the material you have gone over; and then make sure you can answer all your questions.

Finally, if you are having a hard time learning all the vocabulary, you might want to make vocabulary flash cards. Each key term can be written on one side of an index card, and its definition on the other side of the card. You will then have a stack of cards for each chapter. You can go through the stack, looking at the word side and saying the definition, or vice versa, looking at the definition and saying the key term. You can drill yourself or classmates. When you know a particular cold, you can remove it from the stack and concentrate on the remaining ones that you are still uncertain about. The night before an exam you can quickly review the entire stack.

We hope this Preface has given you good ideas about how to enjoy biology and do well in your course. We also hope this Study Guide will prove to be a valuable aid to you in your learnings. We cannot predict exactly how your instructor will test you in your biology course, but by successfully working through each of the exercises in the Study Guide chapters, you will be well on your way toward mastering the material in Raven and Johnson's BIOLOGY. Your should check with your instructor, however, to make sure you understand the format of the exams that will be given to you and the level of detail tat you are expected to know. If you have comments on the Study Guide or suggestions on how it could be improved and made more useful to you, we would be happy to hear from you. Write to us care of the Biology Editor, College Division, Mosby-Year Book, Inc., 11830 Westline Industrial Drive, St. Louis, Missouri 63146.

In closing, we wish you good luck, excitement, and appreciation of life as you explore the world of biology!

Margaret Gould Burke
Ronald M. Taylor

Acknowledgement

We wish to give our sincere thanks for the fine editorial support we have received in writing this Study Guide; for the excellent clerical help of our typists and for the understanding of our families and friends while we became asocial creatures meeting writing deadlines.

TABLE OF CONTENTS

1: THE SCIENCE OF BIOLOGY

IN THE GRAND SCHEME

Biology is the scientific study of life. This is a neat and simple definition, but it covers a fascinating and diverse world. This textbook is an introduction to the world of biology, and in it you will learn what living organisms are made of, how they function, and how they have evolved and continue to do so. Our study of life will be a scientific one, following the scientific method of asking questions, collecting data, making and testing hypotheses, and formulating theories. All the information, hypotheses, and theories presented in this textbook have been derived by countless scientists following such procedures. Biological knowledge has been steadily built up and refined over hundreds of years. Today our biological knowledge is increasing at a phenomenal rate, and biology has assumed an ever more important role in all of our lives. Only through understanding biology can we hope to address and solve vital medical and ecological problems, for example, and help improve the quality of life for all organisms on this planet. We begin our study of biology by examining the theory of evolution by natural selection - what it says, the evidence on which Darwin based his theory, and how the theory has withstood the test of time. We start with this theory because it forms the foundation of modern biology.

CHAPTER OUTLINE

THE NATURE OF SCIENCE (pp. 3-7)
      inductive reasoning
  Testing Hypotheses
      experiments
  Controls
  The Importance of Prediction
  Theories
  The Scientific Method
HISTORY OF A BIOLOGICAL THEORY: DARWIN'S THEORY OF EVOLUTION (pp. 7-9)
      species change
DARWIN'S EVIDENCE (pp. 9-12)
  What Darwin Saw
      fossils
      geographic distributions
      oceanic islands
  Darwin and Malthus
  Natural Selection
      survival of the fittest
PUBLICATION OF DARWIN'S THEORY (p. 12)
EVOLUTION AFTER DARWIN: TESTING THE THEORY (pp. 12-14)
  The Fossil Record
  The Age of the Earth
  The Mechanism of Heredity
  Comparative Anatomy
  Molecular Biology
WHY IS BIOLOGY IMPORTANT TO YOU? (p. 14)
HOW THIS TEXT IS ORGANIZED TO HELP YOU LEARN BIOLOGY (pp. 14-18)

KEY TERMS

p. 3: biology, deductive reasoning, science, inductive reasoning
p. 4: hypothesis, experiment
p. 5: variable, control
p. 6: theories
p. 7: scientific method, evolution, immutable
p. 8: glyptodont
p. 9: endemic
p. 11: geometric progression, arithmetic progression, natural selection, artificial selection
p. 13: homologous, <u>Archaeopteryx</u>
p. 14: analogous
p. 18: cell biology, genetics, ecology

TOPIC EXERCISES

1. Use the following four terms to complete a flowchart that diagrams the scientific method. Briefly explain how the method works. Terms: experiments, hypotheses, questions, theory. Flowchart: _____ --> _____ --> _____ --> _____.

2. It took Darwin many years to formulate his theory of evolution by natural selection, and he used many different pieces of evidence and ideas of different people in the process. Briefly describe the contribution made by each of the following to Darwin's thoughts:

Item	Contribution
fossils	
geographic distribution of species	
oceanic islands	

3. Explain Darwin's theory of evolution by natural selection in your own words.

WHO'S WHO

Complete the following chart:

Scientist	Contribution to Biology
Charles Darwin	a. _____
b. _____	contributed to Darwin's theory by suggesting populations grow geometrically but are limited by nature
Alfred Russel Wallace	c. _____
d. _____	contributed to Darwin's theory by proposing that the earth was very old and species had emerged and gone extinct throughout its history

LEARNING CHECKLIST

1. List the four major components of the scientific method and how they work. What role do controls play?
2. What was the common perception of species before and after Darwin formulated his theory of evolution?
3. List three things that Darwin saw during his 5-year voyage around the world that helped him later develop his theory of evolution.
4. Name three people that influenced Darwin and tell what they contributed to the development of his theory.
5. List five different types of evidence that exist today that have helped strengthen and support Darwin's theory.

MINI EXAM

A. Circle the letter of the one best answer for each question.

1. Darwin spent 5 years sailing around the world on the
   a. H.M.S. Species
   b. H.M.S. Beagle
   c. H.M.S. Evolution
   d. H.M.S. Tortoise

2. Darwin explained his theory of evolution in a book called
   a. On the Origin of Species
   b. The Principles of Population
   c. Survival of the Fittest
   d. Around the World in Eighty Days

3. Which of the following is not part of the scientific process?
   a. making predictions
   b. asking questions
   c. using creative insight
   d. proving theories are true
   e. collecting data

4. The study of the way individual traits are transmitted from one generation to the next is called
   a. ecology
   b. genetics
   c. cell biology
   d. homology
   e. analogy

5. Which of the following did not help Darwin formulate his theory of evolution?
   a. fossil evidence that species had changed over time
   b. closely related species on oceanic islands
   c. belief that the earth was approximately 4000 years old
   d. evidence of artificial selection in domestic animals
   e. all of the above did help Darwin

6. Structures that have the same evolutionary origin even though they may now have different structures or functions are said to be
   a. endemic
   b. analogous
   c. homologous
   d. immutable
   e. geometric

7. Where did Darwin observe closely related species of finches and closely related species of tortoises?
   a. the Galapagos Islands
   b. Tierro del Fuego, South America
   c. the Cape Verde Islands
   d. Australia
   e. England

8. Who wrote an essay on population growth that helped Darwin formulate his theory of evolution?
   a. Charles Lyell
   b. Eratosthenes
   c. Alfred Russel Wallace
   d. Thomas Malthus
   e. Karl Popper

9. Using general principles to analyze specific cases is called
   a. deductive reasoning
   b. inductive reasoning
   c. neutral selection
   d. artificial selection

10. Which of the following pairs are analogous structures?
    a. the front leg of a horse and a human arm
    b. the front leg of a frog and a bat wing
    c. the wing of a bird and a bat wing
    d. the front flipper of a porpoise and a human arm
    e. the wing of a bird and a butterfly wing

11. How old was Darwin when he began his voyage around the world?
    a. 5
    b. 22
    c. 30
    d. 59
    e. 75

12. Which of the following has provided direct fossil evidence of the evolutionary relationship between reptiles and birds?
    a. glyptodonts
    b. tortoises
    c. pigeons
    d. finches
    e. <u>Archaeopteryx</u>

13. Of the following biological levels of organization, which represents the smallest or lowest level?
    a. organs
    b. populations
    c. cells
    d. organisms
    e. biome

14. According to Darwin's theory of evolution
    a. all individuals have an equal chance of surviving and reproducing
    b. species are immutable
    c. tortoises are the modern descendents of glyptodonts
    d. all of the above
    e. none of the above

15. You are conducting an experiment to examine the influence of temperature on the rate at which a substance dissolves in water. You put 10 grams of sugar into 200 milliliters of water that is 5°C. Which of the following would be a possible control for this experiment?
    a. Put 20 grams of sugar into 200 milliliters of water that is 5°C.
    b. Put 10 grams of sugar into 400 milliliters of water that is 5°C.
    c. Put 10 grams of salt into 200 milliliters of water that is 40°C.
    d. Put 10 grams of sugar into 200 milliliters of water that is 20°C.
    e. Put 5 grams of sugar and 5 grams of salt into 200 milliliters of water that is 10°C.

B. Provide the appropriate term to complete each statement.

1. Hypotheses are tested by conducting _____.
2. The study of how organisms interact with their environment and with each other is called _____.
3. Biology is a science that uses _____ reasoning.
4. A _____ is a type of fossil armadillo that Darwin saw in South America.
5. Species that have evolved in a particular place and are unique to that area are said to be _____ to that area.
6. _____ structures have similar structure and function, but different evolutionary origins.
7. The numbers 3, 6, 9, 12, and 15 represent a(n) _____ progression.
8. Saying that species are _____ means that they do not change.
9. When dog breeders choose which individual dogs they will use as parents for the next litter and base this decision on the dogs' characteristics, they are carrying out _____ selection.
10. The scientific study of living organisms and how they have evolved is called _____.
11. In scientific experiments, each factor that influences a process is called a(n) _____.

C. Briefly answer each of the following questions.

1. Can a scientific theory ever be proved to be true?

2. Explain the statement "species evolve, but selection acts on individuals."

3. Why do you think biology is important?

CHAPTER 1 ANSWERS

TOPIC EXERCISES

1. Questions --> hypotheses --> experiments --> theory. A scientist asks questions about the world around him or her and formulates possible explanations to answer the questions and to explain what has been observed. Experiments are then performed to test the hypotheses. If the results do not support a hypothesis, the hypothesis is rejected and a new one is formulated. When a hypothesis has been tested many times and all the evidence supports it, it is considered to be a theory.

2. Fossils: exhibited progressive changes in characteristics over time and resembled living species, suggesting that species were not immutable but gradually change over time, living species arose from fossil species. Geographic distribution: different places with similar climates do not have the same species, evidence that species diversity is not caused strictly by climate diversity; closely related species tend to be found in the same general area, suggesting that organisms change gradually as they move from one area to another. Oceanic islands: often have unique endemic species closely related to each other but also resembling species on the nearest mainlands, suggesting that individuals from the mainland had colonized the islands and the isolated populations had gradually changed and evolved into new species over time.

3. Evolution is the process of species or populations changing over time, natural selection is the mechanism that causes the gradual changes. Individuals vary in their characteristics, and some individuals will have traits that make them more likely to survive and reproduce compared to other members of their population. They pass those "good" traits on to their offspring which in turn are more likely to reproduce and pass on the traits. Gradually, over many generations, the traits become more and more common in the population. This is how evolutionary change occurs and new species are formed with new characteristics: by differential survival and reproduction of individuals with different traits.

WHO'S WHO

a. formulated theory of evolution by natural selection.
b. Thomas Malthus
c. had similar ideas to Darwin's on evolution, stimulated Darwin to publish his ideas.
d. Charles Lyell

LEARNING CHECKLIST

1. Questions - scientists observe the world around them and ask questions about it; hypotheses - scientists formulate possible explanations to answer their questions and explain what they have observed; experiments - scientists test their hypotheses by conducting experiments to see if a particular hypothesis can be disproved (shown it is not the right explanation); theory - if a particular hypothesis has been tested many times and not disproved it is called a theory and assumed to be true although it is always subject to future revision. Control experiments allow researchers to determine how one particular variable influences a particular process. (pp. 3-7)

2. Before Darwin, most people believed that each species had been specially created by God and was unchangeable. After Darwin published his theory of evolution, people gradually accepted the idea that species change (i.e., they evolve). (pp. 7-8, 12)

3. Fossils, geographic distribution of species, species on oceanic islands (pp. 9-10)

4. Charles Lyell - earth is very old and species have been in flux over the ages; Thomas Malthus - populations grow geometrically but are limited by nature; Alfred Russel Wallace - similar ideas on evolution and natural selection, spurred Darwin to publish his ideas. (pp. 9, 11, 12)

5. An extensive fossil record; radioactive dating of the earth indicating it is approximately 4.5 billion years old; knowledge of the mechanisms of heredity; comparative anatomy of species; molecular biology, especially the biochemistry of genes (the genetic or hereditary material). (pp. 13-14)

MINI EXAM

A.
1. b	2. a	3. d	4. b	5. c	6. c
7. a	8. d	9. a	10. e	11. b	12. e
13. c	14. e	15. d			

B.
1. experiments	2. ecology	3. inductive
4. glyptodont	5. endemic	6. Analogous
7. arithmetic	8. immutable	9. artificial
10. biology	11. variable	

C. 1. No; as the textbook says, there is no absolute truth in science. A theory can be disproved if data from a legitimate experiment do not agree with the theory. But a theory can never be proved to be true because we can never perform all the possible experiments to test it. It is always possible in the future that someone will design an experiment that will provide new information that will require the theory to be revised or rejected. Theories represent our current best understanding, but are always open to revision and replacement. (pp. 3-7)

2. Evolution states that species change gradually over time. A single individual does not evolve; an individual does not change its genetic characteristics during the course of its life. But an individual <u>will</u> be acted on by selection. It will either survive, reproduce, and pass on its genetic traits to the next generation (selected for) or it will not survive or will not reproduce as much as other individuals (selected against). Because of the differential reproduction of individual members of a population, some traits get passed to the next generation in greater numbers than do other traits, and thus the overall nature of the population (what traits it has) changes with each generation. Over time the population can evolve into a new species. (pp. 7-14)

3. There is no single answer to this question; it is a personal opinion. Biology may be important to you for immediate and practical reasons, such as you need the course to graduate from college or you hope to have a career in some field of biology. On a more fundamental level, biology is important to everyone because we are living organisms and biology is the study of life. Only by understanding life can we hope to maintain it and improve its quality. (p. 14)

2: THE NATURE OF MOLECULES

IN THE GRAND SCHEME

Our study of life begins with an examination of chemistry because all living organisms are composed of chemicals, and all life processes follow chemical rules. All matter, living and nonliving, is made up of atoms. Atoms can interact by transferring or sharing electrons and forming molecules. Atoms and the bonds that hold them together contain energy; this energy is harnessed and utilized by the chemistry of life. The single most important molecule for life as we know it is water. Water's unique and vital properties are a direct consequence of its chemistry.

CHAPTER OUTLINE

KEY TERMS

p. 21:   atoms, electrons, nucleus, protons, neutrons, atomic number, atomic mass
p. 22:   isotopes, radioactive decay, radioactive, half-life, neutral atom, ions
p. 23:   orbital, energy, potential energy
p. 24:   oxidation, reduction, energy levels, shells
p. 25:   elements, periodic table, octet rule, rule of eight
p. 26:   molecules, compound, chemical bond, ionic bond, covalent bond
p. 27:   chemical reaction, diatomic

TOPIC EXERCISES

1.   Draw and label a picture of a carbon-12 atom and a carbon-14 atom. Your diagram should show energy levels, protons, neutrons, electrons, and the nucleus. List the atomic number and atomic mass of each atom.

2.   Use atomic diagrams to illustrate what happens to electrons when an ionic bond is formed and when a covalent bond is formed.

3.   Draw a drop of water containing five water molecules. Show the covalent bonds with solid lines and the hydrogen bonds with dotted lines. Use (+) and (-) signs to indicate the electronegativity of each atom.

LEARNING CHECKLIST

1.   Explain the structure of an atom using the following terms: proton, neutron, electron, nucleus, orbital, energy level.
2.   What single component determines the atomic number of an atom? What two components determine the atomic mass?
3.   Distinguish between isotopes and ions in terms of the relative numbers of their atomic components.
4.   What three major tendencies guide the interactions of all atoms?
5.   In what situations do you find ionic bonds, covalent bonds, and hydrogen bonds?
6.   What is lost or gained when a molecule is oxidized or reduced?
7.   What four elements are most abundant in living organisms? List four reasons why they are so abundant.
8.   Describe the molecular structure of water in terms of the arrangement of atoms and their electronegativity.
9.   List six biologically important properties of water.
10.   What determines the pH value of a substance? List the pH value of acids, bases, and neutral substances.
11.   How do buffers work, and why are they biologically important?

MINI EXAM

A. Circle the letter of the one best answer for each question.

1. Which chemical bond is the strongest?
    a. ionic bond   c. double covalent bond
    b. single covalent bond   d. hydrogen bond

2. Two isotopes of the same element differ in their number of
    a. protons   d. energy levels
    b. neutrons   e. bonds
    c. electrons

3. The atomic mass of an element is determined by its total number of
   a. orbitals
   b. electrons and protons
   c. electrons and neutrons
   d. protons and neutrons
   e. nuclei

4. Consider elements with the atomic numbers listed below. Assuming the atoms were neutral, which of them would be least chemically reactive?
   a. 1
   b. 8
   c. 16
   d. 4
   e. 10

5. The greater the energy of an electron,
   a. the closer it orbits to the nucleus
   b. the farther it orbits from the nucleus
   c. the greater the number of other electrons that can share its orbital
   d. the more likely it is to be transferred rather than shared

6. Which of the following pH values represents the greatest concentration of H^+ ions?
   a. 4
   b. 10
   c. 2
   d. 7
   e. 12

7. Which of the following pH values represents the strongest acid?
   a. 4
   b. 10
   c. 2
   d. 7
   e. 12

8. Of the following elements, which is the least common in living organisms?
   a. sodium
   b. oxygen
   c. hydrogen
   d. nitrogen
   e. carbon

9. In ionic bonds,
   a. electrons are shared unequally between atoms
   b. electrons are shared equally between atoms
   c. neutrons are transferred between atoms
   d. protons are shared equally between atoms
   e. electrons are transferred between atoms

10. Carbon-14 has a half-life of approximately
    a. 5600 years
    b. 5600 days
    c. 5600 centuries
    d. 600 years
    e. 5000 years

11. The chemical properties of an atom are primarily determined by the number of
    a. neutrons it has in its nucleus
    b. isotopes it forms
    c. protons it has in its nucleus
    d. energy levels it has
    e. electrons it has in its outermost energy level

12. Hydrophobic interactions are exhibited by
    a. ions
    b. hydration shells
    c. polar molecules
    d. nonpolar molecules
    e. all of the above

13. Which of the following statements about water is false?
    a. water molecules are polar
    b. it takes very little heat to change the temperature of water
    c. all living organisms contain water
    d. ice is less dense than liquid water
    e. none; all these statements are true

14. During oxidation, molecules
    a. gain energy
    b. gain neutrons
    c. lose electrons
    d. lose carbon
    e. are converted to oxygen atoms

15. Dmitri Mendeleev
    a. created the periodic table
    b. discovered the first known isotope
    c. carried out the first oxidation reaction
    d. developed the pH scale
    e. discovered the structure of atoms

16. The maximum number of electrons that can be held in the K and L energy levels are
    a. 2 and 4, respectively
    b. 8 and 6, respectively
    c. 4 and 8, respectively
    d. 2 and 8, respectively
    e. 4 and 16, respectively

17. Potassium has an atomic number of 19. How many electrons are in the outermost energy level of a neutral potassium atom?
    a. 1
    b. 2
    c. 3
    d. 4
    e. 5

18. Which of the following pairs list atoms with the same chemical properties?
    a. ^{12}C and ^{13}C
    b. ^{8}O and ^{16}S
    c. ^{10}Ne and ^{18}Ar
    d. all of the above
    e. none of the above

19. Which of the following statements about orbitals is true?
    a. All orbitals have the same shape
    b. Orbitals pinpoint the exact location of electrons.
    c. s orbitals are dumbbell-shaped
    d. the K energy level contains both s and p orbitals
    e. none of the above

B. Provide the appropriate term to complete each statement.

   1. The cohesiveness and surface tension of water are caused by the _____ bonds between its molecules.
   2. The nucleus of an atom contains _____ and _____.
   3. In a neutral atom, the number of _____ equals the number of _____.
   4. A(n) _____ is a substance that prevents pH from fluctuating very much.

5. A covalent bond in which two pairs of electrons are shared between two atoms is called a(n) _____ bond.

6. _____ has a higher specific heat than water because it is more _____ than water.

7. An unstable isotope that tends to break up into elements with lower atomic numbers is called _____.

8. The _____ rule states that atoms tend to fill their outermost energy levels with the maximum number of electrons.

9. If a substance dissolves in water, it is said to be _____ in water.

C. Briefly answer each of the following questions.

1. If you dip the corner of a paper towel into a drop of water, why does the wet area spread along the paper towel?

2. For any particular element, which of the three subatomic particles (protons, neutrons, and electrons) is most constant? Explain.

3. Why does sweating cool us off?

CHAPTER 2 ANSWERS

TOPIC EXERCISES

1.

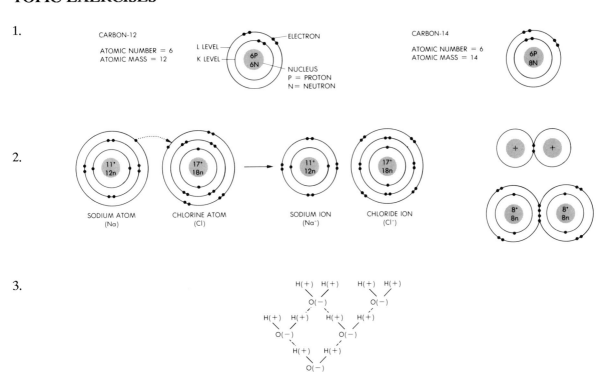

2.

3.

LEARNING CHECKLIST

1. An atom is composed of a central nucleus that contains protons and neutrons. Electrons circle around the nucleus in paths called orbitals. Each orbital is at a specific energy level; the further out an electron orbits, the higher the energy level. (p. 21, 23-24)

2. atomic number = the number of protons in the nucleus; atomic mass = the number of protons plus the number of neutrons in the nucleus. (p. 21)

3. Isotopes are atoms of the same element that have different numbers of neutrons (but the same number of protons) in their nuclei. Ions are atoms that are not neutral; the number of electrons does not equal the number of protons, so the atom carries a positive or negative charge, depending on whether the protons outnumber the electrons or vice versa. (pp. 21-23)

4. (a) tendency for electrons to occur in pairs
    (b) tendency for atoms to balance positive and negative charges
    (c) tendency for atoms to completely fill their outer energy level (pp. 23-25)

5. Ionic bonds occur when one or two electrons are transferred from one atom to another. The resulting ions are attracted to each other because of their opposite charges. Covalent bonds occur when atoms are held together because they share electrons. Hydrogen bonds occur when the slightly positive H of a polar molecule (such as water) is attracted to a slightly negative atom of another polar molecule. (pp. 26-27, 31)

6. During oxidation, a molecule loses one or more electrons, and energy is released. During reduction, a molecule gains one or more electrons, and energy is stored in the molecule. (p. 24)

7. nitrogen (N), oxygen (O), carbon (C), hydrogen (H).
    (a) All form gases, could interact in early atmosphere and dissolve in early oceans on earth. (b) Can all form covalent bonds and thus molecules with each other. (c) Their chemical bonds can be broken. (d) Water is a major component of all living organisms, thus H and O are abundant. (p. 28)

8. One O atom forms a single covalent bond with two H atoms. The H form bond angles of 104.5 degrees with the O. The O has a greater electronegativity than the H, so it attracts the shared electrons more. As a result, the water molecule is polar, with the oxygen end being slightly negative and the H ends being slightly positive. (pp. 30-31)

9. (a) It is polar. (b) It clings to other polar molecules. (c) It stores heat. (d) It is a strong solvent. (e) It organizes or excludes nonpolar molecules. (f) It ionizes. (pp. 30-36)

10. pH is determined by the H^+ concentration; the lower the pH value, the greater the H^+ concentration because pH is defined as the negative logarithm of H^+ concentration. pH < 7 = an acid, pH = 7 is neutral, pH > 7 = a base. (pp. 34-36)

11. Buffers prevent pH from fluctuating drastically by taking up or releasing H^+ ions as needed. They are biologically important because most living cells and biologically important molecules are sensitive to pH changes and can only function properly within a narrow pH range. (p. 36)

14

MINI EXAM

A. 1. c 2. b 3. d 4. e 5. b 6. c
    7. c 8. a 9. e 10. a 11. e 12. d
    13. b 14. c 15. a 16. d 17. a 18. d
    19. e

B. 1. hydrogen 2. protons, neutrons 3. protons, electrons
    4. buffer 5. double 6. ammonia, polar
    7. radioactive 8. octet 9. soluble

C. 1. The polar water molecules are attracted to and adhere to the polar paper towel molecules. As the water molecules are pulled along the paper towel, they bring other water molecules along with them because of the cohesion between them. The cohesion is caused by hydrogen bonds. (pp. 31-32)

   2 Protons. Different atoms of the same element can differ in the number of neutrons they have, as in the case of isotopes, or in the number of electrons they have, as in the case of neutral versus positive or negative ions. But if you change the number of protons, you have a different element. (pp. 21-22)

   3. When we sweat, water evaporates from our bodies. It takes energy to make water evaporate, so sweating is a way of using up or getting rid of excess heat energy. We get rid of 586 calories of heat with every gram of water that evaporates from our bodies. (p. 33)

3: THE CHEMICAL BUILDING BLOCKS OF LIFE

IN THE GRAND SCHEME

In the previous chapter we learned that all matter is composed of atoms. The atoms of living organisms are arranged into large, complex macromolecules. Life is built upon these macromolecules. They store energy for later use, form membranes, provide structural support, help control chemical reactions within the organism, and store the hereditary information that is used to direct every aspect of the organism's life and is passed on to the next generation. The four major categories of macromolecules are carbohydrates, lipids, proteins, and nucleic acids.

FOR REVIEW

Hydrophobic interactions: Nonpolar molecules tend to bond or clump together in water solutions because the polar water molecules form hydrogen bonds among themselves and exclude or push aside the nonpolar molecules. This forcing together of nonpolar molecules contributes to the shapes of biologically important molecules such as phospholipids and proteins.

Reduced carbon compounds: Carbon has an atomic number of 6 and has four electrons in its outer energy level. It thus tends to form covalent bonds with other atoms so that four pairs of electrons are shared and its outer energy level is filled. As the carbon gains these shared electrons, it is reduced. Organic molecules, the molecules of living organisms, are built by carbon bonding to other atoms, especially hydrogen, oxygen and other carbon.

Covalent bonds: In a covalent bond, electrons are shared between two atoms. Carbon, the backbone of all organic molecules, forms four covalent bonds. Covalent bonds represent stored energy: forming a molecule with covalent bonds is a way of storing energy; breaking covalent bonds is a way of releasing energy that can be used to perform some work. Covalent bonds are strong enough that they do not break easily and thus organisms don't fall apart spontaneously.

CHAPTER OUTLINE

THE BUILDING BLOCKS OF ORGANISMS (pp. 40-42)
    functional groups
  Building Macromolecules
  dehydration and hydrolysis reactions
CARBOHYDRATES (pp.42-47)
  Sugars are Simple Carbohydrates
    glucose
  Transport Disaccharides
  Starches are Chains of Sugars
  Cellulose is a Starch that is Hard to Digest
LIPIDS (pp. 47-50)
  Fats
    glycerol
    fatty acids
  There are Many Other Kinds of Lipids
    phospholipids
    prostaglandins

PROTEINS (pp. 50-56)
   Amino Acids are the Building Blocks of Protein
   Polypeptides are Chains of Amino Acids
      structures
NUCLEIC ACIDS (pp. 56-59)
      nucleotides
   DNA
   RNA
   Which Came First, DNA or RNA?

KEY TERMS

p. 40:   macromolecules, organic molecules, functional groups, hydroxyl group, kinases, polymer
p. 41:   dehydration reaction
p. 42:   catalysis, enzymes, hydrolysis reaction, carbohydrates, empirical formula, monosaccharides
p. 43:   glucose, structural isomers
p. 44:   stereoisomers, disaccharide,
p. 45:   maltose, sucrose, lactose, polysaccharides, starches, amylose, amylopectin, pectins
p. 46:   glycogen, cellulose,
p. 47:   chitin, fats, lipids, glycerol, fatty acids
p. 48:   triglyceride, saturated fatty acids, unsaturated fatty acids, polyunsaturated fats, oil, oleic acid, linoleic acid
p. 49:   phospholipid, lipid bilayer, steroids
p. 50:   terpenes, prostaglandins, proteins, enzymes, peptides
p. 51:   amino acid, amino group
p. 53:   peptide bond
p. 54:   polypeptides, primary structure
p. 55:   secondary structure, tertiary structure, quaternary structure, disulfide bridges, denaturation
p. 56:   globular proteins, fibrous proteins, nucleic acids, deoxyribonucleic acid (DNA), ribonucleic acid (RNA), nucleotides, phosphodiester bond
p. 57:   adenine (A), guanine (G), purines, cytosine (C), thymine (T), uracil (U), pyrimidines, helix, double helix
p. 58:   scanning-tunneling microscope

TOPIC EXERCISES

1. Complete the following chart pertaining to macromolecules:

Molecule	Subunits	Function	Examples
Disaccharides	a.	b.	Lactose, sucrose
c.	d.	Energy storage	Glycogen, pectin
e.	f.	Structural	Cellulose
Fats	g.	h.	Cooking oils
i.	Amino acids	j.	Enzymes
k.	Amino acids	Movement	Muscles
l.	m.	Contain hereditary information	DNA, RNA

2. Match the following numbers with the appropriate statement. A number may be used more than once.

Numbers: 0, 1, 2, 3, 4, 5, 6, 12, 20

Statements:
_____ a. the number of different nitrogenous bases in DNA
_____ b. the number of carbon atoms in a glucose molecule
_____ c. the number of fatty acids in a molecule of fat
_____ d. the number of different chemical classes of amino acids
_____ e. the number of chains of nucleotides in a DNA molecule
_____ f. the number of glycerols in a molecule of fat
_____ g. the number of hydrogen atoms in a glucose molecule
_____ h. the number of different nitrogenous bases in RNA
_____ i. the number of simple sugars in a disaccharide
_____ j. the number of carbon-carbon double bonds in a saturated fatty acid
_____ k. the number of oxygen atoms in a glucose molecule
_____ l. the number of different amino acids found in proteins
_____ m. the number of chains of nucleotides in most RNA molecules

LEARNING CHECKLIST

1.   How are dehydration and hydrolysis reactions related to constructing or breaking apart macromolecules?
2.   List the building block unit of carbohydrates, the type of carbohydrates used for short-term energy storage, for long-term energy storage, for transport, and for structural purposes.
3.   List the two building blocks of fats. Why are fats energy rich?
4.   Besides fats, what are four other types of biologically important lipids?
5.   What is the building block unit of proteins? How do these building blocks differ from each other?
6.   Distinguish between the primary, secondary, tertiary, and quaternary structures of proteins.
7.   What is the building block unit of nucleic acids? Of what three subunits are each of these building blocks themselves composed?
8.   List three structural differences and one functional difference between DNA and RNA.

MINI EXAM

A. Circle the letter of the one best answer for each question.

1. The functional group $-NH_2$ is a(n)
   a. carboxyl group
   b. amino group
   c. hydroxyl group
   d. phosphate group
   e. carbonyl group

2. Which of the following is not a lipid?
   a. chitin
   b. terpenes
   c. steroids
   d. prostaglandins
   e. unsaturated fat

3. Glucose is a
   a. protein
   b. disaccharide
   c. nucleic acid
   d. monosaccharide
   e. starch

4. Double helix describes the structure of a molecule of
   a. protein
   b. disaccharide
   c. starch
   d. monosaccharide
   e. DNA

5. Triglycerides contain fatty acids and
   a. glucose
   b. glycogen
   c. glycerol
   d. guanine
   e. an amino group

6. Animals store glucose in the form of
   a. amylose
   b. glycogen
   c. glycerol
   d. guanine
   e. cellulose

7. What is the yield of chemical energy, on average, for every gram of carbohydrate and every gram of fat that is utilized?
   a. 4 kcal each
   b. 9 kcal each
   c. 40 kcal and 90 kcal, respectively
   d. 90 kcal and 40 kcal, respectively
   e. none of the above

8. In the formation of a macromolecule, what type of bond would join two amino acid subunits?
   a. ionic bond
   b. phosphodiester bond
   c. hydrogen bond
   d. peptide bond

9. In the formation of a macromolecule, what type of reaction would join two subunits together?
   a. hydrophobic reaction
   b. hydrolysis reaction
   c. dehydration reaction
   d. denaturation reaction

10. The sequence of amino acids in a polypeptide is called the
    a. primary structure
    b. secondary structure
    c. tertiary structure
    d. quaternary structure

11. The globular shape of a protein is called the
    a. primary structure
    b. secondary structure
    c. tertiary structure
    d. quaternary structure

12. In a DNA molecule, what holds nitrogenous bases together from one polymer chain to the other?
    a. phosphodiester bonds
    b. ionic bonds
    c. disulfide bridges
    d. peptide bonds
    e. hydrogen bonds

13. Assuming they all had the same number of carbon atoms, which of the following has the most C-H bonds?
    a. an unsaturated fat
    b. a polyunsaturated fat
    c. a polysaccharide
    d. a saturated fat

14. Why is cellulose so difficult for most animals to digest?
    a. they don't have the proper enzyme to break the bonds between subunits
    b. cellulose is made up of chitin, which is indigestible
    c. the bonds holding cellulose subunits together are extremely strong, stronger than in any other macromolecule
    d. there are many hydrogen bonds holding the subunits together

15. What happens during a hydrolysis reaction?
    a. protein coils into its secondary structure
    b. the bond between two subunits of a macromolecule is broken
    c. saturated fats become unsaturated
    d. a bond is formed between two subunits of a macromolecule
    e. water breaks ionic bonds

16. Which of the following is not a disaccharide?
    a. sucrose   d. amylose
    b. maltose   e. all of the above are disaccharides
    c. lactose

17. The general term for a large molecule made up of many similar subunits is
    a. polymer   d. helix
    b. functional group   e. kinase
    c. peptide

18. Dehydration and hydrolysis reactions involve removing or adding _____ to macromolecule subunits.
    a. C and O   d. COOH and H
    b. CH and NH_2 e. OH and H
    c. C and H

19. The empirical formula for carbohydrate is
    a. $(CHO)_2$ d. $(C_2HO)_n$
    b. $(CH_2O)_n$ e. $(C_nH_nO_n)_2$
    c. $2(CHO)_n$

20. Which of the following nitrogenous bases is found in DNA but is not found in RNA?
    a. adenine   d. thymine
    b. guanine   e. uracil
    c. cytosine

21. What type of macromolecule carries out catalysis in biological systems?
    a. proteins called enzymes
    b. carbohydrates called starches
    c. lipids called steroids
    d. nucleic acids called DNA
    e. carbohydrates called sugars

22. In nucleic acids, the purine nitrogenous bases are
    a. uracil and thymine   d. adenine and guanine
    b. cytosine and guanine   e. guanine and thymine
    c. thymine and cytosine

B. Provide the appropriate term to complete each statement.

1. _____ have the same empirical formulas but different molecular or bond structures.
2. The most abundant protein in your body is collagen which is a type of _____ protein.
3. Cell membranes are made up of phospholipids arranged in a(n) _____.
4. Groups of atoms that have specific chemical properties, are parts of molecules, and participate in chemical reactions are called _____.
5. _____ amino acids have side groups that contain an organic ring with alternating single and double bonds.
6. _____ refers to a protein losing its three dimensional structure.
7. Hereditary information is stored in macromolecules called _____.

C. Briefly answer each of the following questions.

1. The double helix structure of DNA has been compared to a spiral staircase. What makes up the sides of the staircase and what the steps? What holds these parts together?

2. How do the side groups of amino acids determine the structures of proteins?

CHAPTER 3 ANSWERS

TOPIC EXERCISES

1.
   a. monosaccharides
   d. monosaccharides
   g. glycerol and 3 fatty acids
   j. catalysis
   m. nucleotides

   b. transport
   e. polysaccharide
   h. energy storage
   k. proteins

   c. starches
   f. monosaccharides
   i. proteins
   l. nucleic acid

2.
   a. 4   b. 6   c. 3   d. 5   e. 2   f. 1
   g. 12   h. 4   i. 2   j. 0   k. 6   l. 20
   m. 1

LEARNING CHECKLIST

1. Subunits are joined together to form a macromolecule by dehydration reactions; an OH group is pulled off of one subunit, an H is pulled off another, and then the two subunits are joined by a covalent bond. Macromolecules are broken apart into their constituent subunits by hydrolysis reactions; the covalent bond between two subunits is broken, and an OH is added to one of the subunits, H to the other (pp. 41-42)

2. Simple sugars (monosaccharides) are the building blocks. Short-term energy storage = monosaccharides; long-term energy storage = polysaccharides called starches; transport = disaccharides; structural = polysaccharides such as cellulose and chitin. (pp. 42-47)

3. Each molecule of fat contains three fatty acids bound to one glycerol. Fats are energy rich and thus very efficient at storing energy because of the large number of C-H bonds contained in the fatty acids. C-H bonds represent stored energy, and fats have many more of them than do carbohydrates. (pp. 47-49)

4. phospholipids, steroids, terpenes, prostaglandins. (pp. 49-50)

5. Amino acids are the building blocks. Each amino acid has a central carbon atom with an amino group, a carboxyl group, a hydrogen atom, and a side group attached to it. Each amino acid has its own unique side group that confers upon it specific chemical properties. (pp. 51-53)

6. Primary structure = the particular sequence of amino acids that makes up a polypeptide; secondary structure = the folds or coils that occur in the polypeptide caused by the stiffness of the peptide bond and hydrogen bonding between nearby amino acids; tertiary structure = the complex globular shape of some proteins caused by hydrophobic interactions; quaternary structure = the structure assumed by two or more polypeptide chains in forming one protein molecule. (pp. 54-55)

7.   Building blocks = nucleotides. Each nucleotide consists of a 5-carbon sugar, a phosphate group, and a nitrogenous base. (p. 56)

8.   Structural differences: (a) they contain different sugars (RNA = ribose, DNA = deoxyribose); (b) DNA has the bases adenine (A), guanine (G), cytosine (C), and thymine (T), whereas RNA has A, G, C, and uracil(U); (c) DNA is double-stranded (two chains of nucleotides), RNA is single-stranded. Functional differences: DNA serves as the master plan for storing the hereditary information; RNA is the working copy - it is formed from the DNA master and is then used to specify the production of specific proteins. (pp. 57-59)

MINI EXAM

A.   1. b   2. a   3. d   4. e   5. c   6. b
        7. e   8. d   9. c   10. a   11. c   12. e
        13. d   14. a   15. b   16. d   17. a   18. e
        19. b   20. d   21. a   22. d

B.   1. Structural isomers   2. fibrous   3. lipid bilayer
        4. functional groups   5. Aromatic   6. Denaturation
        7. nucleic acids

C. 1.   The sides are made up of alternating phosphate groups and 5-carbon sugars, the steps are made of two nitrogenous bases. The bases are held together by hydrogen bonds. The phosphate group of one nucleotide is linked to the sugar of the next nucleotide by a phosphodiester bond. (pp. 56-57)

   2.   Each amino acid has a side group with its own particular chemical properties (e.g., nonpolar, polar, aromatic), and it is the side group that makes each amino acid unique. The sequence of amino acids (with their side groups) determines the primary structure of the polypeptide, and this in turn determines what sort of secondary and tertiary structures the polypeptides will have as nearby side groups interact with each other (e.g., forming hydrogen bonds, interacting hydrophobically, or forming disulfide bridges). (pp. 51-55)

4: THE ORIGIN AND EARLY HISTORY OF LIFE

IN THE GRAND SCHEME

As living organisms ourselves, we humans are fascinated by life and all its processes. Life is not a simple or clear-cut phenomenon; it is difficult to define precisely and essentially impossible to know for sure how it arose on our planet. We can describe the attributes of living organisms and reach an understanding of life, but there will still be gray areas (such as viruses) and even legal debates (such as when is a person no longer alive). We can also explore many theories on the origin of life on earth, but biology is a science and in our study of biology we are concerned with scientific explanations based on the best scientific data that are available. Life arose slowly as inanimate chemicals underwent reactions and gradually became more complex and accumulated in the oceans. Fossil and isotopic evidence indicates that true, cellular organisms existed on earth by about 3.5 billion years ago, when the planet was already about 1 billion years old. The original transition from nonliving, complex molecular aggregates to living prokaryotic cells was a gradual one, and the continued evolution and diversification of life into all the forms that exist on earth today have also been gradual. Conditions that led to the initial origin of life on earth no longer exist here; today, all life on earth comes from already existing life, not from inanimate chemicals.

FOR REVIEW

Oxidation and reduction: Oxidation involves the removal of electrons from a molecule, reduction involves the addition of electrons to a molecule. The electrons contain energy, so removing or adding electrons also removes or adds energy to the molecule. The atmosphere around the early earth was a reducing one, making it relatively easy for complex, energy-rich organic molecules to form as hydrogen protons and accompanying electrons were added to carbon and other atoms. In today's oxidizing atmosphere, the spontaneous evolution of life from simple inanimate chemicals is no longer possible.

Covalent bonds: Covalent bonds are formed when one or more pairs of electrons are shared between two atoms. The chemistry of life is based on organic molecules, and organic molecules are built on a backbone of carbon. Each carbon atom forms four covalent bonds with other atoms. Life arose on earth as atoms formed covalent bonds with each other and complex organic molecules were formed.

Proteins: Proteins are vital components of living organisms. They play structural roles and control chemical reaction rates. They are made up of chains of amino acids. With the formation of amino acids and then proteins in the "primeval soup" of the early oceans, one of the key ingredients of living organisms was present and helped lead to the evolution of life.

Nucleic acids: DNA and RNA are the two types of nucleic acids. Hereditary information is stored in DNA as a sequence of nucleotides. RNA is the "working copy" nucleic acid that is responsible for the production of particular proteins based on the hereditary information it is carrying from the DNA. Recent experiments have shown that RNA may have been one of the first macromolecules to form during the evolution of life. A hereditary system is a prerequisite for all living organisms.

CHAPTER OUTLINE

THE ORIGIN OF ORGANIC MOLECULES (pp. 62-65)
    reducing atmosphere
NATURE OF LIFE PROCESSES (pp. 65-68)
ORIGIN OF THE FIRST CELLS (pp. 68-69)
    coacervates and microspheres

THE EARLIEST CELLS (pp. 70-71)
    Living Fossils
        unusual bacteria
    Methane Producing Bacteria
        anaerobic
    Photosynthetic Bacteria
        oxygen production
    The Origin of Modern Bacteria
THE APPEARANCE OF EUKARYOTIC CELLS (pp. 71-72)
IS THERE LIFE ON OTHER WORLDS? (pp. 72-74)

KEY TERMS

p. 62:   Hadean times, geochemists
p. 63:   reducing atmosphere, oxidizing atmosphere, ultraviolet radiation, ozone
p. 66:   life
p. 67:   cells, metabolism, photosynthesis, coacervates
p. 68:   protocells, microspheres
p. 69:   prevital, kaolinite
p. 70:   prokaryotes, nucleus, organelle, eukaryotic, bacteria, anaerobically
p. 71:   cyanobacteria

TOPIC EXERCISES

1. For each of the following dates, list the major event in the evolution of life on earth that is believed to have occurred then.
    a. 4.5 billion years ago
    b. 3.5 billion years ago
    c. at least 3 billion years ago
    d. about 1.5 billion years ago

2. For each of the following pairs of events, circle the member of the pair that appeared first on the earth.
    a. prokaryotes, coacervates
    b. reducing atmosphere, oxidizing atmosphere
    c. eukaryotes, prokaryotes
    d. unicellular organisms, multicellular organisms

WHO'S WHO

Complete the following chart:

Scientist	Contribution to Biology
Miller & Urey	a. _____
b. _____	Proposed theory that first protocells were coacervates
Fox	c. _____

Scientist	Contribution to Biology

d. _____   Proposed theory that first macromolecule was RNA, because RNA can act as an enzyme, assembling new RNA molecules from an RNA template

LEARNING CHECKLIST

1. Why do biologists study evolution rather than other explanations of the origin of life on earth?
2. What are the four fundamental properties of all living organisms? What other two characteristics are common to most living organisms?
3. Briefly describe what conditions were like on the early earth with regard to the atmosphere and the availability of energy and water.
4. Name two types of organic molecules that were formed during the Miller-Urey experiments.
5. Describe the process of chemical evolution that led to the appearance of the first true cells - and thus life - on earth.
6. List in chronological sequence (starting with the first to appear on earth), two major types of prokaryotes that lived during ancient times for which we have evidence of their existence.
7. What is one major difference between prokaryotes and eukaryotes as indicated by their names?
8. Is it likely that life exists elsewhere in the universe?

MINI EXAM

A. Circle the letter of the one best answer for each question.

1. Which of the following organisms alive today is likely to be most similar to the first life forms that evolved on the earth?
   a. methane-producing bacteria   d. dinosaurs
   b. cyanobacteria   e. humans
   c. algae

2. Which of the following gases is <u>least</u> likely to have existed in the early atmosphere of the earth?
   a. NH_3 d. H_2O
   b. CO_2 e. O_2
   c. N_2

3. Clays may have played an important role in the origin of life by providing
   a. sources of energy for the newly formed organisms
   b. shelter from ultraviolet radiation
   c. sources of methane for the first bacteria
   d. sites for the aggregation of amino acids and thus formation of proteins
   e. the minerals necessary for the formation of the complex organic molecules of heredity

4. How old is the earth?
   a. 4.5 billion years old   d. 1.5 billion years old
   b. 3.5 billion years old   e. 0.5 billion years old
   c. 2.5 billion years old

5. How long did the earth exist before life appeared on it?
   a. 4.5 billion years
   b. 2.7 billion years
   c. 1 billion years
   d. 1 million years
   e. 3 thousand years

6. Which of the following was not a source of energy on the early earth?
   a. lightning
   b. ozone
   c. ultraviolet radiation
   d. volcanic eruptions
   e. soil radioactivity

7. How long have bacteria lived on the earth?
   a. 4.5 billion years
   b. 3.5 billion years
   c. 2.5 billion years
   d. 1.5 billion years

8. Within our own solar system, the most likely candidate for having life on it is
   a. our moon
   b. Jupiter
   c. Venus
   d. SETI
   e. Europa, a moon of Jupiter

9. The oldest fossils found so far date back to the
   a. Cambrian Period
   b. Archean Era
   c. Phanerozoic Era
   d. Proterozoic Era

10. Multicellular fossils appear at the beginning of the
   a. Proterozoic Era
   b. Precambrian Period
   c. Archean Era
   d. Phanerozoic Era
   e. Cambrian Period

11. Which of the following traits evolved last (i.e., most recently)?
   a. prokaryotic cells
   b. eukaryotic cells
   c. multicellularity
   d. photosynthesis
   e. heredity

12. Approximately what percentage of today's atmosphere is oxygen?
   a. 21%
   b. 73%
   c. <1%
   d. 50%
   e. 13%

13. What gas in today's atmosphere shields us from ultraviolet radiation?
   a. ozone
   b. nitrogen
   c. oxygen
   d. carbon dioxide
   e. carbon monoxide

14. Miller and Urey's experiments proved that
   a. life evolved on earth from inanimate chemicals
   b. coacervates were the first type of protocells
   c. complex organic molecules can form spontaneously under conditions that probably existed on the early earth
   d. RNA can act as an enzyme and assemble new RNA molecules from RNA templates
   e. bacteria were the first type of living organism to appear on the earth

15. Which of the following is <u>not</u> a characteristic of all living organisms?
    a. reproduction
    b. heredity
    c. metabolism
    d. movement from place to place
    e. all of the above <u>are</u> characteristic of all living organisms

16. Which of the following is <u>not</u> found in a lipid coacervate droplet or a proteinoid microsphere?
    a. the ability to grow
    b. a nucleus
    c. a two layer boundary
    d. division by pinching in two
    e. the ability to carry out chemical reactions

17. The Miller-Urey experiments yielded
    a. urea
    b. hydrogen cyanide
    c. amino acids
    d. all of the above
    e. none of the above

18. What did Miller and Urey use as a source of energy in their experiments?
    a. lightning
    b. UV light
    c. an electrical spark
    d. radioactivity
    e. volcanoes

19. The oxygen that is present in our atmosphere comes primarily from the
    a. eruption of volcanoes
    b. breakdown of ozone
    c. breathing of animals
    d. plants, algae, and bacteria
    e. none of the above

20. Amino acids make up approximately what percentage of the dry weight of each cell in your body?
    a. 100%
    b. 50%
    c. 25%
    d. 5%
    e. 1%

21. Which of the following has been proposed as a type of protocell?
    a. coacervate
    b. microsphere
    c. both of the above
    d. none of the above

22. According to the scientific theory of the origin of life on earth, life arose spontaneously from inanimate chemicals. Do scientists think this process is still going on on our planet today?
    a. yes, it probably is
    b. no, because conditions on earth have changed and are no longer conducive to spontaneous evolution of life

23. Which of the following criteria is necessary and sufficient to define life?
    a. movement
    b. sensitivity
    c. complexity
    d. all of the above
    e. none of the above

24. Which of the following possible explanations of the origin of life on earth allows testable hypotheses to be constructed?
    a. evolution
    b. special creation
    c. extraterrestrial origin
    d. all of the above
    e. none of the above

B. Provide the appropriate term to complete each statement.

1. Today's atmosphere on earth is a(n)_____ one.
2. Another name for prokaryotes is _____.
3. The processes by which all living organisms assimilate energy and use it to grow is called _____.
4. _____ is a term meaning that oxygen is not present or is not used.
5. Silicate clays such as _____ may have played an important role in the origin of life because of their large, internal surface area and chemical properties.
6. The building blocks of all organisms are _____, which are complex organized assemblages of molecules enclosed within membranes.

C. Briefly answer each of the following questions.

1. Why was the evolution of aerobic photosynthesis so important to the history of life on this planet?
2. Do you think life exists elsewhere in the universe? Why or why not?

CHAPTER 4 ANSWERS

TOPIC EXERCISES

1. a. formation of earth
    b. evolution of first life - anaerobic prokaryotic cells
    c. evolution of photosynthetic prokaryotes - oxygen-producing cyanobacteria
    d. evolution of unicellular eukaryotes

2. a. coacervates
    b. reducing atmosphere
    c. prokaryotes
    d. unicellular organisms

WHO'S WHO

    a. demonstrated that simple and complex organic molecules could form from inorganics and an energy source, under conditions thought to have existed on the early earth
    b. Oparin
    c. proposed theory that first protocells were proteinoid microspheres
    d. Cech

LEARNING CHECKLIST

1. Because biology is a science and biologists are scientists. They are interested in a scientific explanation, one that allows hypotheses to be developed and tested and that deals with data that can be obtained and examined. Explanations based on faith with no material evidence is beyond the scope of science and biology. (p. 62)

2.   cellular organization, growth and metabolism, reproduction, and heredity; movement and sensitivity to stimuli. (pp. 66-68)

3.   The atmosphere was a reducing one with little or no O_2. There were tremendous amounts of energy available from solar (ultraviolet) radiation, lightning, volcanic eruptions, heat, and radioactivity. The atmosphere contained a lot of water vapor and oceans gradually formed as the earth cooled and the vapor condensed and fell as rain. (pp. 62-64)

4.   various types of amino acids, and adenine, one of the nitrogenous bases of nucleotides (pp. 64-65)

5.   Nobody knows the precise details, but organic molecules gradually became more complex as they formed new bonds with other atoms and molecules. This chemical evolution led to the formation of aggregates or clumps of molecules with many properties similar to cells. These protocells (i.e., lipid coacervates or proteinoid microspheres) continued to evolve. Ones that were stable and could grow and divide were selected for. At some point the macromolecules necessary for a system of heredity evolved, and the line from protocell to true cell was crossed. (pp. 68-69)

6.   anaerobic methane-producing bacteria; oxygen-producing photosynthetic cyanobacteria (pp. 70-71)

7.   prokaryotic cells lack a nucleus; eukaryotic cells have a nucleus ("karyon" in Greek means kernal or nucleus). (pp. 70, 72)

8.   yes (pp. 72-74)

MINI EXAM

A.   1. a   2. e   3. d   4. a   5. c   6. b
      7. b   8. e   9. b   10. d   11. c   12. a
      13. a   14. c   15. d   16. b   17. d   18. c
      19. d   20. b   21. c   22. b   23. e   24. a

B.   1. oxidizing   2. bacteria   3. metabolism
      4. Anaerobic   5. kaolinite   6. cells

C. 1. Organisms that carry out aerobic photosynthesis produce O_2 as a by-product and release it into the oceans and atmosphere. After the evolution of aerobic photosynthesis by bacteria such as cyanobacteria, O_2 began accumulating in the atmosphere. Eventually, the atmosphere changed from reducing to oxidizing. This meant that conditions were no longer conducive for the spontaneous evolution of more life from chemicals. It also meant that oxygen was now available to be utilized metabolically and that a protective layer of ozone could develop in the atmosphere and shield life on the earth from harmful UV radiation. (pp. 63, 70-71)

   2. The question asked for your personal opinion and as of yet we have no definite proof that life does exist on other worlds besides our own. However, considering the vast number of other stars and planets in the universe, the odds seem pretty good that some of them have conditions favorable for the evolution of life and that we are not alone. Of course, life forms elsewhere may be very different from life as we know it here on Earth. (pp. 72-74)

5: CELL STRUCTURE

IN THE GRAND SCHEME

Just as we do not know exactly when life began, we do not know exactly what shape it first assumed. We don't even know if it had a specific shape or was amorphous. Ultimately, however, life was packaged in structures we now call cells.

Even the simplest and smallest of cells must be able to communicate and cope with its environment to survive, grow and reproduce. It is awesome to contemplate that the tiny microscopic specks we call bacteria must perform all of the life functions. They can perform them so well that some can defeat our bodies defenses and cause considerable bodily harm -- even death. Yet, these bacteria are the simplest of cells. Because they are to simple, lacking even a nucleus, we call them Prokaryotes.

More complex cells including the ones making up our own bodies, are called Eukaryotes. The name is derived from the possession of nuclei to deal with life in general and the diversity cells display both a commonality and diversity of structures . Such commonality and diversity of structures by which cells perform remarkable feats is the substance of this chapter.

FOR REVIEW

Proteins: Proteins are long, unbranched chains of amino acids. Because of the variation of carbon chains attached to the central carbon of each amino acid, any change in the amino acid sequences imparts a different shape to the chain. The architecture of the molecule is also varied by folds of the chain in different planes.

Formation of lipid bilayers: Phospholipids are polar modified fats. One end (containing the glycerol) is hydrophilic. The fatty acid tails are hydrophobic. In water, such phospholipids tend to form two layered sheets with the hydrophobic ends to the inside and the hydrophilic ends facing outside toward the water.

Distinction between prokaryotic and eukaryotic cells: Eukaryotic DNA is packaged in membrane bound structures called nuclei which are lacking in prokaryotic cells. The interior of eukaryotic cells is compartmentalized by membranes whereas, compartmentalization is lacking in prokaryotic cells. Both prokaryotic and eukaryotic cells may have cell walls. However, prokaryotic cell walls are chemically complex, whereas those of eukaryotic cells are of cellulose.

Evolution of eukaryotes: The first eukaryotes were unicellular. The appearance of multicellular forms did not occur until hundreds of millions of years later.

CHAPTER OUTLINE

WHAT ARE CELLS LIKE? (pp. 79-80)
      Surrounding Membranes
      Nuclear Region
      Semifluid matrix
          cytoplasm
          organelles
MOST CELLS ARE VERY SMALL (pp. 80-83)
    The Cell Theory
        All organisms are composed of one or more cells
        Cells are the smallest living things
        Cells arise only by division of previous cells

KEY TERMS

p. 90:   rough ER, smooth ER
p. 91:   nucleus
p. 92:   nuclear envelope, nuclear pores, chromosomes, ribosome, ribosomal RNA, nucleoli
p. 93:   Golgi bodies, Golgi complex, glycoproteins
p. 94:   glycolipids, cisternae, microbodies, peroxisomes, glyoxysomes
p. 95:   lysosomes, primary lysosome, secondary lysosome, aerobic
p. 96:   oxidative metabolism, mitochondria, cristae, inner matrix, outer compartment
p. 97:   thylakoid, granum
p. 98:   leukoblast, amyloplast, plastid, microtubules, tubulin, basal body
p. 99:   cytoskeleton, polymerization, actin, tubulin, organizing centers
p. 100: vimentin, keratin
p. 101: flagella, 9 + 2 structure
p. 103: cilia

TOPIC EXERCISES

1. In the table below, compare eukaryotes with prokaryotes.

Topic	Eukaryotes	Prokaryotes
DNA Arrangement	yes	No
Interior Compartments	yes	No
Cell Walls	No	yes
Internal Sacs	yes	No

2. Below is a list of eukaryotic organelles. Beside each, list the organelle's function.

   a. nucleus   DNA

   b. endoplasmic reticulum   synthes cellular products

   c. Golgi bodies   Fed Ex collects/pkag sends cellular products

   d. lysosomes   degestive enzyme

   e. microbodies   metabolic enzyme

   f. mitochondria   oxidating metabolism

   g. chloroplasts   carries photosynt

   h. chromosomes   genetic/cellular info

   i. ribosomes   polypeptides

3. Components of the cytoskeleton differ in size, function and chemical composition. Compare them in the table below.

Topic	Size	Function	Composition
actin filaments	7 mm	all shape	
microtubules	25 mm	motor movement	
intermediate filaments	8-10 mm	structural	

WHO'S WHO IN BIOLOGY

a. first described cells   *Hooke*

b. first attributed cells to plants   *Schleiden*

c. first attributed cells to animals   *Schwann*

d. first observed living cells   *Leeuwenhoek*

e. first developed a stain used to distinguish two classes of bacteria   *Gram*

LEARNING CHECKLIST

1. What are the three principles of the cell theory?
2. List four ways in which eukaryotic cells differ from those of prokaryotes.
3. What is the function of the plasma membrane?
4. Describe the structure of the plasma membrane.
5. List the membrane bound structures associated with the endoplasmic reticulum.
6. Explain the importance of the nucleus and its components.
7. What is believed to be the origin of eukaryotic endosymbiotic organelles?
8. List the components of the cytoskeleton.
9. What functions are performed by components of the cytoskeleton and how do they relate to the nuclear envelope?

MINI-EXAM

A. Circle the letter of the one best answer for each question.

1. Cellular components found in both eukaryotic and prokaryotic cells include
   a. nuclear region, but not a plasma membrane
   b. cytoplasm, but one nucleoli
   c. cell walls, but not flagella
   d. organelles, but not a nucleus
   e. a plasma membrane, but not cytoplasm

2. The first living cells were observed by
   a. Hooke
   b. Schleiden
   c. Schwann
   d. Leeuwenhoek
   e. Gram

3. As a cell increases in size,
   a. volume increases more rapidly than surface area
   b. surface area increases more rapidly than volume
   c. volume increases at the same rate as surface area
   d. surface area will increase more than volume but the difference is insignificant
   e. volume will increase more than surface area but the difference is insignificant

4. The structure of bacterial cell walls is
   a. more simple than those of animals but more complex than those of plants
   b. the same as those of plants but different from those of animals
   c. the same as those of animals but more complex than those of plants
   d. more complex than those of plants or animals
   e. more simple than those of plants or animals

5. Energy-producing organelles include
   a. lysosomes
   b. ribosomes
   c. nucleus
   d. mitochondria
   e. nucleoli

6. All organelles listed below are derived from membranes except
   a. chromosomes
   b. Golgi bodies
   c. nucleus
   d. rough ER
   e. lysosomes

7. Which of the following is an organelle involved in gene expression?
   a. mitochondria
   b. peroxisomes
   c. ribosomes
   d. glyoxosomes
   e. vacuoles

8. The characteristic the makes eukaryotic chromosomes unique is
   a. their ability to be condensed into a small package
   b. their ring-type structure
   c. that they are composed of RNA
   d. that they have carbohydrate cross-links in their DNA
   e. that they are composed of DNA

9. Nucleoli are involved in
   a. manufacture of chromosomal proteins
   b. membrane formation
   c. cellular metabolism within the nucleus
   d. manufacture of ribosomes
   e. synthesis of heterochromatin

10. The photosynthetic pigments in chloroplasts are located on/in the
    a. stroma
    b. cristae
    c. exoskeleton
    d. cytoskeleton
    e. thylakoids

11. Microtubules are composed of
    a. protein
    b. carbohydrate
    c. glycolipid
    d. glycoproteins

12. All of the following statements are true of the nucleus except that
    a. it is a permanent organelle
    b. it is isolated from the cytoplasm by a two-layered membrane
    c. it is not visible during cell division
    d. its membrane is derived from the endoplasmic reticulum
    e. it contains the cell's hereditary information

13. The organelles that carry digestive enzymes
    a. in plant cells are peroxisomes
    b. are ribosomes in all cells
    c. in animal cells are glyoxosomes
    d. in eukaryotic cells are lysosomes
    e. in prokaryotic cells are desmosomes

14. The digestion of lysosomes by themselves
    a. is fairly common
    b. does not occur, but the reason is not known
    c. is prevented by the structure of their membrane
    d. is prevented by maintaining a very low internal pH
    e. is why they are stored in the Golgi complex until needed

15. Ribosomal RNA is found in/on all of the following except
    a. Golgi body
    b. chloroplast
    c. endoplasmic reticulum
    d. mitochondria

16. Some organelles are believed to have been acquired by eukaryotic cells as endosymbionts
    a. One of the earliest organelles to be acquired was the Golgi complex
    b. One such organelle is the prokaryotic chloroplast
    c. One such organelle is the prokaryotic flagella
    d. One example is the energy-producing organelle, the chloroplast.
    e. the ribosome is the classic example of such an organelle.

17. Which of the following is not a component of the cytoskeleton?
    a. tubulin
    b. chitin
    c. keratin
    d. vimentin

18. Eukaryotic cilia are most similar to
    a. those of motile bacteria
    b. eukaryotic flagella
    c. microvilli found in intestines of some eukaryotic organisms
    d. the cilia of prokaryotic fossils
    e. prokaryotic flagella

19. Bacterial cells are simpler than those of eukaryotic cells, including the absence of
    a. true cytoplasm
    b. DNA
    c. a plasma membrane containing phospholipids
    d. lysosomes
    e. a chemically complex cell wall

20. The nucleolus is
    a. a class 1 organelle
    b. a class 2 organelle
    c. a class 3 organelle
    d. an unclassified organelle
    e. None of the above

B. Provide the appropriate term to complete each statement.

1. Granna contain disk-shaped compartments called _____.
2. Proteins embedded in the cell membrane that identify the type of cell are called _____.
3. Proteins intended for export from a cell have a string of attached amino acids referred to as _____.
4. The living together of two organisms in close association is called _____.
5. Mitochondria are thought to have originated from _____ bacteria (with regard to oxygen needs)
6. Microtubules are often cross-linked by molecules of _____.
7. The kind of lysosome with the lower pH is the _____ lysosome.
8. Bacterial cells stained with gram's stain are said to ge gram positive if they stain a _____ color.
9. Proteins permitting entry of glucose into the cell are called _____.
10. When chlorophyll production ceases, chloroplasts become _____.

C. Briefly answer each of the following questions.

1. Why are cells generally small in size?
2. How do the membrane bound organelles interact with each other?
3. Compare the two eukaryotic energy producing eukaryotic organelles, mitochondria and chloroplasts.

CHAPTER ANSWERS

TOPIC EXERCISES

1.

Eukaryotes	Prokaryotes
DNA arranged in chromosomes	DNA not in chromosomes
Interiors compartmentalized	No interior compartments
Cell walls often lacking; cellulose present	Cell walls present and complex
Vacuoles or vesicles generally present	Vacuoles and vesicles generally absent

2.	(a) contains genetic information
	(b) synthesizes and channels cellular products
	(c) collects, packages, and delivers cellular products
	(d) contains digestive enzymes
	(e) contains metabolic enzymes
	(f) engages in oxidative metabolism
	(g) carries photosynthesis
	(h) contains genetic and cell regulation information
	(i) forms polypeptides

3.

Topic	Size	Function	Composition
actin filaments	7 nm	alters cell shape and aids in movement	actin
microtubules	25 nm	Maintains cell shape and aids in movement	tubulin
intermediate filaments	8-10 nm	Form durable structures	vimentin or keratin

WHO'S WHO IN BIOLOGY

a. Robert Hooke
b. Matthias Schleiden
c. Theodor Schwann
d. Antonie van Leeuwenhoek
e. Hans Christian Gram

LEARNING CHECKLIST

1.	The three components of the cell theory are (a) all organisms are composed of one or more cells that perform the life functions of metabolism and heredity (b) cells are the smallest living things and are the basic organizational unit of all organisms (c) cells arise only by division of a previously existing cell. (p. 81)

2.	(a) Eukaryotes have nuclei in which chromosomes, made of DNA and protein, are contained by a membrane (b) the interiors of eukaryotic cells are subdivided into compartments by a system of membranes (c) the walls of eukaryotes, if present, are simple in composition compared to those of prokaryotes (d) eukaryotic cells contain internal sacks such as vacuoles. (pp. 86-87)

3.	The plasma membrane contains the cell and regulates passage of material into and out of the cell. Markers in the membrane identify the cell. (pp. 88-89)

4.	The plasma membrane is made up of a bilayered membrane of phospholipids in which proteins are embedded, and through some proteins extend. (pp. 88-89)

5.	The endomembrane system includes the endoplasmic reticulum, nuclear envelope, Golgi complex, lysosomes, microbodies, and the plasma membrane. Though the plasma membrane is not actually an endomembrane, it is continuous with and interacts with the endomembranes (p. 88)

6.   The nucleus contains the cell's hereditary material, the chromosomes and directs the cell's precesses. Its membrane regulates passage of materials into and out of the nucleus. The nucleolus, within the nucleus, synthesizes mRNA needed to make ribosomes. (pp. 91-93)

7.   It is believed that both mitochondria and chloroplasts were once free-living organisms that developed an endosymbiotic relationship with eukaryotic cells and have since been incorporated as cellular components. (p. 85)

8.   The cytoskeleton is made of actin filaments, microtubules and intermediate filaments. (pp. 98-101)

9.   Actin filaments and intermediate filaments anchor to proteins in the plasma membrane and regulate the cell shape. Actin filaments change the cell's shape which intermediate filaments limit changes in cell size and shape. Both filaments act as anchorages for organelles. Actin filaments and microtubules interact to provide locomotion for the cell. (pp. 99-101)

MINI-EXAM

A.
1. b	2. d	3. a	4. d	5. d	6. a
7. c	8. a	9. d	10. c	11. a	12. c
13. d	14. b	15. a	16. d	17. b	18. b
19. d	20. c				

B.
1. thylakoids	2. markers	3. signal sequences
4. symbiosis	5. aerobic	6. dynein
7. secondary	8. purple	9. channel-forming proteins
10. leucoplasts		

C. 1.   Cell size is limited by their surface to volume ration and internal logistics. As cells increase in size, their volume increases at a greater rate than their surface area. Surface area is important in the exchange of materials with its environment. Internally, the nucleus can exercise control of cell functions better if distance over which control must be exercised is small. (p. 81)

2.   (a) the nuclear envelope is continuous with the endoplasmic reticulum (ER) and regulates passage of substances into the ER (b) the endoplasmic reticulum synthesizes various substances in response to the direction of the nucleus and provides channels through which its products may abe distributed to the appropriate destination (c) the Golgi complex stores, packages and releases substances manufactured in the ER (d) microbodies, peroxisomes, and glyoxosomes are thought to be derived from the ER. They contain enzymes used in the cells metabolism. Peroxisomes render peroxides produced in metabolism harmless (e) Lysosomes, formed by the Golgi complex, contain digestive enzymes that are used in metabolism and for the destruction of faulty cell components. (pp. 89-101)

3.   The mitochondria derive energy from nutrients within the cell. The chloroplast utilizes solar energy to manufacture nutrients for the cell., The mitochondria function under aerobic conditions, whereas chloroplasts function under anaerobic conditions. (pp. 95-97)

6: MEMBRANES

IN THE GRAND SCHEME

The membranes that enclose cells, in many ways, function much like the walls of our houses. The walls protect us from physical and biological elements in our environment. The walls help us preserve the temperature of our choosing. We have doors through which selected objects and materials may be passed. Windows allow us to sense conditions and events in our external environment. We, as intelligent beings, operate the windows and doors to our advantage. the membrane of a cell must be largely self regulating, constantly and automatically sensing internal and external conditions and regulating the interaction.

Cells are enclosed in a membrane that is compatible with the internal and external environment and, at the same time, regulates the passage of materials. The membrane is a highly adjustable double layer of phospholipid. Into this membrane are built proteins that regulate passage of substances into and from the cell. There are also receptors that provide information about the environment and markers that identify the cell to others. Passage through the membrane may be in bulk or an atom or molecule at a time. There are complex energy management systems that generate energy from some processes and use energy for others. Cells also have attachment and communication systems with which they interact with neighbors. The cell is a remarkable microcosm!

FOR REVIEW

Polar nature of water: Oxygen atoms attract electrons more strongly than do hydrogen atoms. This relationship causes the oxygen end of the molecule to be electron rich and the hydrogen end of the molecule to be electron poor. Thus, the water molecule has one pole that is more negative and another that is more positive.

Hydrogen bonds: The weak attraction of positive ends of polar molecules to the negative ends of other polar molecules is referred to as a hydrogen bond.

Structure of fat molecules: Fat molecules are composed of one molecule of a three carbon alcohol called glycerol to which are attached three fatty acids.

Hydrophobic: Because water molecules are polar and form bonds with other polar molecules, nonpolar molecules are pushed aside. This segregation gives the impression of nonpolar molecules withdrawing from water molecules as if fearing the water. Such nonpolar molecules are called hydrophobic.

Types of membrane proteins: Three types of proteins are found in all membranes: channel-forming proteins, receptors, and markers.

CHAPTER OUTLINE

THE LIPID FOUNDATION OF MEMBRANES (pp. 108-110)
    Phospholipids
        polarity
    Phospholipids Form Bilayer Sheets
        hydrophilic versus hydrophobic
    The Bilipid Layer is Fluid
ARCHITECTURE OF THE PLASMA MEMBRANE (pp. 110-114)
      Lipid bilayer foundation
      Transmembrane proteins
      Network of supporting fibers

KEY TERMS

p. 108: plasmaslema, plasma membrane, phospholipids
p. 109: lipid bilayer
p. 115: diffusion, solution, solvent, solutes
p. 117: osmosis, hypertonic, hypotonic, isotonic, hydrostatic pressure, osmotic pressure
p. 118: extrusion, contractile vacuoles, turgor pressure, generalized endocytosis
p. 119: phagocytosis, pinocytosis
p. 120: exocytosis, osmosis, selective permeability
p. 121: anions, facilitated diffusion
p. 122: active transport
p. 123: sodium-potassium pump

TOPIC EXERCISES

1. The architecture of the plasma membrane includes lipid bilayer, transmembrane proteins, supporting fibers and exterior proteins, and glycolipids. Summarize this architecture in the following manner:

   a. Describe the organization of the phospholipid bilayer.
   b. List the transmembrane proteins and their functions.
   c. List the functions of supporting fibers.
   d. List the functions of the exterior proteins and glycolipids.

2. In the first column below is a term that describes the environment with respect to a cell. In the second column, indicate the direction the water would flow (in, out or neither.)

   a. Isotonic   =

   b. Hypertonic   ↑ out

   c. Hypotonic   ↓ in

3. List the characteristics indicated for each of the following processes as to (1) concentration gradient, (2) energy requirement, and (3) selectivity.

Topic	Concentration Gradient	Energy Requirement	Selectivity
Osmosis	c̄	∅	none
Facilitated diffusion	c̄	∅	selective
Active transport	against	yes	selective

LEARNING CHECKLIST

1. Describe the structure of phospholipid and relate that structure to its interaction with water.

2. How are phospholipids organized into membranes?

3. List the four components of a cell membrane and state the function of each.

4. What are six ways that a cell regulates interactions with its environment?

5. What is the difference between diffusion and osmosis?

6. Compare diffusion, facilitated diffusion and active transport.

7.   How does the sodium-potassium pump work?

8.   What are the biological consequences associated with coupled channels?

9.   What are the functions of cell surface receptors and markers?

10.   How do plants and animals differ in direct cellular communication?

MINI EXAM

A. Circle the letter of the one best answer for the following questions.

1. If one gram of sugar was dissolved in 100 milliliters of water,
   a. water is the solute and sugar is the solvent
   b. water is the solution and sugar is the solute
   c. sugar is the solute and water is the solvent
   d. sugar is the solution and water is the solvent
   e. sugar and water are both solutes in the solution

2. The energy for the sodium-potassium pump comes from
   a. ATP   d. ADP
   b. coupled channels   e. polyploid channels
   c. anion pump

3. _____ is/are responsible for the production of almost all the ATP that you harvest from the food you eat.
   a. coupled channels   d. endocytosis
   b. chemiosmosis   e. coated pits
   c. sodium-potassium pump

4. A net gain of water tends to occur
   a. in a hypotonic solution from a hypertonic solution
   b. in an isotonic solution from a hypertonic solution
   c. in a hypertonic solution from a hypotonic solution
   d. in a hypotonic solution from an isotonic solution
   e. in one isotonic solution from another isotonic solution of the same composition

5. Which of the following might be a cell surface marker?
   a. VDL particle   d. LDL particle
   b. glycolipid   e. aminolipid
   c. phospholipid

6. A cell engaging in a phagocytosis must be
   a. engulfing a live organism
   b. transporting bulk solid material
   c. engulfing a dead organism
   d. transporting bulk dissolved nutrients
   e. acquiring a liquid

7. The transport of solutes across a membrane to a region of lower concentration by way of a specific channel is
   a. active transport
   b. simple diffusion
   c. osmosis
   d. facilitated diffusion
   e. facilitated osmosis

8. The sodium-potassium pump is a good example of
   a. a proton pump
   b. coupled channels
   c. an anion pump
   d. receptor-mediated endocytosis
   e. polyploid channels

9. Anions are always
   a. neutral
   b. negative
   c. positive
   d. electrons
   e. protons

10. A single celled eukaryote is solving a permeability problem by using its cytoskeleton to engulf a dissolved nutrient.
    a. This is a good example of active transport
    b. The cell is engaged in pinocytosis
    c. Such behavior is called facilitated diffusion
    d. Such bulk acquisition of nutrients is called phagocytosis
    e. Action of this kind must be accomplished with a contractile vacuole

11. Plants rely upon turgor pressure to maintain their shape. To achieve turgor pressure they
    a. circulate an isotonic solution throughout their structures
    b. must keep their cells hypotonic to the environment at all times
    c. create a positive osmotic pressure by keeping cells hypertonic to the environment
    d. undergo a process unique to plants called selective wilting
    e. maintain a high internal hydrostatic pressure by keeping their cells hypotonic to their environment

12. A system that uses other energy sources to generate ATP is the
    a. sodium-potassium pump
    b. anion pump
    c. anabolic pump
    d. proton pump
    e. electron pump

13. A contractile vacuole is a mechanism of
    a. endocytosis
    b. pinocytosis
    c. extrusion
    d. facilitated diffusion
    e. intrusion

14. Receptor-mediated endocytosis involves trapping the desired substance in
    a. coated pits
    b. contractile vacuoles
    c. lysosomes
    d. coupled channels
    e. plasmodesmata

15. Substances transported by facilitated diffusion
    a. are limited to solvents
    b. must have their movement coupled to that of another substance
    c. may flow to a region of higher concentration by expenditure of energy
    d. move passively through specific channels from an area of greater concentration to one
       of lower concentration
    e. are restricted to only one direction through the membrane

16. "Self" markers on cells are
    a. MHC proteins   c. PTI proteins
    b. LDL proteins   d. SMP proteins

17. The sodium-potassium pump
    a. pumps both ions into the cell
    b. pumps both ions out of the cell
    c. pumps sodium in and potassium out
    d. pumps sodium and potassium in and protons out
    e. pumps sodium out and potassium in

18. Which of the following intercellular connections are exclusive to plants?
    a. adhering junctions   d. gap junctions
    b. organizing junctions   e. plasmodesmata
    c. communicating junctions

19. One step in the sodium-potassium pump cleaves ATP into
    a. ADP + P_i c. AMP + P_2
    b. AMP + ADP   d. cAMP + P_1

20. Particles are enclosed in a vesicle that moves to the plasma membrane and fuse with it
    and release the particles on the other side of the membrane.
    a. The process described is called exocytosis
    b. The kind of action is usually referred to as extrusion
    c. These events represent a typical example of endocytosis
    d. The process is simply osmosis
    e. Due to the energy requirements, this process is active transport

B. Provide the appropriate term to complete the statement.

1. Cells organized into highly specialized groups are collectively called ___tissues___.
2. Another correct name for plasma membrane is ___plaslemma___.
3. The "lipid bilayer" refers to two layers of ___phospholipids___ molecules.
4. Random movement of molecules of one substance among those of another resulting in uniform distribution
    is called ___diffusion___.
5. Diffusion resulting in a net movement of water into a cell is called ___osmosis___.
6. Increases in hydrostatic pressure resulting from an inward diffusion of water is called ___osmosis pressure___.
7. ___Pressure___ is the internal pressure that keeps plant cells rigid.
8. Paramecium uses organelles called _____ to extrude water.
9. ___exocytosis___ is the extrusion of material form a cell by discharge from a vesicle through the cell
    surface.
10. A membrane containing channels that will transport only certain kinds of molecules is said to be _____
    selectively permeable

C. Briefly answer each of the following questions.

1. Describe the movement of substances into and out of a cell with various relative concentrations.

2. Explain bulk movement of substances through a cell with and without receptor mediation.

3. What is the importance of selective permeability in biological systems?

CHAPTER ANSWERS

TOPIC EXERCISES

1. a. the phospholipid bilayer is composed of two layers of phospholipids. In each layer of phospholipids all phospholipid molecules are oriented n the same way; that is, all polar hydrophilic ends face in one direction and all nonpolar hydrophobic ends face the other. The two layers of phospholipids that make up the bilayer are oriented so that the nonpolar hydrophobic portions of the two layers face each other on the inside of the bilayer. Thus, both outside surfaces of the bilayer are polar and hydrophilic.

   b. Transmembrane proteins are:
      (a) channel formers that provide passage of substances through the membrane.
      (b) receptors that recognize and complex with substances such as hormones.
      (c) markers that identify the cell.

   c. Supporting fibers help maintain cell shape and anchor components against tendencies to drift.

   d. Exterior proteins and glycolipids act as identity markers.

2. a. neither
   b. out
   c. in

3.

Topic	Concentration Gradient	Energy Requirement	Selectivity
Osmosis	with	none	none
Facilitated diffusion	with	none	selective
Active transport	against	required	selective

LEARNING CHECKLIST

1. Phospholipids are formed from a molecule of glycerol onto which two fatty acids and one phosphocholine molecule has been substituted. The two fatty acids lie parallel to each other and on the opposite side from that of the phosphocholine. the phosphocholine end is water soluble while the fatty acid end is not water soluble. These ends are often referred to as hydrophilic and hydrophobic respectively. (pp. 108-110)

2. In biological membranes, the phospholipids arranged in parallel layers with the fatty acid hydrophobic ends facing each other and the hydrophilic ends forming the two surfaces of the membrane. (pp. 110-114)

3. (a) Lipid bilayer foundation serves as a flexible barrier to permeability and a foundation for the other

components.

(b) Transmembrane proteins provide channels for the passage of molecules and information through the membrane.

(c) The network of supporting fibers provides cells shape, with flexibility, and provide anchorage for cellular components.

(d) Exterior proteins and glycolipids provide identity markers for the cell's components. (pp. 110-115)

4.   (a) Passage of water
    (b) passage of bulk materials
    (c) selective transport of molecules
    (d) reception of information
    (e) expression of cell identity
    (f) physical connection with other cells. (p. 115)

5.   Diffusion is the net movement of molecules of any substance to regions of lower concentration as a result of random spontaneous molecular motion. Osmosis is the diffusion of water, but not solutes, through a membrane. (pp. 115-117)

6.   Both simple diffusion and facilitated diffusion are processes in which substances flow down their concentration gradient. An enzyme is required to "facilitate" the passage through a membrane in the latter. Active transport also requires a facilitating enzyme, but at the expense of energy, the substance is moved without regard for concentration gradient. (pp. 121-126)

7.   The sodium-potassium pump is a membrane bound protein with changing conformation. Sodium outside the cell binds to the protein whose conformation gives it an affinity for sodium ions. Energy from the breakdown of ATP to ADP plus a phosphate group alters the conformation which leaves the sodium ions facing the exterior and which has a low affinity for sodium. The sodium is released from the cell. The new conformation has an affinity for potassium ions which become attached. Phosphate ions become attached to the protein which changes conformation again, releasing the phosphate group gained from ATP and delivering the potassium to the cell's interior. (see figure 6-20 in the text.) (pp. 123-126)

8.   Coupled channels are a resource for cells somewhat analogous to a toll road. The transport of one substance provides the energy for the transport of another. (pp. 124-126)

9.   Surface receptors provide information to the cell that possesses them. Surface makers provide identity information of other cells. (pp. 127-128)

10.   Plants establish cytoplasmic connections through matching holes in their cell walls called plasmodesmata. Animals establish cytoplasmic connections through cellular connections called gap junctions. (pp. 129-130)

MINI EXAM

A.

1. c	2. a	3. b	4. c	5. b	6. d
7. d	8. b	9. b	10. b	11. c	12. d
13. c	14. a	15. d	16. a	17. c	18. c
19. a	20. a				

B.

1. tissues	2. plasmalemma	3. phospholipid
4. diffusion	5. osmosis	6. osmotic pressure
7. turgor pressure	8. contractile vacuole	9. exocytosis
10. selectively permeable		

C. 1. When two solutions of different concentrations are separated by a membrane, the more concentrated solution (containing more solute) is said to be hypertonic with respect to the less concentrated. The less concentrated is said to be hypotonic with respect to the more concentrated. Both the solute and solvent tend to flow down their concentration gradient. The ability to make such a movement depends upon the permeability of the membrane. Permeability permitting, there would be net movement of solute from the side with greater solute concentration, whereas there would be a net movement of solute toward the region of higher solute concentration (thus, lower solvent concentration.) If both solutions were of equal concentration, they are said to isotonic to each other and, though random movement would occur, there would be no net movement. (pp. 115-118)

2. Bulk passage of substances into and out of a cell is accomplished by forming a membranous bag around the substance and transporting the bagged substance into the cell from the surface of dumping them out the cell through surface. Inward transport is called endocytosis. (see figure 6-15 in the text) Special names are given to endocytosis according to the nature of the imported substance. If the substance is solid, the process is called phagocytosis. If the substance is liquid, the process is called pinocytosis. endocytosis may be generalized, in which case the cell has only some control over substances taken in. Specialized receptors enable the cell to take in or expel specific substances in processes called receptor-mediated endocytosis or receptor-mediated exocytosis respectively. (pp. 118-120)

3. Selective permeability provides a measure of control over its interactions with its environment, rather than being left at its mercy. (pp. 120-121)

7: ENERGY AND METABOLISM

IN THE GRAND SCHEME

Energy is a requirement of life. Living is hard work; energy must be expended to perform all the processes that occur in organisms. Chemical reactions, cellular functioning, running, growing, reproducing--all require energy. Without a steady source of usable energy, organisms would die. As we will see in the next two chapters, photosynthetic organisms use the sun as their energy source and convert solar energy to chemical energy. That chemical energy is then used by the photosynthesizers themselves and by essentially all other organisms. In this chapter we learn the fundamentals of energy and metabolism: what energy is, how it can be transformed and transferred, how chemical energy and reactions operate in living organisms, and how such systems are controlled.

FOR REVIEW

Nature of chemical bond: Chemical bonds hold atoms together to form molecules. In ionic bonds, electrons are transferred between atoms, and the resulting ions are attracted to each other. In covalent bonds, pairs of electrons are shared between atoms. Chemical bonds represent stored energy, potential energy. When a chemical bond is broken, energy is released. If the bond being broken is within an organism, the organism may use the released energy to help carry out its life processes.

Protein structure: A protein consists of one or more polypeptide chains. Each polypeptide chain consists of a particular sequence of amino acids. This sequence is referred to as the primary structure, and it determines the chemical properties and further structures of the protein. The pleated folding or helical coiling of the chain is called the secondary structure of the protein. The tertiary structure refers to the complex, three-dimensional globular structure assumed by some proteins as their polypeptide chains bend and ball up. Finally, a protein is said to have a quaternary structure if it has more than one polypeptide chain; quaternary structure refers to how these chains are shaped and associated with each other. The structure of a protein is responsible for the way it functions.

Nucleotides: Nucleotides are the building block units of nucleic acids. Each nucleotide consists of a five-carbon sugar, a phosphate group, and a nitrogenous base. Nucleotides are also components of other biologically important compounds such as ATP and the coenzyme NAD^+.

Proton pump: The proton pump establishes a proton gradient across a cell membrane and uses that gradient to produce ATP, the universal energy currency. Protons are actively pumped across the membrane, and their diffusion back through special channels is coupled with the production of ATP. The cell (and organism) can then use the ATP to perform work. The energy needed to pump the protons is supplied by photosynthesis or the breakdown of energy-rich molecules.

CHAPTER OUTLINE

WHAT IS ENERGY? (pp. 135-136)
    kinetic and potential
THE LAWS OF THERMODYNAMICS DESCRIBE HOW ENERGY CHANGES (pp. 136-137)
    entropy
FREE ENERGY (pp. 137-138)
OXIDATION-REDUCTION: THE FLOW OF ENERGY IN LIVING THINGS (pp. 138-139)
ACTIVATION ENERGY: PREPARING MOLECULES FOR ACTION (pp. 139-141)
    catalysis

ENZYMES: THE WORKERS OF THE CELL (pp. 141-146)
 How Enzymes Work
  active sites
 Factors Affecting Enzyme Activity
  Temperature
  pH
 How Enzyme Activity is Regulated
 Coenzymes are Tools Enzymes Use to Aid Catalysis
  NAD$^+$
ATP: THE ENERGY CURRENCY OF LIFE (pp. 146-148)
BIOCHEMICAL PATHWAYS: THE ORGANIZATIONAL UNITS OF METABOLISM (pp. 148-150)
 How Biochemical Pathways Evolved
 How Biochemical Pathways are Regulated
  feedback
THE EVOLUTION OF METABOLISM (pp. 150-151)

KEY TERMS

TOPIC EXERCISES

1. Complete the following graphs to illustrate an endergonic reaction and an exergonic reaction. Be sure to label the reactants, products and activation energy. Indicate for each reaction whether the products or reactants contain more energy.

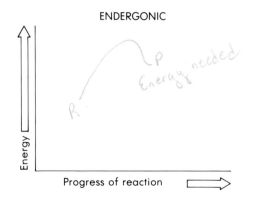

ENDERGONIC

Energy

Progress of reaction

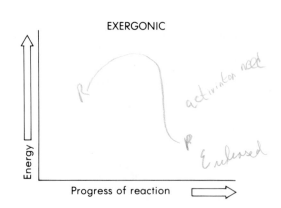

EXERGONIC

Energy

Progress of reaction

2. If an enzyme had the shape shown below, draw what its substrate would look like. Use these caricatures to show how enzymes function and then how drastic changes in temperature or pH affects the enzyme.

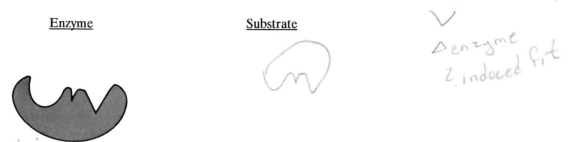

Enzyme   Substrate

3. Diagram how ATP, ADP and inorganic phosphate (P_i) are cycled and recycled in living organisms and how energy is involved in this cycling by filling in the blanks on the following figure. Terms to fill in: ADP, ATP, energy added, energy released, P_i.

LEARNING CHECKLIST

1. List the two states in which energy can exist. List seven forms of energy.
2. State briefly the First and Second Laws of Thermodynamics.
3. What single phrase defines free energy?
4. What three things are lost by a molecule undergoing oxidation? What three things are gained by a molecule being reduced?
5. What is the relationship between the activation energy and the speed of a chemical reaction? Does a catalyst increase or decrease the activation energy and rate of a reaction?
6. Name the place on an enzyme where the substrate binds. What must match if the binding and catalysis are to occur?
7. List two factors that affect enzyme activity by affecting enzyme shape.
8. List three general types of substances that bind to enzymes and influence their functioning. State briefly what effect each has on the enzyme.
9. What is the universal energy currency of all cells? What are its three components? What is formed when one of its high-energy bonds is broken?
10. In what direction did biochemical reactions most likely evolve?
11. Which evolved first, aerobic or anaerobic metabolism?

MINI EXAM

A. Circle the letter of the one best answer for each question.

1. The First Law of Thermodynamics states that energy can be
   a. created
   b. destroyed
   c. converted
   d. all of the above
   e. none of the above

2. The universal energy currency for all cells is
   a. ATP
   b. NAD^+
   c. ADP
   d. P_i
   e. O_2

3. Enzymes
   a. make endergonic reactions proceed spontaneously
   b. lower the activation energy of a reaction
   c. are not very specific in their choice of substrates
   d. are needed in large quantities because they are used up during catalysis

4. To what category of macromolecules do enzymes belong?
   a. carbohydrates
   b. lipids
   c. steroids
   d. nucleic acids
   e. proteins

5. NAD^+ is a(n)
   a. enzyme
   b. coenzyme
   c. active site
   d. high-energy bond
   e. allosteric activator

6. Which of the following is a reduced compound?
   a. CO_2
   b. O_2
   c. N_2
   d. NAD^+
   e. NADH

7. In an endergonic reaction,
   a. the reactants contain less free energy than the products
   b. the reactants contain more free energy than the products
   c. no activation energy is required
   d. catalysis cannot occur
   e. substrates outnumber enzymes

8. The energy of random molecular motion is called
   a. heat energy
   b. free energy
   c. enthalpy
   d. potential energy
   e. activation energy

9. The energy available to do work in a system is called
   a. entropy
   b. activation energy
   c. thermodynamics
   d. free energy
   e. heat energy

10. During cellular respiration, glucose is
    a. reduced
    b. oxidized

    b

11. A catalyst will make a reaction
    a. stop
    b. slow down
    c. speed up
    d. go in a different direction
    e. you can never tell

    c

12. When molecules are reduced they gain
    a. energy   d. all of the above
    b. electrons   e. none of the above
    c. hydrogen protons

    d

13. Which of the following statements about enzymes is true?
    a. some substrates can make enzymes change shape slightly
    b. all enzymes have the same pH optimum
    c. the active sites of all enzymes have the same three-dimensional shape
    d. all of the above
    e. none of the above

    a

14. Cofactors
    a. break hydrogen bonds in proteins
    b. help facilitate enzyme activity
    c. increase activation energy
    d. are very rare in living organisms
    e. are linked to ATP by high-energy bonds

    b

15. Approximately how much energy is released when one of the high-energy bonds in ATP is broken?
    a. 700 cal/mole   d. 70 kcal/mole
    b. 7 cal/mole   e. 700 kcal/mole
    c. 7 kcal/mole

    c

16. Consider the hypothetical biochemical pathway H --> I --> J --> K --> L. Which step most likely evolved first?
    a. H --> I   d. J --> K
    b. I --> J   e. K --> L
    c. I --> H

    e

17. Why do drastic changes in temperature and pH of a system alter enzyme activity?
    a. they change the three-dimensional shape of the enzyme
    b. they disrupt hydrogen and ionic bonds in the enzyme
    c. they disrupt hydrophobic interactions in the enzyme
    d. all of the above
    e. none of the above

    d

18. The loss of an electron by a molecule is called
    a. oxidation   d. enthalpy
    b. reduction   e. allosteric inhibition
    c. induced fit

    a

19. In the chemical equation G = H - TS, the term G stands for
    a. entropy
    b. disordering influences
    c. enthalpy
    d. free energy
    e. ordering influences

B. Provide the appropriate term to complete each statement.

1. All other forms of energy can be converted into _heat_.
2. The set of all chemical reactions carried out by an organism is called _metabolism_.
3. The energy that must be supplied to destabilize existing chemical bonds and get reactions to proceed is called _activation_ energy.
4. In a(n) _exer_ reaction, the products contain less free energy than the reactants.
5. The _2nd_ Law of Thermodynamics states that disorder in the universe is constantly increasing.
6. Disorder or energy that is no longer available to do work is called _entropy_.
7. The _substrate_ is the molecule that an enzyme binds to and acts on.
8. ATP contains _2_ (number) high-energy bonds.
9. Sequences of reactions, in which the product of one reaction becomes the substrate of another reaction, are called _biochemical pathways_.
10. Enzymes that can be controlled by having nonsubstrate molecules binding and changing their shape are said to be _allosteric_.
11. RNA molecules that can act like enzymes and catalyze reactions are called _ribozymes_

C. Briefly answer each of the following questions.

1. Why is feedback inhibition an efficient way to regulate biochemical pathways?

2. Acid rain is a serious environmental problem. Using your knowledge of enzyme activity, explain why acid rain kills organisms.

CHAPTER 7 ANSWERS

TOPIC EXERCISES

1.

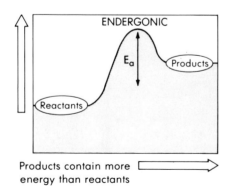

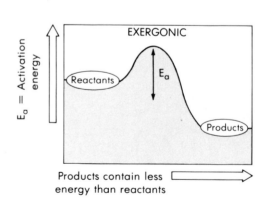

2.   Substrate must fit into the active site of the enzyme, e.g.,

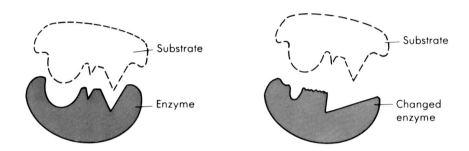

Drastic changes in temperature or pH change the shape of the enzyme active site, making it impossible for the substrate to bind properly.

3.   a. ATP
        b. ADP
        c. P$_i$
        d. energy added
        e. energy released

LEARNING CHECKLIST

1.   States = kinetic energy (energy of motion) and potential energy (stored energy). Forms = mechanical force, heat, sound, electrical, light, radioactive radiation, magnetic. (pp. 135-136)

2.   First Law of Thermodynamics: energy can be neither created or destroyed, but can be converted from one form to another. Second Law of Thermodynamics: energy spontaneously converts to less organized forms, disorder in the universe constantly increases (p. 136)

3.   The energy in a system available to do work (pp. 137-138)

4.   In both cases: an electron, a hydrogen proton, and energy. (p. 139)

5.   The greater the activation energy, the slower the reaction will proceed. A catalyst lowers the activation energy and therefore increases the rate of the reaction. (pp. 139-141)

6.   Active site. The three-dimensional shapes of the substrate and the active site must match or fit each other. (p. 142)

7.   Temperature, pH. (pp. 143-144)

8.   Inhibitors: cause allosteric changes that reduce or stop enzyme's activity; activators: cause allosteric changes that enhance enzyme activity; cofactors: necessary components that enhance enzyme activity. (pp. 144-146)

9.   ATP; ribose, adenine and a triphosphate group; ADP + P$_i$ (and energy is released). (pp. 146-147)

10.   Backward, with final reactions in the pathway evolving first, and earlier reactions evolving later. Pathways became longer and more complex as more reactions evolved and were "added on." (pp. 148-149)

11.   Anaerobic (p. 150)

MINI EXAM

A.   1. c   2. a   3. b   4. e   5. b   6. e
       7. a   8. a   9. d   10. b   11. c   12. d
       13. a   14. b   15. c   16. e   17. d   18. a
       19.d

B.   1. heat   2. metabolism   3. activation
       4. exergonic   5. Second   6. entropy
       7. substrate   8. two   9. biochemical pathways
       10. allosteric   11. ribozymes

C. 1. Feedback inhibition is efficient because it prevents energy from being wasted on unnecessary reactions. As the final product of a pathway builds up, it inhibits the first step from occurring. This shuts down the pathway and prevents additional production of the final product. The pathway runs - and running it takes activation energy - only when there is need for the final product. (pp. 144-145, 149-150)

   2. When acid is added to an environment it alters the pH of the soil or water. Organisms using the soil or water also have their internal pH levels altered. If the change in pH is too great and cannot be controlled by buffers, enzymes in the organism's cells may be denatured. Once enzymes lose their proper shape, they can no longer function properly and biochemical pathways slow down or even stop. Organisms cannot live if their metabolism has been disrupted too severely. (pp. 143-144)

8: CELLULAR RESPIRATION

IN THE GRAND SCHEME

As you learned in the last chapter, organisms need a continual input of energy if they are to stay alive. Work must be done if an organism or cell is to live, and energy must be expended for work to be done. All living organisms--from bacteria and protists to fungi, plants, and animals--obtain energy by carrying out cellular respiration. They break down energy-rich food molecules and then use the released energy to synthesize ATP, the universal energy currency. The food molecules are oxidized, and ADP is reduced to ATP. Glycolysis, the conversion of glucose to pyruvate, is the first stage of cellular respiration for all organisms and results in the net production of 2 ATP for each molecule of glucose. What happens next depends on what molecules are available to act as electron acceptors. If oxygen is present, oxidative respiration (aerobic metabolism) occurs and 32 ATP are generated by chemiosmosis for each initial molecule of glucose. These 32 ATP, plus the 2 from glycolysis and 2 more from substrate-level phosphorylation in aerobic respiration, result in a net yield of 36 ATP. If oxygen is not present, fermentation (anaerobic metabolism) occurs and an organic molecule acts as the final electron acceptor instead of oxygen. Anaerobic metabolism yields only the 2 ATP from glycolysis for each initial glucose molecule.

FOR REVIEW

Glucose: Glucose is a six-carbon sugar, a monosaccharide. Its molecular formula is $C_6H_{12}O_6$. It is the primary energy-storing molecule of living organisms. Each of its seven C-H bonds are energy-storing bonds. When those bonds are broken during the oxidation of glucose, energy is released. Many different food molecules can be converted to glucose, and all living organisms contain large amounts of glucose. Cellular respiration essentially begins with glucose.

Chemiosmosis: The vast majority of ATP that is produced by aerobic organisms comes from chemiosmosis. In this process a proton pump forces protons across a cell membrane through special channels, making the proton concentration higher outside the membrane than inside. Following the concentration gradient, the protons diffuse back in across the membrane through a second type of special channel. Passage through this second channel causes ATP to be synthesized. It takes energy to run the proton pump, and therefore it takes energy to synthesize ATP by chemiosmosis.

Oxidation-reduction: Oxidation is the loss of an electron by an atom or molecule, reduction is the addition of an electron to an atom or molecule. The electrons are frequently accompanied by a hydrogen proton. Since electrons represent energy, oxidation involves the release of energy from the atom or molecule, and reduction stores energy in the atom or molecule. Whenever one substance is oxidized, another substance is reduced since the electrons taken from the oxidized substance must go somewhere (i.e., to the reduced substance). Oxidation-reduction reactions transfer energy within living organisms.

ATP: ATP is the universal energy currency of all cells. Almost every type of work that cells and organisms do is powered by ATP. High-energy covalent bonds link the three phosphate groups. When one of those bonds is broken, ADP and an inorganic phosphate are left, and 7.3 kcal/mole of energy are released. This is enough energy to drive endergonic reactions in the cell or perform other work. ATP is constantly being synthesized and broken down in living cells as it cycles and recycles between ADP + P_i and ATP. The energy required to synthesize ATP from ADP + P_i comes from photosynthesis or cellular respiration.

Exergonic and endergonic reactions: Free energy is the energy in a system that is available to do work. If the products of a reaction contain more free energy than the reactants, the reaction is endergonic. If the reactants contain more free energy than the products, the reaction is exergonic. Spontaneous reactions are exergonic.

Endergonic and exergonic reactions are often coupled in living systems: the energy released by exergonic reactions is used to drive endergonic reactions.

CHAPTER OUTLINE

KEY TERMS

TOPIC EXERCISES

1. Complete the following chart outlining the various carbon compounds involved in cellular respiration.

Beginning stage	Carbon end carbon compound(s)	Product(s)
Glycolysis	Glucose	a. _pyruvate_
b. _fermentation_	c. _pyruvate_	Various: e.g., ethanol, lactic acid, CO_2
Oxidation of pyruvate	Pyruvate	d. _acetyl CoA_ e. _CO_2_
Citric acid cycle	f. _acetyl CoA_, Oxaloacetate	g. _CO_2_ h. _oxaloacetate_

2. Complete the chart below. For each of the following stages of cellular respiration, indicate which of the following substances are produced in that stage. Substances: ATP, FAD^+, $FADH_2$, NAD^+, NADH
A substance may be listed more than once.

Stage	Substance(s) produced
Glycolysis	a. _NADH_ b. _ATP_
Fermentation	c. _NAD^+_
Oxidation of pyruvate	d. _NADH_
Citric acid cycle	e. _NADH_ f. _ATP_ g. _$FADH_2$_
Electron transport chain	h. _NAD^+_ i. _ATP_ j. _FAD^+_

3. Fill in the blanks below to complete the story of what happens in the electron transport chain of cellular respiration. Each blank should be filled with the name of one substance.
   a. Electrons are taken from _NADH_ and _$FADH_2$_, which
   b. then revert to _NAD_ and _FAD_.
   c. The electrons are passed along the transport chain, a series of carrier molecules (electron acceptors) such as _cytochromes_
   d. The final electron acceptor is _O_2_, which
   e. combines with the electrons and H^+ to form _H_2O_.
   f. As the electrons travel the transport chain, they provide energy to drive proton pumps, which causes _ATP_ to be produced by chemiosmosis.

LEARNING CHECKLIST

1. What two general types of reactions are coupled in living systems? Which one supplies the energy to drive the other?
2. Name the two processes that cells use to synthesize ATP.
3. What are the three basic stages of aerobic cellular respiration?
4. What are the four stages of glycolysis?
5. What is the net yield of ATP for every molecule of glucose that goes through glycolysis? What process produces the ATP?
6. What is the net yield of ATP for every molecule of glucose that goes through fermentation? Through oxidative respiration?
7. What type of molecule acts as the final electron acceptor in fermentation? In oxidative respiration?
8. List four different products of fermentation.
9. What are the three end-products of the oxidation of pyruvate?
10. Not counting the carbon compounds that are recycled, what are the four products of the citric acid cycle?
11. What is the function of the electron transport chain in oxidative respiration?
12. Where do each of the following processes of oxidative respiration take place in eukaryotes: glycolysis, oxidation of pyruvate, citric acid cycle, electron transport, and chemiosmosis?
13. In oxidative respiration, how many ATP are generated by substrate-level phosphorylation? By chemiosmosis?

MINI EXAM

A. Circle the letter of the one best answer for each question.

1. Which of the following is <u>not</u> a product of fermentation?
   a. CO_2
   b. O_2
   c. ethanol
   d. lactic acid
   e. all of the above <u>are</u> products of fermentation

2. What substance is produced by the oxidation of pyruvate and feeds into the citric acid cycle?
   a. pyruvate
   b. glucose
   c. acetyl-CoA
   d. O_2
   e. CO_2

3. Fermentation has an efficiency level of approximately
   a. 2%
   b. 5%
   c. 20%
   d. 50%
   e. 78%

4. Hans Krebs discovered (worked out the details of)
   a. glycolysis
   b. fermentation
   c. the oxidation of pyruvate
   d. the citric acid cycle
   e. electron transport and chemiosmosis

5. Oxidative respiration has an efficiency level of approximately
   a. 2%
   b. 63%
   c. 14%
   d. 7%
   e. 38%

6. In aerobic cellular respiration, which generates more ATP, substrate-level phosphorylation or chemiosmosis?
   a. substrate-level phosphorylation
   b. chemiosmosis
   c. both generate the same amount of ATP
   d. neither generates any ATP

7. What role does O_2 play in oxidative respiration?
   a. it plays no role
   b. it combines with acetyl-CoA at the start of the citric acid cycle
   c. it is given off as a by-product during the oxidation of pyruvate
   d. it combines with H_2O to help drive the formation of ATP
   e. it is the final electron acceptor at the end of the electron transport chain

8. During oxidative respiration, $FADH_2$ is produced in
   a. glycolysis
   b. the oxidation of pyruvate
   c. the citric acid cycle
   d. the electron transport chain
   e. fermentation

9. NADH is produced during
   a. glycolysis
   b. the oxidation of pyruvate
   c. the citric acid cycle
   d. all of the above
   e. none of the above

10. Organisms that do not have the ability to produce or synthesize their own food are called
    a. anaerobic
    b. autotrophs
    c. exergonic
    d. catabolic
    e. heterotrophs

11. The proper sequence of stages in glycolysis is
    a. glucose mobilization, cleavage, oxidation, ATP generation
    b. cleavage, glucose mobilization, ATP generation, oxidation
    c. glucose mobilization, oxidation, cleavage, ATP generation
    d. ATP generation, oxidation, glucose mobilization, cleavage
    e. oxidation, cleavage, ATP generation, glucose mobilization

12. During what stage of cellular respiration is the most ATP synthesized?
    a. glycolysis
    b. oxidation of pyruvate
    c. citric acid cycle
    d. fermentation
    e. chemiosmosis

13. Catabolic processes
    a. make complex molecules from simpler ones
    b. break complex molecules into simpler ones
    c. occur only in autotrophs
    d. occur only in heterotrophs
    e. none of the above

14. What substance is regenerated by fermentation?
    a. O_2
    b. NAD^+
    c. acetyl-CoA
    d. ATP
    e. glucose

15. Which of the following is a multienzyme complex?
    a. glyceraldehyde-3-phosphate (G3P)
    b. NAD
    c. FAD
    d. pyruvate dehydrogenase
    e. all of the above

16. During chemiosmosis in oxidative respiration, protons are pumped
    a. out of the cell
    b. out of the mitochondria into the cell cytoplasm
    c. out of the matrix into the outer compartment of the mitochondria
    d. out of the cell cytoplasm into the matrix of mitochondria
    e. out of the nucleus and into the mitochondria

17. Each molecule of $FADH_2$ results in the production of how many ATP molecules during oxidative respiration?
    a. 2   d. 18
    b. 3   e. 36
    c. 4

18. Which of the following organisms carries out cellular respiration?
    a. a corn plant   d. a bacterium
    b. a dog   e. all of the above
    c. a yeast

19. Humans usually obtain more of their energy from oxidizing
    a. proteins   d. alcohol
    b. glucose   e. water
    c. fatty acids

B. Provide the appropriate term to complete each statement.

    1. At the end of oxidative respiration, ATP moves out of the mitochondria and into the cytoplasm by the process of _____.
    2. The generation of ATP by coupling strongly exergonic reactions with the synthesis of ATP from ADP and P_i is called _____.
    3. The oxidation of food molecules to obtain energy is called _____.
    4. No matter whether oxygen is present or not, the first stage in the oxidation of glucose is always _____.
    5. The oxidation of _____ is the second stage of oxidative respiration.
    6. If O_2 is present, the complete catabolism of four molecules of glucose will yield _____ molecules of ATP.
    7. At the end of the electron transport chain, one molecule of O_2 combines with 4 _____ and _____ (number) electrons to form _____.
    8. Fermentation is also known as _____ metabolism.
    9. The reactions of the citric acid cycle take place in the _____ of the mitochondria.
    10. The oxidation of fatty acids is called _____.
    11. In the citric acid cycle, the electron acceptor _____ is an integral part of the mitochondrion inner membrane.

C. Briefly answer each of the following questions.

    1. Drowning, suffocation, and carbon monoxide poisoning all kill a person by preventing sufficient oxygen from reaching his or her cells. Using what you now know about oxidative respiration, explain why the lack of oxygen kills the person.

66

2. Why are wines alcoholic? Why don't wines have alcoholic contents higher than about 12%?

3. Some animals that live in deserts and other very dry places can survive without having to drink water. They obtain some water from the food they eat, but many also rely on "metabolic water." What do you suppose is metabolic water? (Hint: Think about what happens at the end of the electron transport chain).

4. If fermentation is so inefficient compared with oxidative respiration, why does it still exist?

CHAPTER 8 ANSWERS

TOPIC EXERCISES

1. | a. pyruvate | b. fermentation | c. pyruvate |
    | d. acetyl-CoA | e. CO_2 | f. acetyl-CoA |
    | g. oxaloacetate | h. CO_2 | |

2. | a. ATP | b. NADH | c. NAD^+ |
    | d. NADH | e. ATP | f. $FADH_2$ |
    | g. NADH | h. ATP | i. FAD^+ |
    | j. NAD^+ | | |

3. | a. NADH, $FADH_2$ | b. NAD^+, FAD^+ | c. cytochromes (or cytochrome c) |
    | d. O_2 | e. H_2O | f. ATP |

LEARNING CHECKLIST

1. Exergonic and endergonic reactions are coupled. Exergonic supply the energy to drive endergonic. (p. 154)
2. Substrate-level phosphorylation, chemiosmosis (p. 155)
3. Glycolysis, oxidation of pyruvate, citric acid cycle (pp. 156-157)
4. Glucose mobilization, cleavage, oxidation, ATP generation (p. 161)
5. 2 ATP; substrate-level phosphorylation (pp. 161-163)
6. 2 ATP (from glycolysis); 36 ATP (pp. 161, 174)
7. An organic molecule; oxygen (pp. 164-166, 172)
8. NAD^+, CO_2, ethanol, lactic acid (also acetic acid, butyric acid, proprionic acid) (pp. 164-166)
9. Acetyl-CoA, NADH, CO_2 (pp. 166-167)
10. ATP, CO_2, NADH, $FADH_2$ (pp. 168-171)
11. To take electrons from NADH and $FADH_2$, and use them to drive proton pumps, which results in the chemiosmotic synthesis of ATP (pp. 172-173)
12. Glycolysis = cell cytoplasm; pyruvate oxidation, citric acid cycle, electron transport and chemiosmosis = inside mitochondria of cell (p. 176)
13. 4 ATP; 32 ATP (p. 174)

MINI EXAM

A.
1. b	2. c	3. a	4. d	5. e	6. b
7. e	8. c	9. d	10. e	11. a	12. e
13. b	14. b	15. d	16. c	17. a	18. e
19. c					

B.
1. facilitated diffusion	2. substrate-level phosphorylation	3. cellular respiration
4. glycolysis	5. pyruvate	6. 144
7. H^+, 4, H_2O	8. anaerobic	9. matrix
10. beta-oxidation	11. FAD^+	

C. 1. Oxygen is the final electron acceptor at the end of the electron transport chain in oxidative respiration. If no oxygen is present, the preceding electron acceptors in the chain cannot pass on their electrons; the chain essentially becomes backlogged or jammed and stops functioning. Without the electron transport chain, there is no chemiosmotic synthesis of ATP. Chemiosmosis is responsible for 32 of the 36 ATP produced from each molecule of glucose that goes through oxidative respiration. Without chemiosmosis, ATP cannot be synthesized rapidly enough to do all the work that must be done to keep the person alive (e.g., pumping the heart, carrying out vital biochemical pathways). (pp. 172-174)

2. Wines contain alcohol because of the yeast that live in the grape juice. The yeast carry out fermentation because conditions are anaerobic in the wine vat or bottle where the wine is being made. The species of yeast used in winemaking produce ethyl alcohol (ethanol) as a by-product of fermentation, and thus ethanol is added to the grape juice. Natural wines do not have alcohol levels higher than about 12% because at higher levels the alcohol becomes toxic to the yeasts and kills them, thus preventing any further fermentation or further production of alcohol. (pp. 164-166)

3. Metabolic water is the water formed at the end of the electron transport chain of oxidative respiration. Oxygen is the final electron acceptor. It combines with electrons and hydrogen protons to form water. This metabolic water (formed by the processes of metabolism within the organism) can be used to help meet the water needs of cells and organisms. (pp. 172-173)

4. Fermentation may be inefficient compared with oxidative respiration, but it is better than nothing. The ATP yield from glucose may be small under anaerobic conditions, but there is some yield. Fermentation allows organisms to live in otherwise uninhabitable anaerobic environments and also allows normally aerobic cells to keep functioning (albeit at a reduced level) under temporarily anaerobic conditions (e.g., muscle cells during strenuous exercise). (pp. 164-166)

9: PHOTOSYNTHESIS

IN THE GRAND SCHEME

Life as we know it on the earth today depends on photosynthesis. When organisms first evolved the ability to photosynthesize, they evolved the ability to convert solar energy into chemical energy. The first photosynthesizers evolved approximately 3.4 billion years ago and were anaerobic. They used sunlight as a source of energy to synthesize ATP. Approximately 2.5 billion years ago, aerobic photosynthesizers evolved. They used solar energy to produce not only ATP, but also a reduced compound called NADPH. Oxygen gas, O_2, was produced as a by-product of this process. The two energy-rich compounds, ATP and NADPH, provided the energy to convert carbon dioxide to glucose in another series of reactions. Glucose, you remember, is the beginning compound of cellular respiration. It is oxidized to provide the energy to synthesize the ATP that keeps organisms alive. Essentially then, photosynthetic organisms capture solar energy and convert it to chemical energy. This chemical energy is then utilized by the photosynthesizers and by all other organisms to fuel their life processes. Almost every single food chain on earth can be traced back to green plants or other photosynthetic organisms. Of equal importance to life as we know it is the production of O_2 during aerobic photosynthesis. It is the sole source of the oxygen that we and all other aerobic organisms need to stay alive. Without aerobic photosynthesis there would be no O_2 in the atmosphere or in bodies of water, there would be no oxidative respiration, and there would be no us or any other aerobic organism.

FOR REVIEW

Electron energy levels: Electrons orbit around the nucleus of their atom in specific paths called orbitals and at specific energy levels. The further out from the nucleus that an electron is, the greater the energy it contains. Moving the electron closer to the nucleus lowers its energy as energy is released. Similarly, if energy is added to the electron, it is raised to a higher energy level and orbits further from the nucleus. When electrons absorb light energy, they are raised to higher energy levels.

Chloroplasts: Chloroplasts are the organelles that carry out photosynthesis in the cells of eukaryotic plants and algae. They apparently are endosymbionts, derived from anaerobic photosynthetic bacteria. They have a complex internal structure consisting of disk-shaped sacs called thylakoids that are stacked into grana.

Chemiosmosis: Chemiosmosis is one of the two ways of synthesizing ATP. A proton pump first uses energy to force protons out across a membrane against their concentration gradient. The protons then diffuse back in across the membrane through special channels. This diffusion back in is coupled with the conversion of ADP + P_i to ATP.

Oxidation-reduction: Oxidation is the loss of an electron and therefore the loss of energy, too; reduction is the gain of an electron and energy. Hydrogen ions often accompany the electrons in their movements. When one substance is oxidized, another substance in the reaction is reduced since the electron must be transferred to something. Oxidation-reduction reactions are a key way that energy is transferred within living systems.

Glycolysis: Whether under anaerobic or aerobic conditions, glycolysis is the first stage in the process of cellular respiration. During glycolysis, glucose is converted to pyruvate, more ATP is produced than is used up, and NAD^+ is reduced to NADH. What happens next depends on whether the cell is in an anaerobic environment (fermentation occurs) or in an aerobic environment (oxidative respiration occurs). This chapter shows that the glucose that is the foundation for cellular respiration comes from photosynthesis.

CHAPTER OUTLINE

KEY TERMS

p. 180: photoelectric effect, photons, electromagnetic spectrum
p. 181: gamma rays, radio waves, absorption spectrum, pigments, carotenoids
p. 182: beta-carotene, vitamin A, retinal, chlorophylls, porphyrin ring, accessory pigment
p. 184: photoefficiency, light reactions, dark reactions, photosynthetic membranes, chloroplasts, primary photoevent,
p. 185: reducing power, carbon fixation, photocenter, P_{700}
p. 186: ferredoxin, green sulfur bacteria, cyclic photophosphorylation
p. 188: photosystem II, photosystem I, P_{680}, nicotine adenine dinucleotide phosphate ($NADP^+$)
p. 189: oxidant, protein Z
p. 190: abiotic synthesis, glycolysis, nitrogen fixation
p. 191: ribulose 1,5 bisphosphate (RuBP), phosphoglycerate (PGA), heterocysts, chemoautotroph
p. 192: C_3 photosynthesis, Calvin cycle
p. 193: thylakoids, grana, stroma
p. 194: RuBP carboxylase, photorespiration
p. 195: C_4 photosynthesis, phosphoenolpyruvate, bundle-sheath cell
p. 196: crassulacean acid metabolism (CAM), stomata

TOPIC EXERCISES

1. The substances listed below are present either at the beginning or the end of the light reactions of photosynthesis. Fill in the chart by listing which substance is present to start with, and what it has been converted to by the end of the light reactions. (e = electrons)

Substances:	Start	End
$ADP + P_1$		ATP
ATP		
$H^+ + e + O_2$		H_2O
H_2O	$H+e+O_2$	$H+eO_2$
$NADP^+$		NADPH
NADPH		

2. Use the following terms to complete the diagram of the Calvin cycle. A term may be used more than once.

Terms

1. $ATP \rightarrow ADP + P_i$

2. CO_2

3. glucose and other sugars

4. $NADPH \rightarrow NADP^+$

5. PGA

6. RuBP

Calvin cycle

a. _CO₂_

b. _RuBP_

c. _PGA_

d, e. _ATP, NADPH_

g. _①_

f. _3_

Glyceraldehyde phosphate

3.   In the following stylized drawing of a chloroplast give the name of the part indicated by each letter and tell what part of photosynthesis takes place there.

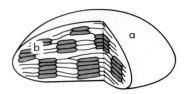

Name	Process
a. Stoma	Calvin
b. thylakoid	lite react

WHO'S WHO

Complete the following chart.

Scientist	Contribution to Biology
a. Hertz	demonstrated existence of electromagnetic waves and photoelectric effect
b. Einstein	explained photoelectric effect
Calvin	c. cycle (dark react

LEARNING CHECKLIST

1.   What are the two general types of photosynthetic pigments? Do they absorb a narrow or wide range of light wavelengths?
2.   What are the three major chemical processes that occur during photosynthesis?
3.   In cyclic photophosphorylation, what molecule donates excited electrons to ferredoxin? Where do the electrons eventually wind up? What is produced along the way? How is it produced?
4.   What pigment molecule donates excited electrons in photosystem II?
5.   What two energy-rich compounds are produced during the light reactions in plants (photosystems II and I)? What compound is the ultimate source of the electrons that get transported in these light reactions?
6.   What gas is produced during the light reactions of photosynthesis?
7.   What carbon compound joins with carbon dioxide at the beginning of the Calvin cycle? Name two carbon compounds that are produced from glyceraldehyde phosphate later in the cycle. What provides the energy to drive the Calvin cycle?
8.   State where the light and dark reactions occur in a plant cell.
9.   Name two environmental conditions that tend to promote photorespiration rather than carbon fixation. Name two different strategies that have evolved in different plants to circumvent photorespiration.

MINI EXAM

A. Circle the letter of the one best answer for each question.

1.   During what stage of photosynthesis is O_2 produced?
     a. cyclic photophosphorylation
     b. the light reactions involving photosystems I and II
     c. carbon fixation
     d. the Krebs cycle
     e. O_2 is not produced during photosynthesis

2. The pigment molecules responsible for photosynthesis are located in the
   a. mitochondria
   b. cytoplasm of the cell
   c. stroma of the chloroplast
   d. thylakoid membrane of the chloroplast
   e. all of the above

3. Both carotenoids and chlorophylls
   a. are pigments
   b. absorb photons of wide energy ranges
   c. contain porphyrin rings
   d. all of the above
   e. none of the above

4. Which of the following is the correct sequence for the movement of electrons during the light reactions of plants?
   a. P_{680} --> P_{700} --> water --> NADP
   b. water --> P_{700} --> NADP --> P_{680}
   c. P_{700} --> P_{680} --> NADP --> water
   d. P_{680} --> water --> P_{700} --> NADP
   e. water --> P_{680} --> P_{700} --> NADP

5. What pigment is used in human vision?
   a. chlorophyll <u>a</u>
   b. beta-carotene
   c. retinal
   d. vitamin A
   e. ferredoxin

6. During what stage of photosynthesis are ATP and NADPH converted to ADP + P_i and $NADP^+$?
   a. the light reactions
   b. the dark reactions
   c. both of the above
   d. none of the above

7. Water vapor exits and CO_2 enters a leaf through the
   a. stomata
   b. grana
   c. porphyrin rings
   d. photons
   e. stroma

8. Which of the following organisms have the greatest problem with photorespiration?
   a. C_4 plants
   b. heterotrophs
   c. C_3 plants
   d. CAM plants
   e. chemoautotrophs

9. What energy-rich organic compound is produced as a result of the Calvin cycle?
   a. NADPH
   b. CO_2
   c. ATP
   d. H_2O
   e. glucose

   e

10. High-energy photons
    a. have long wavelengths
    b. have short wavelengths
    c. are more likely to produce red light than blue light
    d. cannot be absorbed

    b

11. Light that is visible to humans occupies what part of the electromagnetic spectrum?
    a. the entire upper half
    b. the entire lower half
    c. a small portion in the middle
    d. the entire spectrum
    e. visible light is not part of the electromagnetic spectrum

12. During photosynthesis, photons raise electrons to higher energy levels. These excited electrons belong to what compound?
    a. H_2O
    b. ATP
    c. RuBP
    d. glucose
    e. chlorophyll

13. Which of the following occurs during the light reactions of plants?
    a. electron transport
    b. chemiosmosis
    c. splitting of water
    d. all of the above
    e. none of the above

14. When water is split during photosynthesis, what is the first substance to receive its electrons?
    a. ferredoxin
    b. protein Z
    c. $NADP^+$
    d. P_{700}
    e. P_{680}

15. Green sulfur bacteria carry out
    a. cyclic photophosphorylation
    b. noncyclic photophosphorylation
    c. both of the above
    d. none of the above

16. The earliest photosynthesizers probably used what as a source of hydrogen?
    a. H_2S
    b. H_2O
    c. CO_2
    d. $C_6H_{12}O_6$

17. How many carbon atoms are in a molecule of RuBP?
    a. O
    b. 1
    c. 2
    d. 3
    e. 5

18. Which of the following is mismatched?
    a. Photosystem I - uses the P_{700} molecule in its photocenter
    b. PGA - a 3-carbon compound
    c. heterocysts - carry out nitrogen fixation
    d. CAM plants - open their stomata during the day and close them at night to avoid photorespiration
    e. C_4 plants - expend ATP to concentrate CO_2 in bundle-sheath cells to avoid photorespiration

19. Which of the following statements about photosynthesis is true?
    a. The light reactions can occur only in the light, the dark reactions only in the dark.
    b. Photorespiration is more efficient at producing glucose than is photosynthesis.
    c. The light reactions produce the energy-rich compounds that are used to run the dark reactions.
    d. All of the above are true.
    e. None of the above are true.

20. Which of the following statements accurately describes the relationship between photosynthesis and cellular respiration?
    a. Photosynthesis occurs only in autotrophs, cellular respiration occurs only in heterotrophs.
    b. Photosynthesis uses solar energy to convert inorganics to energy-rich organics, respiration breaks down energy-rich organics to synthesize ATP.
    c. Photosynthesis involves the oxidation of glucose, respiration involves the reduction of CO_2.
    d. The primary function of photosynthesis is to use solar energy to synthesize ATP, the primary function of cellular respiration is to break down ATP and release energy.
    e. Photosynthesis and cellular respiration occur in separate, specialized organelles; the two processes cannot occur in the same cell at the same time.

b

B. Provide the appropriate term to complete each statement.

1. The units of energy in light are called _photons_.
2. Molecules that absorb light are called _pigments_.
3. The dark reactions of photosynthesis are also known as _Calvin cycle_ or _carbon fixation_.
4. In plants and algae, all photosynthetic reactions take place in the organelles called _chloroph_.
5. The membrane-bound protein that accepts electrons from P_{700} in photosystem I is called _ferrodoxin_.
6. During the light reactions, O_2 is produced when molecules of _H_2O_ are split.
7. At the beginning of the Calvin cycle, RuBP combines with _CO_2_.
8. In chloroplasts, stacks of thylakoids are called _grana_.
9. _RuBP_ is the enzyme that initiates carbon fixation or _photo resp_ depending on local conditions.
10. Chlorophyll molecules use _Mg_ atoms as their source of electrons to be excited by photons.

C. Briefly answer each of the following questions.

1. What is meant by the bumper sticker that says: "Have you thanked a green plant today?"
2. Briefly describe the interdependent relationship between the light and dark reactions of a green plant.
3. Compare the roles of electron transport and of water in oxidative respiration and aerobic photosynthesis.

CHAPTER 9 ANSWERS

TOPIC EXERCISES

1.
Start	End
a. ADP + P_i	ATP
b. H_2O	$H^+ + e + O_2$
c. $NADP^+$	NADPH

(Note: the vertical listing makes no difference here, e.g., whether H_2O is on the line above or below $NADP^+$. The important point is that the horizontal row is correct - what you start with, what you wind up with).

2. a. CO_2
   b. RuBP
   c. PGA
   d.,e. ATP --> ADP + P_i, NADPH --> $NADP^+$
   f. glucose and other sugars
   g. ATP --> ADP + P_i

3.   Name   Process

   a. stroma   Calvin cycle (dark reactions)

   b. thylakoid   light reactions

WHO'S WHO

   a. Hertz
   b. Einstein
   c. discovered (worked out details of) the dark reactions of photosynthesis

LEARNING CHECKLIST

1.   carotenoids and chlorophylls; carotenoids absorb wide range of light wavelengths; chlorophylls absorb narrow range (pp. 181-182)

2.   light reactions, dark reactions, rejuvenation of pigment (pp. 184-185)

3.   a chlorophyll pigment molecule called P_{700}; back at the P_{700}; ATP; by chemiosmosis run by electron transport (pp. 185-187)

4. P_{680} (pp. 187-188)

5.   ATP and NADPH (p. 188); water (p. 189)

6. O_2 (p. 189)

7.   RuBP; glucose, RuBP; ATP and NADPH (pp. 191-193)

8.   light reactions: in the thylakoids of the chloroplasts and across the thylakoid membranes; dark reactions: in the stroma of the chloroplast (pp. 193-194)

9.   high temperature and high O_2/low CO_2 levels; crassulacean acid metabolism (CAM) and C_4 photosynthesis (pp. 194-197)

MINI EXAM

A.   1. b   2. d   3. a   4. e   5. c   6. b
     7. a   8. c   9. e   10. b   11. c   12. e
     13. d   14. b   15. a   16. a   17. e   18. d
     19. c   20. b

B.   1. photons   2. pigments   3. the Calvin cycle, carbon fixation
      4. chloroplasts   5. ferredoxin   6. water
      7. CO_2 8. grana   9. RuBP carboxylase, photorespiration
      10. magnesium

C. 1.   Without green plants, we wouldn't be here. They produce O_2 as a by-product of the light reactions of photosynthesis, and this O_2 is released and becomes part of the atmosphere. We use the O_2 to carry out oxidative respiration; without it we would die. As heterotrophs, we also depend on the autotrophic plants as the ultimate source of the energy-rich organic compounds that we utilize as food, but cannot synthesize by ourselves. (pp. 184-193, this chapter; pp. 156-174, chapter 8)

   2.   The light reactions produce the ATP and NADPH that provide the energy to run the dark reactions. The dark reactions, in turn, convert the ATP and NADPH back to ADP + P_i and $NADP^+$ that can then be recycled and used to keep the light reactions running when light and water are available. (pp. 184-193)

   3.   In both respiration and photosynthesis, electron transport is used to produce ATP by chemiosmosis. In respiration, water is formed as an end product when oxygen acts as the final electron acceptor at the end of the electron transport chain. In photosynthesis, on the other hand, water is the ultimate source of the electrons that get transported. (pp. 184-190, this chapter; pp. 172-174, chapter 8)

10: THE CELL CYCLE: MITOSIS

IN THE GRAND SCHEME

Each cell living at this moment is the product of division of some previous cell. This is as true of people as of one celled organisms. Failure to divide into faithful copies of parent cells can be disastrous. Such is the origin of cancer cells.

A highly structured process has evolved that increases the probability that the products of cell division are, indeed, duplicates of the parent cell. The details of this process make up this chapter. The understanding of these details is vital to understanding the chapters that follow.

FOR REVIEW

DNA: DNA is a double helix of linked nucleotides. The nucleotide sequences of DNA code for specific amino acid sequences of polypeptides essential for the cell's function. The sum of all of these codes makes up the heredity information of the cell.

Chromosomes: Chromosomes are packages of DNA and protein containing the cell's heredity information.

Nuclear envelope: The nuclear envelope contains the nucleus. The envelope consists of two membranes penetrated by pores.

Microtubules: Microtubules are hollow tubes of about 25 nm in diameter composed of a protein called tubulin.

Microtubular organizing center: In cells, microtubules form around structures called organizing centers.

CHAPTER OUTLINE

Reformation of the Nuclei: Telophase
CYTOKINESIS ((pp. 214-215)
COMPARING CELL DIVISION IN EUKARYOTES AND PROKARYOTES (p. 215)

KEY TERMS

p. 203: genome, replication origin, binary fission
p. 205: chromatin, duplex
p. 206: histones, nucleosome, supercoils, heterochromatin, euchromatin, centromere, karyotype
p. 207: gametes, diploid, haploid complement, homologues, cytokinesis
p. 209: interphase, sister chromatids, centromere, kinetochore, condensation, centrioles, tubulin, prophase, spindle fibers, spindle apparatus
p. 212: aster, metaphase, metaphase plate
p. 214: cytokinesis
p. 215: cleavage furrow, cell plate, middle lamella

TOPIC EXERCISES

1. A concept of major importance to the understanding of this and later units is understanding the distinction between the terms <u>haploid</u> and <u>diploid</u>. A subset of this understanding is the distinction between the terms <u>chromosome</u> and <u>chromatid</u>. Complete the following table, and use it to clarify these relationships. The chromosome number for this diploid hypothetical cell is 4, i.e. 2n=4.

End of phase cell cycle	Number of copies of each DNA molecule	Number of centromeres	Number of chromatids	Number of chromosomes
G_1	1	4	4	4
S	2	4	8	4
G_2	3	4	8	4

2. It is common to study the process of mitosis by studying drawings or pictures of various phases. A better understanding that will make following chapters easier to understand is acquired by the following means. List each phase of mitosis and, for each, list the important distinguishing events. At table is given below to guide you. Complete the table and base your study on it.

Phase	Event
Interphase	
Prophase	
Metaphase	
Anaphase	
Telophase	cytokinesis

3. Although distinct phases have not been assigned to events of binary fission, as they have in mitosis, the process is orderly and can be described step-wise. List below the sequence of events as described in this chapter.

a. *genome replication*

b. *" copy attach to inner cell membrane*

c. *cell growth*

d. *new p membr between*

e. *" c wall separates*

LEARNING CHECKLIST

1. Compare euchromatin and heterochromatin.
2. Describe the karyotyping of human chromosomes
3. List and describe the features of the five stages of the cell cycle.
4. List the five stages of mitosis and events occurring in mitosis.
5. How do plant and animal mitosis differ?

MINI EXAM

A. Circle the letter of the best answer for each question.

1. Before cell division in bacteria, the daughter genomes are attached to the:
   a. interior of the cell membrane
   b. centriole
   c. centromere
   d. cell wall

2. In the division of plant cells
   a. cytokinesis occurs at the end of telophase
   b. the formation of the aster by the spindle apparatus occurs at the beginning of metaphase
   c. the centrioles move toward the poles in prophase
   d. a cleavage furrow develops during telophase
   e. the nuclear envelope does not break down until the chromosomal manipulation is complete

3. In the eukaryote chromosome, the DNA is coiled around a complex of:
   a. histamines   c. heterochromatin
   b. nucleotides   d. histones

4. With regard to chromosome number, most human body cells are
   a. haploid   d. tetraploid
   b. monoploid   e. polyploid
   c. diploid

5. DNA that is never expressed genetically is
   a. prochromatin   d. heterochromatin
   b. euchromatin   e. oligochromatin
   c. achromatin

81

6. In the lift cycle of a cell
   a. DNA synthesis occurs in the M phase
   b. the C phase ends the interphase
   c. the genome is replicated in the S phase
   d. the cell resumes normal growth and may spend most of its life span in the G_2 phase
   e. the replication of the parent cell's organelles occurs in the S phase

7. The portion of a chromosome that is genetically expressed is composed of
   a. euchromatin   d. antichromatin
   b. prochromatin   e. exochromatin
   c. heterochromatin

8. In plant mitosis
   a. the formation of the spindle apparatus is an important process in prophase
   b. centrioles are replicated in early metaphase
   c. anaphase includes the division of centromeres
   d. daughter chromosomes are divided by diakinesis
   e. chromosome condensation is completed in interphase

9. In the life cycle of animal cells
   a. synthesis of tubulin and cell membranes occurs in the S phase
   b. daughter cells are formed in the C phase
   c. the M phase is the one in which cells spend the major portion of their life
   d. the G_2 phase is characterized by rapid growth of the cell wall to insure adequate size of progeny
   e. the C phase is the period of chromosome condensation

10. As chromosome condensation occurs,
    a. the thickening and shortening is due to the shortening of histones
    b. the length of the DNA helix is reduced by the strong attraction of hydrogen bonds
    c. chromosomes may continue twisting until a structural arrangement called hypercoil is formed
    d. RNA transcription is simplified
    e. Nucleosomes with the DNA wrapped around them twist into supercoils

11. Replication of bacterial DNA begins at a location called the
    a. replication origin   d. cell plate
    b. centriole   e. kinetochore
    c. centromere

12. In the life cycle of a cell, each chromosome contains two chromatids at the end of the
    a. G_1 phase   d. C phase
    b. M phase   e. S phase
    c. G_2 phase

13. Two nearly identical copies of one of the chromosomes makes up a pair of
    a. diplogues   d. haplogues
    b. heterologues   e. monologues
    c. homologues

14. The coiling of the long DNA thread that makes up a chromosome
    a. is the result of the contraction of the spiral protein connected to the ends of the DNA thread
    b. is initiated by the tight coiling of the two nucleosomes attached to the kinetochore
    c. occurs because of the break down of tubulin that results in its shortening
    d. is a consequence of the tension placed upon the DNA helix by the movement of centromeres
    e. begins as the DNA wraps tightly about a core made up of eight histones

15. In comparing plant and animal cell division,
    a. one must have a microscope with very high resolution to observe the subtle differences
    b. an obvious difference is the formation of a cell plate by plant cells in cytokinesis
    c. the distinction is made by the presence of nucleosomes in plant cells until late prophase
    d. the primary feature is the distinctive centriole in plant cells that is absent in animal cells
    e. the process is virtually the same in those animal cells that have cell walls as it is in plants

16. In both plant and animal mitosis, metaphase is highly recognizable because
    a. a line of condensed chromosomes can be seen in the equatorial plane, the same distance from each aster
    b. of the appearance of the metaphase plate that will eventually separate the two daughter cells.
    c. the nuclear membrane and nucleolus are both absent
    d. only then are the chromosomes aligned in a plane equidistant from the poles
    e. the tubulin is arranged in a "spindle" with the centrioles at each end

17. Gametes of a person whose general body cells contain 46 chromosomes contain only 23 chromosomes. This smaller number is called
    a. septaploid   c. monoploid
    b. diploid   d. haploid

18. During anaphase of mitosis
    a. centromeres split, freeing kinetochores which are dragged toward the poles as tubulin is absorbed in aster formation
    b. in animal cells, centromeres move toward their respective centrioles
    c. kinetochores leave their old centromeres and carry the daughter chromatids toward the poles
    d. euchromatin remains tightly condensed while the heterochromatin opens up and actively controls tubulin activity
    e. in plant cells, the kinetochores move toward polar centrioles, carrying chromosomes with them

19. A nucleosome is
    a. the plant equivalent of the animal centriole toward which chromosomes will move in anaphase
    b. a core unit made of eight histones
    c. a structure in the nucleus that is responsible for RNA formation in the manufacture of ribosomes
    d. exactly what is literal translation indicates, the sum of all nuclear structures
    e. an organelle responsible for the reassembly of the nuclear envelope in telophase

20. In the life cycle of a cell, the spindle apparatus is formed in the
    a. S phase   d. G₁ phase
    b. C phase   e. G₂ phase
    c. M phase

21. Fungal cell division differs from that of both plants and animals by the characteristic of
    a. performing cytokinesis with a cell plate yet having an animal-like aster
    b. leaving the nuclear envelope intact while chromosome manipulation occurs and then forms two new nuclei within the same cell
    c. a spindle composed of the protein, mycelium, rather than tubulin
    d. centrioles being positioned in an acentric manner
    e. chromosomes of pure DNA rather than containing histones

22. The human karyotype
    a. is usually obtained from cheek epithelial cells since their collection involves no discomfort
    b. made by preparing a smear of fresh human peripheral blood on a microscope slide staining them with a special stain and viewing with a special light
    c. is simply a photograph of a polar view of chromosomes on the metaphase plate
    d. is an array of condensed chromosomes consisting of 22 pairs of chromosomes in which the paired members are quite similar and one pair that may contain either similar of dissimilar chromosomes
    e. usually contains 44 diploid chromosomes and two haploid chromosomes

23. In the life cycle of a cell, each chromosome consists of a single chromatid at the end to the
    a. G_2 phase
    b. S phase
    c. G_1 phase
    d. M phase
    e. none of these

24. Part of the variation in the appearances of chromosomes is caused by differences in the placement of the
    a. centromeres
    b. centriole
    c. nucleolus
    d. nucleosome
    e. aster

25. In mitotic prophase
    a. prokaryotic cells have completed replication
    b. animal mitochondria and plant chloroplasts replicate
    c. the cleavage furrow appears in animal cells but does not deepen until cytokinesis
    d. individual chromosomes first become visible and, in plants and animal cells, the nuclear envelope disintegrates
    e. chromosomes become visible as rings of DNA in prokaryotic cells

B. Provide the appropriate term to complete each statement.

1. The _____ is the total complement of genetic information in a cell.
2. The cell division process of prokaryotes is called _____.
3. _____ is permanently condensed chromatin.
4. The complement of chromosomes in sex cells is called the _____ relative to the other body cells.
5. The division of the cytoplasm into daughter cells is called _____.
6. _____ are microtubule organizing centers in animal cells.
7. In animal cells, a radial array of microtubules called a(n) _____ forms at each pole.
8. At metaphase, each centromere contains two protein disks called _____.
9. In anaphase, sister chromatids are moved apart by sliding _____.
10. The final separation of daughter cells in plants is accomplished by the expansion of a partition called the _____.

C. Briefly answer each of the following questions.

1. How do DNA, histones, nucleosomes and RNA relate to the structure of a chromosome?

2. (a) Describe a condensed eukaryotic chromosome (b) What feature of that chromosome is the most reliable indicator of chromosome number?

3. (a) What number and kinds of chromosomes comprise the human genome prior to cell division? (b) What components make up an individual chromosome prior to cell division?

CHAPTER ANSWERS

TOPIC EXERCISES

1.

End of phase cell cycle	Number of copies of each DNA molecule	Number of centromeres	Number of chromatids	Number of chromosomes
G_1	1	4	4	4
S	2	4	8	4
G_2	2	4	8	4

2. a. Genome and organelles replicated; chromosome condensation begins.
    b. Chromosomes become visible, spindle apparatus and poles established, nuclear membrane disperses, and nucleolus disappears.
    c. Chromosomes align on metaphase plate; kinetochores divide
    d. Centromeres divide and daughter chromosomes move to opposite poles
    e. Cell reorganization; cytokinesis

3. a. Genome replication
    b. Genome copies attached to inner cell membrane
    c. Cell growth
    d. New plasma membrane grows between genome copies
    e. New cell wall separates daughter cells

LEARNING CHECKLIST

1. The DNA and histone complex is referred to as chromatin. During cell division, the chromatin condenses greatly. Most of the chromatin resumes its expanded, open form after completion of cell division and the genes become active. This portion of the chromatin is called euchromatin. Part of the chromatin, called heterochromatin, remains condensed and the genes remain inactive. (pp. 205-207)

2. Blood of an individual is sampled. A chemical is added to induce cell division. The mitotic process is arrested during metaphase by the addition of another chemical. Because the chromosomes are in their most condensed state in metaphase, they are easiest to separate and identify at this time. The chromosome array is photographed. The chromosomes are cut out of the photograph and arranged in a prescribed order. (See figure 10-6) The chromosome complement can be inventoried and its normalcy determined. (pp. 206-207)

3. (a) G_1 phase: cell growth
    (b) S phase: genome replication
    (c) G_2 phase: organelles replicate, chromosome condensation and microtubule synthesis.
    (d) M phase (mitosis): microtubule apparatus assembles and manipulates chromosomes. Internal cell components separated into two groups (e) C phase (cytokinesis): Cell divides into two daughter cells. (pp. 207-208)

4.   (a) Interphase (including G_1, S and G_2 phases): chromosomes replicate and condense. Centrioles are replicated and tubulin synthesized.
   (b) Prophase: chromosomes condense. Nuclear membrane breaks down. Spindle apparatus of the protein, tubulin, forms between poles.
   (c) Metaphase: chromosomes align around the inner circumference of the cell, manipulated by microtubules of the spindle apparatus. The phase ends with the division of centromeres. Freed chromatids are attached to the spindle.
   (d) Anaphase: poles are pushed apart sliding microtubules. Sister chromatids move toward poles as tubules attached to their kinetochore shorten.
   (e) Telophase: Mitotic apparatus is disassembled. Nuclei are reformed. Genes resume activity. (pp. 209-214)

5.   When animal centrioles reach the poles radiating tubules brace the centrioles against the cell producing a star-like appearance, the term aster is applied to this array. Plants do not produce asters. In cytokinesis, the division of the cell body into two daughter cells, animals form a cleavage furrow that continually deepens until the cell body is cleaved into two daughter cells. Plants, having a rigid cell wall, synthesize a partition between the two halves of the cell that grows outward until the parent cell is completely divided into two daughter cells. (pp. 212-215)

MINI EXAM

A.

1. a	2. a	3. d	4. c	5. d	6. c
7. a	8. a	9. b	10. e	11. a	12. e
13. c	14. c	15. b	16. d	17. d	18. b
19. b	20. c	21. b	22. d	23. c	24. a
25. d					

B.

1. genome	2. binary fission	3. heterochromatin
4. haploid complement	5. cytokinesis	6. centrioles
7. aster	8. kinetochores	9. spindle fibers
10. cell plate		

C. 1.   DNA is a very long, continuous double-stranded fiber that coils around polypeptides called histones. Eight such histones form the core of an assembly called a nucleosome. The nucleosome acts as a form for the coiling of the DNA. Since DNA is the site of RNA synthesis, RNA is associated with chromosomes. (p. 206)

    2.   (a) Prior to cell division, the chromosome consists of duplicate strands attached to each other. the chromatin is folded and condensed, making the chromosome thick except at points of constriction. A structure called the centromere is located at one of the constrictions. The two chromatids are held together by the centromere. (See figure 10-8)
       (b) The chromosome number is determined by counting the number of centromeres. One chromosome is comprised of one centromere and any attached chromatin, whether it contains one or two copies of the DNA. (p. 207)

    3.   (a) Before mitotic division, the human genome contains 46 chromosomes. the complement of 46 chromosomes represent 23 from each parent. Two of the 46 are sex chromosomes. The remaining 44 chromosomes are called autosomes.
       (b) Each chromosome is comprised of two chromatids attached to one centromere. (p. 207)

11: SEXUAL REPRODUCTION AND MEIOSIS

IN THE GRAND SCHEME

Reproduction without sex is not uncommon in the living world. Many simple organisms reproduce by mitosis or binary fission and never mate.

The evolution of sexual reproduction required a new mechanism of chromosome number adjustment. If the nuclei of two organisms fuse, in a process called syngamy, their two genomes are combined in the fusion nucleus. The chromosome number would then be doubled. A doubling of chromosome number with each subsequent generation would cause insurmountable problems. There must be one of two mechanisms to accompany syngamy. There could be a chromosome reduction following syngamy to return the organism to normal chromosome number. Alternatively, there could be a process of reduction of the normal chromosome complement prior to syngamy bringing the chromosome number n the progeny to a normal compliment when the two nuclei merge.

The latter process predominates and was named meiosis. The process involves two successive divisions. The first division reduces the number of chromosomes to half, a condition termed haploid. The second division reduces the chromatid number per chromosome from two to one. The process also includes events that enhance variability. As the first division begins, genes are exchanged between homologous chromosomes from the two parents, with the result that both chromosomes carry genes from the chromosome of the other parent in place of the one inherited from the prior generation. The altered chromosomes are then randomly sorted into the newly forming nuclei. These two events provide virtually infinite variability.

It is believed that syngamy evolved as a mechanism for repairing breaks or deletions in chromosomes by providing an intact template from the mating partner. The variability resulting from sexual reproduction could either enhance or hinder the progeny. A highly successful organism or population will loose genetic stability. The genes gained <u>may</u> be less beneficial than the ones lost in the exchange or vice versa. In any event, evolution thrives on variability.

FOR REVIEW

Microtubules: Microtubules are fine, hollow tubes that make up the spindle apparatus used to move chromosomes around.

Centromere: Each chromosome has a constriction called the centromere, where chromatids of a chromosome are attached to each other and to the spindle apparatus.

Mitosis: Mitosis is a process of cell division resulting in cells genetically identical to the cell from which they were formed.

Homologous chromosomes: Homologous chromosomes are chromosomes from each of two parents that carry genetic information for the same characteristics.

CHAPTER OUTLINE

THE DISCOVERY OF MEIOSIS (p. 219)
SEXUAL VERSUS ASEXUAL REPRODUCTION (pp. 219-220)
THE SEXUAL LIFE CYCLE (pp. 220-221)
     somatic cells versus sex cells
     zygote

KEY TERMS

P. 219: fertilization, syngamy, meiosis, diploid, haploid, sexual reproduction
P. 221: homologous chromosomes, homologues, crossing over
P. 222: synapsis, synaptonemal complex, chiasma, chiasmata
P. 223: terminal chiasmata
P. 226: parthenogenesis

TOPIC EXERCISES

These activities will help you understand the differences between mitosis and meiosis, and between the two divisions of meiosis.

1.　　Mitosis: In the figures provided, show the locations and content of the chromosomes in each phase. For simplicity, assume a diploid chromosome number of two (one homologue from each parent.) Draw the chromosomes with colored markers to distinguish between homologues. Show the number of chromatids per chromosome.

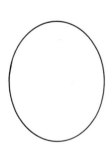
Prophase

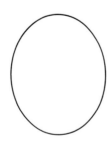
Metaphase

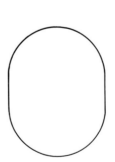
Anaphase

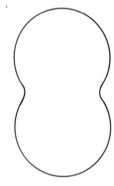
Telophase

2.   Meiosis I: Using the same technique and principles as above, fill in the chromosomes in the figures provided below. When finished, compare them with the set you did for mitosis in number 1 above.

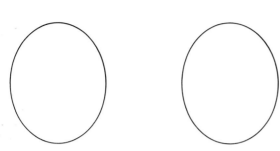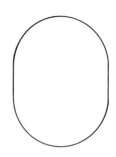

Prophase I   Metaphase I   Anaphase I   Telophase I

3.   Meiosis II: Again, using the same techniques and principles, fill in the chromosomes in the figures provided below for meiosis II. Assume on the resulting cells from number 2 above as a starting point. When finished, compare with mitosis and with meiosis I.

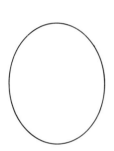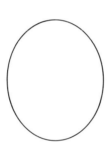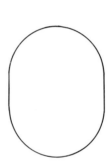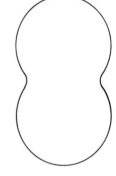

Prophase II   Metaphase II   Anaphase II   Telophase II

LEARNING CHECKLIST

1.   In a physical sense, how is sexual reproduction different from asexual reproduction?
2.   Why are both syngamy and meiosis essential to sexual reproduction?
3.   (a) What is meant by the terms haploid and diploid? (b) How do these terms relate to somatic or gametic cells?
4.   What are the three major properties by which meiosis and mitosis differ?
5.   Compare meiosis II and mitosis.
6.   By what means and through what phases does independent assortment occur in meiosis?
7.   How is it believed that sexual reproduction arose?
8.   Critique the processes of meiosis and sexual reproduction as to (a) genetic and (b) evolutionary consequences.

MINI EXAM

A. Circle the letter of the one best answer for the following questions.

1.   The fertilization of female gamete results in a single cell
      a. which is called a zygote in most eukaryotic organisms, but a human zygote which is called a fetus
      b. which is diploid in most multicellular eukaryotic species but haploid in algae
      c. which undergoes many divisions by binary fission
      d. which is diploid and referred to as a zygote
      e. except in parthenogenic species who form a multicellular mass

2. In prophase I of meiosis
   a. a protein lattice and the two chromatids of a chromosome form a structure called a synaptonemal complex
   b. soon after pairing, homologous chromosomes begin the exchange of genetic material, forming a figure called chiasma
   c. the centromeres are exchanged for kinetochores as the first step of crossing over.
   d. crossing over is initiated by the formation of terminal chiasmata
   e. individual strands of DNA of homologous chromosomes pair closely and precisely

3. Anaphase I differs from mitotic anaphase by
   a. the less tightly coiled chromosomes in anaphase I than those in mitotic anaphase
   b. the placement of the centrioles which is acentric in mitosis but not meiosis
   c. the composition of the chromosomes, in that the anaphase I chromosomes have two chromatids and mitotic anaphase chromosomes have only one chromatid
   d. the number of chromosomes, haploid in mitosis and diploid in meiosis
   e. the absence of cytokinesis in meiosis

4. A zygote divides by
   a. meiosis
   b. syngamy
   c. oogamy
   d. mitosis
   e. fission

5. In comparing meiosis II to mitosis it would be correct to say
   a. the greatest similarity is in the number and contents of the chromosomes
   b. mitosis is not nearly as similar to meiosis II as it is to meiosis I
   c. they are distinctly different, the meiotic division being more complex
   d. the most striking difference is in prophase in which the genes of homologues cross over
   e. that the mechanics of the two processes are essentially the same

6. The meiotic structure shaped like the letter "X" is called a
   a. chiasma
   b. terminal metonema
   c. metonema
   d. terminal chiasma
   e. protonema

7. The crossing over process is thought to have originated from
   a. recombinant DNA
   b. mutation
   c. genetic engineering
   d. gene repair

8. Fusion of haploid gametes to form a diploid cell is
   a. karyogamy
   b. polyploidy
   c. syngamy
   d. heterogamy

9. Unlike gametes, body cells are called
   a. somatic
   b. haploid
   c. semantic
   d. colloid
   e. hepatic

10. Unlike mitotic telophase, in telophase I
    a. the nucleus does not reform before the next prophase
    b. the tubules of the spindle reach all centromeres from each pole
    c. the homologues of one parent are gathered into one nucleus while the homologues of the other parent are collected in the other nucleus
    d. the chromosomes are harder to see because of less condensation
    e. there are two chromatids per chromosome and the genes that make up the chromatids probably differ

11. Most of the cells in the body of higher multicellular eukaryotic organisms are
    a. haploid and in interphase
    b. diploid and somatic
    c. haploid and gametic
    d. diploid and gametic
    e. diploid and undifferentiated

12. Sexual reproduction involves alternation of
    a. mitosis and isogamy
    b. syngamy and meiosis
    c. meiosis and oogamy
    d. heterogamy and meiosis
    e. mitosis and oogamy

13. Most multicellular eukaryotic organisms form gametes by
    a. meiosis
    b. mitosis
    c. parthenogenesis
    d. binary fission
    e. oncogenesis

14. In metaphase I, independent assortment is assured by
    a. the random placement of the homologues on the metaphase plate with regard to accessibility of spindle fibers of the two poles
    b. the law of averages that applies universally
    c. the utter precision by which the homologues from each parent are oriented toward alternate poles
    d. the variation in the availability of specific centromeres because of their face-to-face orientation
    e. the crossing over of genetic material

15. Metaphase II differs from mitotic metaphase in
    a. the dissimilarity of chromatids comprising the chromosomes in metaphase II
    b. the arrangement of chromosomes because of the chiasmata
    c. the number of centrioles per centromere
    d. the spindle position of the two phases
    e. the arrangement of chromosomes on the metaphase plate

16. The complement of chromosomes in a gamete is
    a. haploid
    b. identical
    c. diploid
    d. reversed

17. With respect to modes of reproduction and evolution,
    a. population stability resulting from sexual reproduction has caused it to be universally favored
    b. the diversification resulting from unequal binary fission is responsible for the rapid rate of early evolution
    c. even though asexual reproduction is preferable, it won't work in multicellular organisms
    d. algae have survived stressful situations by evolving an asexual alternative to the usual sexual reproduction
    e. it appears that evolution has overwhelmingly favored sexual reproduction in vertebrates

18. A major way in which metaphase I is different from metaphase II is
    a. the position of the metaphase plate in the cell
    b. the presence of the aster that is no longer visible by metaphase II
    c. the composition of the chromatids that make up the chromosomes
    d. the appearance of the chromosomes because of the persistence of chiasmata in metaphase I
    e. there are fewer centrioles in metaphase II

19. All of the following activities in the sexual cycle increase genetic variability except
    a. fertilization of one gamete by another
    b. cleavage of the zygote into increasing numbers of cells and the induced specialization thereafter
    c. independent assortment in meiosis
    d. crossing over in prophase I of meiosis

20. In prophase I, there is side by side alignment of paired homologues in a process called
    a. syngamy   c. zygosity
    b. phoresis   d. synapsis

B. Provide the appropriate term to complete the statement.

1. _____ is the fusion of haploid gametes to form a diploid cell.

2. The kind of cell division resulting in a reduction in chromosome number is _____.

3. Another term for fertilization is _____.

4. Paired homologues exchange genetic material in a process called _____.

5. At one stage in meiosis a lattice of protein holds homologues chromosomes in precise alignment, forming a complex called the _____.

6. In metaphase I, the points of attachment because of genetic exchange move to the ends of the chromosomes here they are called _____.

7. In comparing mitosis and the two meiotic divisions, it is evident that meiosis II most nearly resembles _ _____, in terms of mechanics.

8. Development of an adult from an unfertilized egg is called _____.

9. _____ reproduction increases the ability to introduce variability.

C. Briefly answer each of the following questions.

1. Explain how terminal chiasmata cause homologous chromosomes to go to opposite poles in meiosis I.

2. In anaphase I, unlike mitosis, both chromatids of a homologue travel together to a pole. This is a byproduct of the terminal chiasmata. Explain.

3. List the stages of meiosis I and the events that characterize each stage.

4. Compare prophase I of meiosis to prophase of mitosis including: (a) proximity of homologues to each other. (b) the physical nature and genetic consequences of the synaptonemal complex and crossing over. (c) spindle attachment to chromosomes.

CHAPTER ANSWERS

TOPIC EXERCISES

1.

Prophase

Metaphase

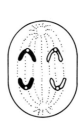
Anaphase

Telophase

2.

Prophase I

Metaphase I

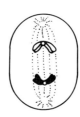
Anaphase I

Telophase I

3

Prophase II

Metaphase II

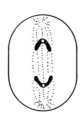
Anaphase II

Telophase II

LEARNING CHECKLIST

1. In sexual reproduction cells from two parents, each containing half the chromosome number of the parent, combine to produce progeny. In asexual reproduction, cells replicate their entire genome and pass one copy to each progeny. (pp. 219-220)

2. All members of a species normally have the same number of chromosomes. Without meiosis, the chromosome number would double with the fusion of cells from the two parents. Meiosis is necessary to adjust the chromosome number so that each generation will have the same number of chromosomes. Likewise, a gamete requires syngamy with another in order to establish the appropriate complement of chromosomes. (p. 219)

3. A diploid cell has a complement of chromosomes conferred by two parents. A haploid cell has half the parental complement of chromosomes. Human somatic cells are diploid, whereas human gametic cells are haploid. (pp. 219-220)

4. Meiosis differs from mitosis in the following ways; (1) homologous chromosomes pair in prophase I an exchange genetic material. (2) homologues remain together through the first meiotic division. (3) chromosomes do not replicate between meiotic divisions. (pp. 220-221)

5. The mechanics of the second meiotic division is essentially mitotic. The resulting cells are, however, haploid and are not genetically the same as they would be in mitosis. (p. 224)

6. When homologues pair on the metaphase plate in metaphase I, they do so randomly with regard to parental source. Consequently, attachment of any homologue to a particular pole is also random. They will be drawn apart to their randomly determined pole in anaphase I. (pp. 223-224)

7. The synaptonemal complex provides the opportunity for repair of breaks in DNA. Thus, those organisms that joined in this manner were able to survive chromosome damage. (pp. 221-223)

8. Sexual reproduction increases genetic variability through independent assortment and crossing over in meiosis and the bringing together two gene lines through fertilization. The consequence is virtually unlimited variation. This is not always beneficial. It is said that one should not "mess with success." New genes for old may be a step backwards for the individual. However, variability is the fuel of the evolutionary engine and sexual reproduction generates variability very rapidly. (pp. 224-229)

MINI EXAM

A.

1. d	2. e	3. c	4. d	5. e	6. a
7. d	8. c	9. a	10. e	11. b	12. b
13. a	14. a	15. a	16. a	17. e	18. d
19. b	20. d				

B.

1. fertilization	2. meiosis	3. syngamy
4. crossing over	5. synaptonemal complex	6. terminal chiasmata
7. mitotic	8. parthenogenesis	9. sexual
10. conservative		

C. 1. Terminal chiasmata hold homologues together in an orientation that allow attachment to only the outward facing centromeres. When microtubules shorten, homologues will be pulled apart and dragged apart and toward apposite poles (pp. 223-224)

   2. Since microtubules do not have access to both sides of a centromere, the two chromatids do not get pulled apart. (pp. 222-223)

3. (a) Prophase I. Chromosomes become microscopically visible. DNA strands of homologues pair side-by-side.
    (b) Metaphase I. Chiasmata become terminal. Homologous pairs align an the metaphase plate.
    (c) Anaphase I. Homologues are segregated. One homologue of each pair goes to each pole, assorted randomly as to parental source.
    (d) Telophase I. New nuclei form, containing one member of each homologous pair. The chromosomes are composed of chromatids that are not identical because of crossing over. Cytokinesis may or may not occur. (pp. 221-224)

4. (a) There is no pairing of homologues in mitosis as in meiosis. Strands of DNA pair precisely, gene for gene, in meiosis.
    (b) The synaptonemal complex is formed by the two homologues and a lattice of protein that holds them in precise register with each other. Genes cross over from the DNA of one homologue to that of another. The two chromosomes remain attached at these points for a while. Eventually, the two chromosomes will move apart, carrying their gene replacement with them. The genetic consequence is, for better or worse, an altered genome.
    (c) Because the two homologous chromosomes are paired, the facing sides of each are not accessible to the spindle fibers. Therefore, each homologue becomes attached to a different pole. (pp. 221-224)

12: PATTERNS OF INHERITANCE

IN THE GRAND SCHEME

"Her mother's eyes, her father's nose" etc., are attributed to our children soon after birth. Similarities from generation to generation have been observed in all familiar plants and animals for centuries. However intriguing the similarities were, the causes of the similarities eluded mankind for a long time. Faulty beliefs were abundant. Even well controlled experiments failed to reveal the secrets of inheritance.

It was Gregor Mendel who built on earlier work and improved on their methods that formed the foundation of the scientific study of inheritance. Mendel added the key step in the experimentation -- quantification. His records of variations of phenotypes resulting from various crosses enabled him to create a model upon which understanding of heredity would be built. He established the Law of Segregation and the Law of Independent Assortment. Mendel also developed the procedure known as the testcross. Reginald C Punnett added his visualization device, the Punnett square. Eventually it was recognized that chromosomes were the bearers of hereditary information and the "factors" of Mendel were genes. The recognition of the genetic effects of gene crossover led to the ability to map chromosomes. Mechanisms of gene interaction were discovered that shed light on phenomena that had not yielded to more simple models. As the succeeding chapters will demonstrate, scientists are now able to deal with genetics on a molecular level and change the course of events through the restructuring of chromosomes.

FOR REVIEW

Scientific method: The scientific method is the experimental testing of a hypothesis formulated after the systematic, objective collection of data.

Chromosomes: Chromosomes, composed of DNA and protein, control the hereditary information for a cell except during cell division, when they are distributed.

Meiosis: Meiosis is a cell division process in which the number of chromosomes is reduced to half of that of the original source cell.

CHAPTER OUTLINE

KEY TERMS

p. 234: hybridization, segregation, true-breeding
p. 236: self fertilization, experimental cross
p. 237: first filial (F_1), dominant, recessive, second filial (F_2)
p. 239: Mendelian ratio, alleles, homozygous, heterozygous, genes, locus, genotype, phenotype
p. 241: Punnett square, testcross
p. 242: Mendel's First Law of Heredity, Law of Segregation
p. 243: dihybrid
p. 244: Mendel's Second Law of Heredity, Law of Independent Assortment
p. 245: binomial distribution, probability
p. 246: mutant, X chromosome, Y chromosome, sex linked
p. 248: crossing over
p. 249: centimorgan, wild type, syntenic, linked, three-point cross
p. 251: epistasis, pleiotropic
p. 253: modified ratio

WHO'S WHO IN BIOLOGY

Scientist	Contribution
Koelreater	_____
Mendel	_____
Punnett	_____
Sutton	_____
Morgan	_____

TOPIC EXERCISES

To better visualize Mendel's experiments and findings, construct Punnett squares and display the genotypes of offspring of various parents. First, some advice on setting up the Punnett squares. The name, Punnett square, is always used even if the figure turns out to be oblong instead of square. The Punnett square consists of intersecting columns, vertical columns for the gametes of one parent and horizontal columns for the other parent. It makes no difference which direction is assigned to which parent. It is first necessary to determine the various genetic contents of the potential gametes of each parent. For instance, a parent who is Ww will form gametes containing W in one and w in the other. No other possibilities exist. A parent who is ww will form only gametes containing w.

1. Try constructing a Punnett square for the parents mentioned above (Ww x ww.) First draw one column for each gamete type of parent number one (Ww.) At the head of each column, place the letter for the gene of one of the gametes (W or w.) Notice that the second parent can only form gametes containing w.

Though you <u>could</u> draw two columns for this parent too, both would be identical and yield exactly the same ratio. Therefore, it is necessary to construct only one intersecting column. The figure formed will be oblong, rather than square. Complete the Punnett square and determine the genotypic and phenotypic ratios for the F_1 generation.

2. Now assume both parents to be Ww as would be possible for the F_2 generation. Complete that Punnett square and determine the genotypic and phenotypic ratios.

3. A more complex problem involves the simultaneous consideration of two traits, such as flower color and seed color. Remember that yellow seeds are dominant to green seeds and purple flowers are dominant over white in peas. The alleles for seed color would be represented by "G" for yellow and "g" for green. To keep the problem relatively simple, consider each parent to be heterozygous for one trait and heterozygous for the other trait. Each is homozygous recessive for the second trait. Thus, the parental genotypes would by WWgg and wwGg. Remember, that one gene for each trait will appear in each gamete. Remember, also that homologues are segregated in anaphase I. Observing some conventions reduces the probability of error. Always put the capital letter first among alleles. However, when showing gamete content or offspring genotypes, kept the letter of the same trait first, regardless of capital. Notice the following of the convention in describing the parental genotypes above. Also, remember that gametes are haploid and parents and offspring are diploid. In diploid genotypes, always group same letters of the alphabet together (WwGg not WGwg.) Complete a Punnett square for the parents described, and determine the genotypic and phenotypic ratios for the F_1.

LEARNING CHECKLIST

1. What were two ancient ideas about inheritance?
2. What were three findings of early genetics prior to Mendel's time?
3. What were the three stages of Mendel's experiment?
4. What did Mendel do differently than his predecessors did that led him successfully postulate his laws where others failed?
5. What are the 5 elements of Mendel's model of heredity?
6. What purpose is the testcross used for?
7. What was Sutton's Theory of chromosomal inheritance?
8. How is gene crossing-over important to gene assortment?

MINI EXAM

A. Circle the letter of the one best answer for each of the following questions.

1. A gene present in the organism but not expressed in its appearance is called:
   a. submissive
   b. recessive
   c. regressive
   d. syntenic

2. The unit for 1% crossing over is a:
   a. centimere
   b. centimendel
   c. centigene
   d. centigrade
   e. centimorgan

3. Which of the following gene sets represents a dihybrid?
   a. wwGg
   b. Wwgg
   c. WwGg
   d. wwgg
   e. WWGG

4. The conventional way of indicating the genes of a heterozygous flower that is red and in which red is dominant over white is:
   a. Rw
   b. Ww
   c. Rr
   d. WW

5. The phenotype of a white flower for which white is recessive is:
   a. white
   b. ww
   c. WW
   d. Ww

6. Joint action of genes resulting in continuous variation is caused by
   a. multiple genes at different loci rather and alleles interacting to affect a single trait
   b. independent assortment of genes of which there are only alleles
   c. multiple alleles for a single locus
   d. epistatic interaction of a single gene
   e. alleles derived from a population having a large gene pool

7. One refers to a gene interaction as epistatic if
   a. one of the genes has a higher centimorgan value than another
   b. one gene has a higher frequency of expression than the other interacting gene
   c. the effect of one gene is modified by another
   d. one allele dominates all other alleles
   e. the genes of one individual modify the genotype of another

8. The practice in Mendel's experiments that was different from all preceding experiments was that of
   a. using a test organism that was sure to show segregation among offspring
   b. crossing varieties exhibiting alternative forms of traits
   c. permitting hybrids to self-pollinate
   d. observation of several generations
   e. keeping of careful count of the resulting phenotypes

9. A testcross is appropriate to determine if a genotype is:
   a. WW or ww
   b. Ww of ww
   c. wW or Ww
   d. WW or Ww

10. The five elements of the model Mendel used to explain his results include all of the following except that
    a. the presence of a given element does not insure that its form of the trait will be expressed
    b. each individual contains two factors that may be different or alike, and that code for a particular trait
    c. the alleles from the two parents do not influence each other in any way
    d. not all copies of a factor are alike
    e. parents transmit their form, but not their physiological traits directly

11. Mendel believed that parents transmitted traits
    a. directly
    b. that were a blend of the traits of both parents
    c. in chromosomes
    d. as discrete factors

12. Mendel's Law of Segregation includes all of the following but
    a. genes located on different chromosomes are segregated independently
    b. when gametes are formed in heterozygous diploid individuals, the two alternative alleles segregate from on another
    c. each gamete has an equal probability of possessing either member of an allele pair
    d. the alternative form of a trait encoded by a gene are specified by alternative alleles of that gene and are discrete

13. One of the concepts that provided the basis of thinking about heredity prior to the twenty first century was
    a. only genes at the same locus can interact
    b. genes, though possessed, may not be expressed
    c. direct inheritance of parental characteristics could not occur
    d. heredity occurs within species but not between species

14. An organism is said to be true breeding if
    a. all offspring resemble it regardless of the other parent
    b. both genes for the trait are dominant
    c. it is homozygous for the trait considered
    d. both genes for the trait are recessive
    e. it is homozygous for all traits

15. A trait is said to be sex-linked if
    a. the gene for the trait is found on the X chromosome only
    b. it occurs in females whose mother displayed the trait
    c. it can be inherited only by males
    d. it occurs in males whose father displayed the trait
    e. it appears only in sexually active individuals

16. In fruit flies, the chromosome combination resulting in females is:
    a. XXyy   c. Yy
    b. Xy   d. XX

17. The ABO blood type is determined by
    a. the combination in offspring of recessive genes for B and O
    b. two alleles, except in the case of type O which results from the absence of a gene
    c. genes located at different loci of the same chromosome
    d. a single pair of alleles for which there are more than two alternatives
    e. unique factors characteristic of the blood of the Rhesus monkey

18. The genotype of a white flower for which white is recessive is
    a. white   c. syntenic
    b. pleiotripic   d. synical

19. An allele is said to be pleiotropic if
    a. it is duplicated on more than one chromosome
    b. it has more than one effect on the phenotype of its recipient
    c. it blends with another allele to produce an intermediate outcome
    d. it occurs more frequently in tropical populations
    e. it varies in its degree of expression in individuals of the same genotype

20 The occurrence of more independently assorted characteristics than there are chromosomes is the result of
    a. linkage   d. segregation
    b. hybridization   e. pleomorphism
    c. crossing-over

B. Provide the appropriate term to complete the statement.

1. Varieties that are uniform from one generation to the next are called _____.

2. The first generation of offspring of a given set of parents is called the _____.

3. A form of a trait that is unexpressed in the presence of the other form is called _____.

4. The form of a trait that is expressed to the exclusion of the other form present is called _____.

5. Alternate genes leading to alternate forms of a trait are called _____.

6. The position of a gene on a chromosome is referred to as its _____.

7. An organism possessing genes for both alternatives of a trait is said to be _____ for that trait.

8. The physical appearance resulting from a pair of alleles is the _____.

9. The _____ is a diagram that facilitates visualization of genetic possibilities.

10. A _____ is used to determine whether an organism displaying the dominant from of a trait has both genes for that alternative.

C. Briefly answer each of the following questions.

1. How are gene segregation and independent assortment different but related?

2. Explain the process of performing a testcross and the interpretation of the results.

3. What causes some syntenic genes to be considered linked whereas other syntenic genes are not?

4. How is gene crossing-over used in genetic map construction?

CHAPTER ANSWERS

WHO'S WHO IN BIOLOGY

Scientist	Contribution
Koelreutter	First successful hybridization of plant species.
Mendel	First quantitative study of genetics.
Punnett	Developed a diagram for representing genetic crosses in an orderly manner.
Sutton	First formulated the chromosomal theory of inheritance.
Morgan	First clear evidence that Sutton's theory was correct.

TOPIC EXERCISES

1.

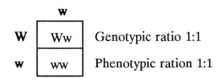

	w
W	Ww
w	ww

Genotypic ratio 1:1

Phenotypic ration 1:1

2.

	W	**w**
W	WW	Ww
w	Ww	ww

Genotypic ratio 1:2:1

Phenotypic ratio 3:1

3.

	Wg	**wg**
wG	WwGg	wwGg
wg	Wwgg	wwgg

Genotypic ratio 1:1:1:1

Phenotypic ratio 1:1:1:1

LEARNING CHECKLIST

1. (a) Heredity occurs within species. (b) traits are transmitted directly. (p. 233)

2. (a) Some forms of an inherited trait can be masked in some generations but appear unchanged again in later generations.
   (b) Forms of a trait segregate among offspring of a cross. (c) Some alternative forms of a trait are more likely to be represented than others. (p. 234)

3. (a) He allowed pea plants to produce seeds by self-fertilization for several generations, assuring constancy of traits.
   (b) He then crossed varieties exhibiting alternative forms of a trait. (c) He permitted the hybrid offspring to produce progeny by self-fertilization for several generations. (p. 236)

4. Mendel's unique technique was to keep a count of the traits of all offspring, thus enabling him to establish predictable ratios for various alternatives (pp. 237-238)

5. (a) Parents do not transmit their characteristics directly to offspring.
   (b) Each individual possesses two factors coding for a given trait.
   (c) Not all copies of a factor are identical. Alternative forms may exist. The alternatives are called alleles.
   (d) The two alleles contributed by the two parents do not influence each other in any way.
   (e) The presence of a particular element does not ensure its expression in the individual inheriting it (pp. 239-240)

6. When dominance occurs in genes, it may not be possible to distinguish the homozygous dominant genotype from a heterozygous genotype by observing the phenotypes. A testcross enables this determination. (pp. 241-242)

7. Sutton's theory contained 4 postulates:
   (a) Since one of the two gametes that unite in fertilization is a sperm with little cytoplasm and each gamete contributes equally to the heredity of offspring, the hereditary material must be in the nucleus.
   (b) Chromosomes segregate in meiosis in a similar manner to that of elements in Mendel's model.
   (c) Gametes carry one copy of each pair of homologous chromosomes. The progeny are diploid and have two copies. In Mendel's model, gametes have one copy of each element; diploid individuals have two copies.
   (d) The behavior of chromosomes in meiosis independently assorts them in a manner similar to factors postulated by Mendel. (pp. 245-246)

8. The crossing-over of genes in meiosis enables genes to be assorted that would otherwise be carried together on the same chromosome. (pp. 247-250)

MINI EXAM

A.
1. b	2. e	3. c	4. b	5. a	6. a
7. c	8. e	9. d	10. e	11. d	12. a
13. d	14. c	15. a	16. d	17. d	18. b
19. b	20. c				

B.
1. true breeding	2. first filial or F_2	3. recessive
4. dominant	5. alleles	6. locus
7. heterozygous	8. phenotype	9. Punnett square
10. testcross		

C. 1. The segregation of homologues in meiosis insures that the alleles that they carry will be contained in different gametes. Thus each gene will be distributed independently of the one on the other homologue. Independent assortment is a consequence of genes for different traits occurring on the same chromosome and staying together. (pp. 243-245)

2. In a testcross, the individual with the dominant trait expressed is crossed with a homozygous recessive individual. If the genotype containing the dominant gene is homozygous, all offspring will exhibit the dominant trait. If the genotype with the dominant gene is heterozygous, fifty percent of the offspring will display the recessive trait. (pp. 241-242)

3. They are located too close together on the chromosome to be assorted independently. (p. 248)

4. The frequency of crossing-over between two genes is proportional to the distance between the genes. If the locus on one and the cross-over is known, their relative location can be calculated. (pp. 249-250)

13: HUMAN GENETICS

IN THE GRAND SCHEME

As in other animals, human infants go on inheriting features of their parents, grandparents, etc. The inheritance of these and other human traits are encoded in 46 chromosomes derived from the pairing of 23 chromosomes from each parent. One of the 23 pairs determines sex. These are called sex chromosomes. The remaining 22 pairs of chromosomes determine other traits and are called autosomes. Many traits are determined by a single pair of genes, called alleles, for which there are only two alternative forms. Other traits are determined by a single pair of genes for which there are multiple alternative forms.

Even when the mechanisms of gene inheritance work perfectly, there are unfortunate outcomes due to combinations of genes from the two parents that result in defective structure or function. Other defects result from errors in the mechanisms of inheritance. Some defects, from either normal or faulty mechanisms, are lethal. Through understanding the hazards, better planning can produce a higher frequency of "bundles of joy" and fewer tragic disappointments.

FOR REVIEW

Karyotypes: The entire complement of one's chromosomes, arranged in an orderly manner, is the karyotype of that individual.

Dominant and recessive traits: When two alternative alleles for a trait occur in the same individual, one may be expressed in the phenotype to the exclusion of the other. The expressed member is called dominant, and the unexpressed member is called recessive.

Sex linkage: Recessive traits transmitted on the X chromosome cause males to inherit those traits more often than females. Such traits are called sex linked.

CHAPTER OUTLINE

HUMAN CHROMOSOMES (pp. 259-263)
    Down Syndrome
    Sex Chromosomes
        The X chromosome
        The Y chromosome
PATTERNS OF INHERITANCE (pp. 263-264)
    A Pedigree: Albinism
MULTIPLE ALLELES (pp. 265-266)
    ABO Blood Groups
    The Rh Blood Group
GENETIC DISORDERS (pp. 266-271)
    Cystic Fibrosis
    Sickle Cell Anemia
    Phenylketonuria
    Tay-Sachs Disease
    Hemophilia
    Huntington's Disease
GENETIC COUNSELING (pp. 271-274)
    Genetic Therapy

KEY TERMS

p. 225: autosomes, sex chromosomes
p. 260: monosomics, trisomics, Down syndrome
p. 261: primary nondisjunction, Barr body
p. 262: Klinefelter's syndrome, Turner's syndrome
p. 263: pedigrees
p. 265: cell surface antigens, co-dominant, type A, type B, type AB, type O, ABO blood groups
p. 266: Rh blood group, erythroblastosis fetalis, mutation
p. 267: genetic disorder, cystic fibrosis, Sickle cell anemia, hemoglobin
p. 268: hemophilia
p. 270: Tay-Sachs disease, gangliosides
p. 271: phenylketonuria (PKU), Huntington's disease
p. 272: high-risk pregnancy, amniocentesis, ultrasound, chorionic villi sampling
p. 273: restriction enzymes, RFLP's

TOPIC EXERCISES

The content of this chapter can be summarized in three categories. Completion of the following activities should help in the mastery of this information.

1. Listed below are some normal characteristics. To the right of each, list the genetic cause.

    A. Femaleness _____

    B. Maleness _____

    C. ABO blood types _____

2. Some genetic defects are caused by undesirable genes inherited by normal genetic mechanisms. These are called "genetic disorders." For each genetic disorder listed below, indicate the gene dominance, and describe the effects of the disorder.

    A. Cystic fibrosis _____ _____

    B. Sickle-cell anemia _____ _____

    C. Tay-Sachs disease _____ _____

    D. Phenylketonuria _____ _____

    E. Hemophilia _____ _____

    F. Huntington's disease _____ _____

3. Some genetic defects are the result of faulty cell division called nondisjunctions. For each syndrome listed, indicate the chromosome pair that failed to separate in meiosis and resulting chromosome combinations.

    A. Down Syndrome _____ _____

    B. Klinefelter's _____ _____

    C. Turner's syndrome _____ _____

LEARNING CHECKLIST

1. What are the two categories of chromosomes that make up the human chromosome complement? How many are there of each?
2. What are the normal complements of sex chromosomes in human males and females?
3. What are the red cell surface markers involved in the ABO system of blood types? What are the possible genotypes with respect to ABO blood type inheritance? What are the corresponding phenotypes?
4. What are the possible combinations of fetal versus parental Rh types? Which combinations pose a potential problem for (a) immediate pregnancy and (b) future pregnancies?
5. How can genes that are detrimental or even lethal persist in a population?
6. How might a couple benefit from genetic counseling?
7. What are two genetic screening techniques?

MINI EXAM

A. Circle the letter of the one best answer for each question.

1. A genetic disorder resulting from a missing blood protein is
    a. sickle-cell anemia
    b. erythroblastosis fetalis
    c. hemopoiesis
    d. hemophilia

2. Klinefelter's syndrome results from a zygote having
    a. XXX
    b. XXY
    c. XYY
    d. YYY

3. The normal human male karyotype contains
    a. one X and one Y chromosome and 23 autosomes
    b. two X chromosomes and 44 autosomes
    c. one X and one Y and 44 autosomes
    d. two X and two Y chromosomes and 23 autosomes
    e. one X and one Y and 46 autosomes

4. One with Turner's syndrome
    a. is a sterile male with female appearance
    b. is a short sterile female with a webbed neck
    c. is a fertile female with male appearance
    d. usually fails to reach puberty
    e. a male who is normal except mental retardation

5. Tay-Sachs disease
    a. causes children that appear normal at birth to die young due to brain deterioration
    b. expresses itself in the adult and results in progressive brain deterioration
    c. results in short stature adults whose brain development ceased about age 5
    d. causes mental retardation in normal appearing adults
    e. stops fetal development and results in stillbirth

6. Klinefelter's disease is caused by nondisjunction of X chromosomes, resulting in
    a. a normal appearing male who may show antisocial tendencies
    b. a mentally retarded female of short stature.
    c. an XXY sterile male with many female characteristics
    d. an XXX female who is sterile but otherwise is normal
    e. an individual with female gentiles, but masculine characteristics

7. Chromosomes may be examined as an aid to genetic counseling by means of
   a. chorionic villi sampling
   b. ultrasound
   c. pedigree examination
   d. X-ray
   e. tissue culture of sediments in mother's urine

8. The genetic disorder whose effects are not seen until after child-bearing years is
   a. Klinefelter's syndrome
   b. Turner's syndrome
   c. Huntington's disease
   d. Tay-Sachs Disease
   e. Cystic fibrosis

9. Huntington's disease is
   a. caused by a homozygous recessive genes and results in progressive brain deterioration
   b. most serious if the individual is homozygous recessive but is expressed in the heterozygous
   c. caused by a dominant allele and is expressed in people over 30 years of age
   d. restricted to American Blacks and their descendants
   e. rare except n Jewish populations

10. A zygote containing one extra autosome
    a. will never develop
    b. may develop into an individual with Downs syndrome
    c. will develop normally
    d. will be unusually talented in some respect, depending an the extra chromosome
    e. will have an extra Barr body

11. A parent who has an AB blood type needs a blood transfusion which of the children whose genotype is shown can donate the blood?
    a. AB
    b. OO
    c. AO
    d. BO
    e. all of the above

12. Cystic fibrosis results from two recessive alleles causing
    a. defective chloride-transport channel function
    b. defective hemoglobin
    c. inability to break down gangliosides
    d. production of brain cell metabolism inhibitor
    e. blood to become fibrous and become unable to flow

13. A zygote missing one autosome but no other chromosomes
    a. is monosomic and will survive but will be impaired in some manner
    b. has only 45 chromosomes and will produce children how have Down syndrome
    c. can develop into either a male or female but will be sterile
    d. is monosomic and will not develop
    e. is trisomic and can successfully mate only with another with the same chromosome number

14. A family of four children have the genotypes AB, AO, BO, and OO. Their parents' genotypes are
    a. AB and OO
    b. AO and OO
    c. BO and OO
    d. AO and BO
    e. AB and O

15. Down syndrome results from and extra chromosome number
    a. 13   c. 21
    b. 15   d. 23

16. Phenylketonuria causes
    a. the body to fail to properly utilize phenylalanine and results in death by age 5
    b. mental retardation and an early death, usually before age 30
    c. mental retardation but has no effect on life span
    d. progressive brain deterioration in the elderly
    e. albinism

17. A Barr body results from an inactive
    a. X chromosome   c. chromosome 22
    b. chromosome 21   d. Y chromosome

18. A person with galactose on the surface of red blood cells is
    a. type A   c. type AB
    b. type B   d. type O

19. Nondisjunction of the X chromosome resulting in YO
    a. produces a zygote that fails to develop
    b. produces a sterile by very masculine male
    c. produces a dwarfed mail who can father only male children
    d. produces a male child who has traits identical to that of the father
    e. produces a male child that will not survive beyond puberty

20. Sickle-cell anemia is a recessive disorder involving poor blood flow because of
    a. absence of factor IX
    b. gangliosides in excess
    c. galactose on red blood cells
    d. defective hemoglobin
    e. galactosamine on red blood cells

B. Provide the appropriate term to complete each statement.

1. Of the 23 pair of chromosomes of the human species, 22 pairs are classed as _____.

2. Down syndrome results from an error in meiosis called _____.

3. Female cells can be identified by the appearance of a(n) _____.

4. X and Y chromosomes are called _____.

5. The _____ chromosome contains mostly inactive genes.

6. With regard to dominance, albinism is a _____ trait.

7. The ABO blood types result from a gene having _____ alleles.

8. A particular mismatch of Rh factors between mother and fetus may result in a potentially fatal condition called _____.

9. Because both A and B alleles for blood type are expressed when present, they are called _____.

10. A detrimental allele occurring with significant frequency in a population produces a condition called _____.

C. Briefly answer each of the following questions.

1. What are the causes, effects, and frequency of Down syndrome?

2. What is the effect of the addition or deletion of (a) an X chromosome or (b) a Y chromosome?

3. In the pedigree shown below, is the trait (a) sex linked or autosome, (b) dominant or recessive, and (c) determined by a single gene or multiple genes. In each case, how do you know?

CHAPTER ANSWERS

TOPIC EXERCISES

1. A. two X chromosomes
   B. X and Y chromosomes
   C. Multiple alleles for surface markers

2. A. Recessive, excess mucus in lungs, pancreas and liver
   B. Recessive defective hemoglobin
   C. Recessive, brain deterioration
   D. Recessive, inability to break down phenylalanine
   E. Recessive, inability to clot blood
   F. Dominant, brain deterioration.

3. A. autosome, three of either chromosome
   B. X, XXY
   C. X, XO

LEARNING CHECKLIST

1. Two of the human chromosomes are sex chromosomes. Forty four are autosomes. (p. 259)

2. Human females have two X chromosomes. Human males have one X and one Y chromosome. (p. 261)

3. Red cells have surface markers for antigens A or B or neither. Considering the absence of a marker for A or B to be represented by O, the possible genotypes are AB, AA, AO, BB, BO or OO. Genotype AB results in phenotype AB. Genotypes AA and AO result in the phenotype A. BB and BO resulting the phenotype B. Genotype OO results in the phenotype O. (pp. 265-266)

4. A fetus may have a mother that is Rh+ and a father that is either Rh+ or Rh-. Such a fetus could be Rh+ or Rh-. Neither case represents any potential hazard. A fetus may have an Rh- mother and a father that is either Rh+ or Rh-. If both parents are Rh- then the fetus will also be Rh- and no problem will result. If the father is Rh+ and the mother Rh-, the fetus could also be Rh+. This usually represents no potential problem for the immediate pregnancy but, lacking intervention represents a problem for future pregnancies involving an Rh+ fetus. (p. 266)

5. Sublethal detrimental genes may be tolerated and passed on. Some lethal traits, such as Huntington's chorea, express themselves after the individual has reached reproductive capacity. (pp. 266-271)

6. Cystic fibrosis: (a) mucus congestion of lungs, liver and pancreas (b) two recessive genes for that trait, (c) 1 in 1800 white children. (p. 267)
    Sickle-cell anemia: (a) defective hemoglobin causing difficulty in transport of oxygen, (b) homozygous for the recessive trait (heterozygous will show some effect) (c) about 2% of american blacks. (p. 267)
    Phenylketonuria: (a) causes phenylalanine to be converted to tyrosine instead of being broken down, (b) homozygous for the allele, (c) 1 in 15,000 infants. (pp. 270-271)
    Tay-Sachs disease:(a) brain deterioration and early death, (b) homozygous for allele, (c) 1 in 3600 Jewish infants of Easter and Central European ancestry. (p. 270)
    Hemophilia:(a) inability to clot blood (b) lack of genes for any of several factors required for blood clotting. Factors VIII and IX are carried and the X chromosome. The lack of these genes on an X chromosome effect males who have only on X chromosome more than females who may have the gene on their other X chromosome. (c) 1 in 7000 in case of the royal hemophilia involving mutant factor IX. (pp. 268-270)

7. Although the genetic defects cannot be cured, parents who learn that it is probable that their child will inherit such a disease may be advised to avoid pregnancy. In the case of PKU, dietary changes may be prescribed. (pp. 271-274)

8. Amniocentesis and chorionic will sampling yield early information about inherited defects. (p. 272)

MINI EXAM

A.

1. d	2. d	3. c	4. b	5. a	6. c
7. a	8. c	9. c	10. b	11. c	12. a
13. e	14. d	15. c	16. b	17. a	18. b
19. a	20. d				

B.

1. autosomes	2. primary nondisjunction	3. Barr body
4. sex chromosomes	5. Y	6. recessive
7. multiple	8. erythroblastosis fetalis	9. co-dominant
10. genetic disorder		

C. 1. Down syndrome is caused by the inheritance of three copies of a segment of chromosome number 21 or 22 either as part of a complete extra chromosome or by translocation of the segment. The symptoms are short stature, poor muscle tone and mental retardation. The disorder occurs in 1 out of every 750 children. (pp. 260-261)

2 (a) XXX results in a female who is sterile but otherwise normal XO in Turner's syndrome, characterized by short stature, webbed neck and immature sex organs that fail to develop at puberty.
   (b) XXY results in Klinefelter's syndrome, characterized by sterility in a male who has many female body characteristics and sometimes diminished mental capacity. XYY results in normal fertile male. This is often associated with antisocial behavior. YO zygotes fail to develop. (pp. 262-263)

3.   (a) The trait is autosomal, not sex linked, as evidenced by equal distribution among sexes.

     (b) The trait is dominant. It occurs only in children whose parents show the trait.

     (c) The trait is single gene trait, occurring about one third of the possible cases. (pp. 263-264)

14: DNA: THE GENETIC MATERIAL

IN THE GRAND SCHEME

What is the cell's hiding place of hereditary information? The large and complex cell of the alga, Acetabularium, was an ideal subject for the investigation. Through grafting, it was determined that the base of the cell in which the nucleus was located always dictated the characteristics of the cell.

What content of the nucleus governs heredity? A substance was isolated that transformed a benign bacterium into a virulent pathogen. Using enzymes to destroy various components of the nucleus, it was determined that the hereditary material of cells was DNA.

Though the hereditary material of cellular organisms was identified, that of viruses was still unknown. Was it a protein coating or the nucleic acid? If a nucleic acid, which one? The study of bacteriophages determined that such viruses utilized DNA. The nucleic acid of tobacco mosaic viruses proved to be RNA.

What is the structure of DNA? The chemical content was learned, but how were these chemicals arranged? Building on earlier x-ray diffraction studies of DNA, modeling experiments led to the conclusion that the DNA molecule was a ladder-like double helix.

It was evident that cells must pass DNA to progeny, yet all cells need a full complement to function. There must be a process in which DNA is copied. Using a heavy isotope of nitrogen, it was demonstrated that the process was semiconservative replication. That is, each new molecule is composed of one half old molecule and one half new molecule. An understanding of the enzyme action in replicating the two complementary strands followed.

How does this large complex molecule of DNA perform its control over cell structure and behavior? It was found that the large molecule was composed of discrete hereditary units called genes. Through the study of single gene mutations, it was discovered that each gene codes for one enzyme or, more precisely, for one polypeptide. The spiral of knowledge continues.

FOR REVIEW

Nature of scientific experiments: the scientific method is the formulation of hypotheses based on a systematic collection of data and the experimental testing of the hypotheses. The process is not mechanical, but involves creative insight and critical thinking.

Structure of DNA: DNA is a complex molecule coding for amino acid sequences in proteins with triplets of nucleotides in the DNA.

Nucleotides: A nucleotide is a segment of a nucleic acid. A nucleotide is composed of (1) a five-carbon sugar, (2) a phosphate group, and (3) an organic nitrogen-containing base.

Structure of proteins: A protein is a long polymer chain of amino acid subunits linked end to end.

The structure of chromosomes: A chromosome is a single, long, double stranded DNA fiber that is often coiled to occupy less space. The typical chromosome contains about 60% protein and 40% DNA. Somewhere on the chromosome is a constriction called the centromere.

CHAPTER OUTLINE

WHERE DO CELLS STORE HEREDITARY INFORMATION? (pp. 281-283)
WHICH COMPONENT OF CHROMOSOMES CONTAINS THE HEREDITARY INFORMATION? (pp. 283-286)
The Griffith-Avery Experiments: Transforming Principle is DNA

KEY TERMS

TOPIC EXERCISES

1. In the section that follows (Who's Who in Biology), you will match contributions to the list of scientists. What was discovered by whom is important, but also important is the basis for their conclusions. For each conclusion listed below state the evidence leading to the conclusion.

    A. In eukaryotes, hereditary information is contained in the nucleus.

    B. The "transforming principle" was a nonprotein.

    C. One gene controls one enzyme.

2. At first the complementarity of the two strands of DNA made it difficult to understand how the two complementarity strands are replicated since DNA polymerase can only replicate DNA in a 3 prime to 5 prime direction. Explain how the two strands are formed.

WHO'S WHO IN BIOLOGY

Complete the following chart.

Scientist	Contribution to Biology
Hammerling	_____ _____
Stewart	_____ _____
Griffith and Avery	_____ _____
Hershey and Chase	_____ _____
Fraenkel-Conrat	_____ _____
Meischer	_____ _____
Levine	_____ _____
Chargaff	_____ _____
Franklin	_____ _____
Watson and Crick	_____ _____
Okazaki	_____ _____
Beadle and Tatum	_____ _____
Sanger	_____ _____

LEARNING CHECKLIST

1. How did Griffith discover the existence of a "transforming principle?"
2. How did Avery discover that the "transforming principle" was DNA not a protein?
3. How was it established that RNA, too, was hereditary material?
4. What were Chargaff's two discoveries? How did these discoveries impact the acceptance of Avery's work?

5. Describe the three dimensional model of DNA as determined by Watson and Crick based on the x-ray crystallography of Franklin.
6. What is meant by semiconservative replication? How was it determined?

MINI EXAM

A. Circle the letter of the one best answer for each question.

1. A gene is a sequence of
   a. enzymes
   b. DNA molecules
   c. nucleotides
   d. amino acids

2. When DNA is replicated, the two strands of DNA separate at one end forming a
   a. replication center
   b. replication junction
   c. replication fork
   d. replication unit
   e. replication zone

3. Nucleotides are linked to each other by
   a. nitrogen-containing bases
   b. nucleoses
   c. three-carbon sugars
   d. five-carbon sugars
   e. phosphodiester bonds

4. When DNA polymerase replicates DNA it always adds new nucleotides to the
   a. 3 prime carbon
   b. 1 prime carbon
   c. 5 prime carbon
   d. 2 prime carbon
   e. 4 prime carbon

5. Chargaff's rules, about nucleotide distribution in DNA state that
   a. C = A
   b. T = G
   c. G = A
   d. A = T

6. Eukayote chromosomes have discrete units that are replicated. These units are called
   a. replication units
   b. replication zones
   c. replication segments
   d. replication quanta

7. A nucleotide is
   a. a five-carbon sugar, a phosphate group and a nitrogen-containing base
   b. a sugar with an attached base containing nitrogen
   c. a six-carbon sugar, a base containing nitrogen and a phosphate group
   d. a nitrogen-containing base with an attached five-carbon sugar
   e. a benzene ring with nitrogen, a base, and an atom of phosphorus

8. Franklin's work with DNA was hampered by
   a. a shortage of electricity
   b. interference from long electromagnetic waves
   c. a lack of crystalline DNA
   d. impurity of x-rays
   e. unavailability of pure RNA

9. Viruses that attack bacteria are called
   a. bacteriophages
   b. bacteriostats
   c. bacterioblasts
   d. bacteriocides

10. Semiconservative replication means
    a. only half a DNA molecule is replicated and the next remains in its original state
    b. a replicated molecule of DNA contains one strand from the old molecule and one new strand
    c. half of the DNA is lost by the action of DNA polymerase
    d. only half of the energy used in the process is conserved
    e. the new molecule resembles only half of the old molecule

11. Which of the following is a part of RNA but not DNA?
    a. adenine   d. uracil
    b. guanine   e. cytosine
    c. thymine

12. Which of the following is a purine?
    a. guanine   c. thymine
    b. uracil   d. cytosine

13. Avery identified the "transforming principle" as
    a. ATP   d. DNA
    b. RNA   e. ADP
    c. CAMP

14. The component that distinguishes one DNA nucleotide from another is the
    a. phosphodiester bond   c. hydrogen bond
    b. base   d. five-carbon sugar

15. The work with <u>Neurospora</u> by Beadle and Tatum led to the
    a. discovery of the transformation principle
    b. one gene-one enzyme hypothesis
    c. discovery of the configuration of DNA
    d. knowledge of the relationship of amounts of thymine to that of adenine
    e. recognition of the nucleus as the site of hereditary material

16. Through the study of bacteriophages, Beadle and Tatum discovered that
    a. the virus encoded its hereditary material in a molecule of polymerase
    b. the viral DNA was in the form of a ring
    c. the hereditary material of the bacteriophage was RNA
    d. viruses lacked hereditary material of their own and required the bacterium to reproduce them
    e. the viral hereditary material was DNA

17. Nucleotides are held together by
    a. hydroxyl bonds   c. electrovalent bonds
    b. phosphodiester bonds   d. hydraulic bonds

18. In the study of the tobacco mosaic virus, Fraenkel-Conrat
    a. hybridized viruses to find that the tobacco mosaic virus used DNA for its hereditary material
    b. found that the tobacco mosaic virus had a different kind of hereditary material than the Holmes ribgrass virus
    c. used a mixture of live and dead viruses to find the cause of tobacco mosaic disease
    d. found that the virus was a bacteriophage that attacked cyanobacteria that were symbiotic with tobacco
    e. showed that the RNA of the tobacco mosaic virus was responsible for the tobacco disease

19. When DNA polymerase builds the complement to the strand ending with a PO_4 group attached to the 5 prime carbon, it
    a. adds continuously to the 3 prime carbon
    b. builds from the 5 prime to 3 prime direction but not continuously
    c. adds continuously to the 5 prime carbon
    d. builds discontinuously in a 3 prime to a 5 prime direction
    e. substitutes the base for the 3 prime carbon on the 5 prime carbon

20. One polypeptide is genetically specified by
    a. one chromosome   d. one enzyme
    b. one nucleotide   e. one base
    c. one gene

B. Provide the appropriate term to complete each statement.

   1. _____ studied Acetabularia to determine the site of hereditary information.

   2. The work of _____ made it clear that some adult plant cells contained a full set of hereditary information.

   3. The discovery of the "transforming principle" is attributed to _____.

   4. _____ and _____, working on bacterial viruses, found that their heredity was directed by DNA.

   5. The work of _____ on tobacco viruses showed that some viruses use RNA in place of DNA.

   6. The discovery of nucleic acids is attributed to _____.

   7. _____ determined the three components of DNA.

   8. _____ discovered the ratio of DNA bases to each other.

   9. The helical structure of DNA was first suggested by _____ as a result of x-ray diffraction.

   10. _____ and _____ suggested the mode of replication of DNA.

C. Briefly answer each of the following questions

   1. How was it first determined that a cell's hereditary material is in the nucleus?

   2. Describe the two strand process of DNA replication.

   3. Explain the one gene-one enzyme hypothesis. What is the evidence that supports this hypothesis?

CHAPTER ANSWERS

TOPIC EXERCISES

1. A. Regeneration of amputated caps of <u>Acetabularia</u> were of the type that would grow on the foot that contained the nucleus
   B. Protein destroying enzymes had no effect on the "transforming principle."
   C. A change of a single nucleotide in DNA results in a change of a single amino acid produced by the cell.

2. DNA polymerase begins at the replication fork and replicates one strand continuously in the 3 prime to 5 prime direction. In the complementary strand, DNA polymerase skips ahead about 1000 nucleotides and replicates its way back. Thus, in the complementary strand, DNA polymerase still replicates from 3 prime to 5 prime but discontinuously.

WHO'S WHO IN BIOLOGY

<u>Scientist</u>	<u>Contribution to Biology</u>
Hammerling	Nucleus is the site of hereditary information.
Stewart	Complete sets of hereditary information are contained in several adult plant cells.
Griffith and Avery	"Transforming principle"
Hershey and Chase	Bacteriophages use DNA
Fraenkel-Conrat	Some viruses use RNA instead of DNA
Meischer	Discovered nucleic acids
Levine	Determined chemical content of DNA
Chargaff	Rules: A = T, and G = C.
Franklin	Helical shape of DNA.
Watson and Crick	Double helix and purine/pyrimidine relationship.
Okazaki	Discovered discontinuous synthesis.
Beadle and Tatum	One gene-one enzyme hypothesis
Sanger	Discovered amino acid sequence of protein.

LEARNING CHECKLIST

1. Griffith mixed dead, coated, virulent bacteria with live, uncoated and avirulent bacteria. He found that the presence of the dead bacteria transformed the live bacteria into a virulent strain. (pp. 283-284)

2. Avery found that protein-destroying enzymes did not effect the transforming principle but DNA-destroying enzymes made the transforming principle ineffective. (p. 284)

3. Fraenkel-Conrat worked with two viruses. Both had RNA for their nucleic acid and a protein coat. One (TMV) caused a mosaic pattern in tobacco leaves and the other (HMV) did not. He formed tow hybrids, each with the other's protein coat. The one with the RNA of TMV and the coat of HMV caused the mosaic but not vice versa. (p. 286)

4. Chargaff discovered that different proteins had different distributions of DNA nucleotides, not a single repeating pattern. However, the amount of the base, A, equalled that of the base, T, and the amount of the base, C, equalled that of the base, G. This eliminated the objection to Avery's work that DNA was a simple repetition of a single base sequence. (p. 288)

5. DNA is a double helix composed of two polynucleotide chains hydrogen-bonded to each other, wrapped around a central axis. (pp. 289-290)

6. Semiconservative replication means that one of the two strands of replicated DNA is a strand of the molecule being replicated. DNA was formed containing a heavy isotope of nitrogen. Replication took place in a medium containing only the lighter nitrogen. The result was DNA containing one heavy strand and one light strand. (pp. 291-292)

MINI EXAM

A.

1. c	2. c	3. e	4. a	5. d	6. a
7. a	8. c	9. a	10. b	11. d	12. a
13. d	14. b	15. b	16. e	17. b	18. e
19. d	20. c				

B.

1. Hammerling	2. Stewart	3. Griffith and Avery
4. Hershey and Chase	5. Fraenkel-Conrat	6. Meischer
7. Levine	8. Chargaff	9. Franklin
10. Watson and Crick		

C. 1. Hammerling discovered that regeneration of parts in the single celled alga, Acetabularia, occurred only when the nucleus bearing foot was present. Grafting experiments showed that the foot, not parts without a nucleus, controlled the appearance of the parts regenerated from the graft. (pp. 281-283)

2. When replication is to occur, strands of DNA separate, forming a replication fork. DNA polymerase uses each strand for a template. On the strand beginning with the 3 prime end, nucleotides are connected sequentially. On the strand beginning with the 5 prime end, the polymerase will skip ahead 1000 nucleotides or more and fills back in the 3 prime to 5 prime direction. (pp. 291-293)

3. The one gene-one enzyme hypothesis holds that each gene codes for one enzyme (actually, only polypeptide.) Beadle and Tatum worked with the mold, Neurospora, having single gene mutations. They found that each mutated gene altered the peptide formed by a single amino acid. (pp. 294-297)

15: GENES AND HOW THEY WORK

IN THE GRAND SCHEME

The nucleus of a cell is somewhat analogous to the office of an architect. In the form of DNA, the master plans for the molecules that are to be made by the cell are housed and protected in the nucleus. A disposable working copy of the plan, transcripted as a coded sequence complementary to the master plan in a molecule of messenger RNA, is sent to the construction site. The site is the ribosome which has its own instruction set in the molecules of ribosomal RNA. Polypeptides that may be either end products or enzymes needed to make the end product are formed by the ribosome from amino acids delivered by molecules of transfer RNA.

Genes specify the polypeptides to be formed. Much of the process and regulation of gene expression is now understood, An enzyme, RNA polymerase, selects and reads the appropriate strand of the appropriate segment of DNA. Using the DNA strand as a templet, RNA polymerase synthesizes a single stranded molecule of mRNA. The molecule of mRNA is attached and transported to a ribosome. An enzyme precisely positions the molecule of mRNA on the surface of the ribosome. Molecules of tRNA bearing amino acids are positioned sequentially on the mRNA molecule in the appropriate sequence. Adjacent amino acids are coupled to each other to form a polypeptide chain and the associated molecules of tRNA are released. The polypeptide grows in this manner until it is complete. The polypeptide is then released.

Constant gene expression would result in ill timing and excesses of polypeptides. Gene expression is regulated by proteins that stimulate or inhibit the gene's expression. Genes are constructed with receptor sites for the regulators interspersed strategically among the segments that code for the polypeptides. A model for regulation of gene expression is the **lac** system of the bacterium, Escherichia coli.

FOR REVIEW

Structure of DNA and RNA: DNA and RNA are nucleic acids. Both are made of nucleotides linked by phosphate groups. The sugar in RNA is ribose. The sugar of DNA has one less oxygen atom per molecule, thus, deoxyribose. RNA is single stranded whereas DNA is double stranded. Both contain the bases adenine, guanine and cytosine. DNA also has thymine, whereas RNA has uracil.

Ribosomes: Ribosomes are microstructures found in the cytoplasm and on the rough endoplasmic reticulum. They are the sites of protein synthesis.

Enzymes and enzyme activity: Enzymes are protein catalysts of specific reactions. In order to function, an enzyme must physically conform to the shape of the substrate.

Structure of eukaryotic chromosomes: Eukaryotic chromosomes are very long, often coiled molecules of DNA with some protein. Each contains a constriction, called the centromere, by which sister chromatids are held together, and by which the chromosomes are attached to the microtubules for movement.

CHAPTER OUTLINE

CELLS USE RNA TO MAKE A PROTEIN (pp. 301-302)
  ribosomes
 Ribosomal RNA
 Transfer RNA
 Messenger RNA
AN OVERVIEW OF GENE EXPRESSION (pp. 302-303)
 Transcription

KEY TERMS

TOPIC EXERCISES

In organizing the information of this chapter for study, there appear to be three categories: (1) understanding the "major players" and an overview of the "plot", (2) understanding the protein synthesis process, and (3) understanding gene regulation. The following activities should help gain this understanding.

1. Beside each substance listed below, briefly describe its function, and beside each process, give a brief description.

   A. rRNA

   B. tRNA

   C. mRNA

   D. Transcription

   E. Translation

2. Listed below are the steps in protein formation. Briefly describe the action that occurs for each step.

   A. Initiation complex formation

   B. Positioning of incoming tRNA

   C. Coupling of amino acids

   D. Translocation and elongation

   E. Release of polypeptide

3. Below is an outline of the "**lac** system." Under each step are terms for you to define (d) or to describe its function (f).

   A. Coding sequence
      1. operon (d)

   B. Ribosome recognition site
      1. leader region(d)

      2. transcription unit (d)

   C. RNA polymerase binding site
      1. promoters (f)

   D. Regulatory protein binding site
      1. operator (f)

   E. CAP site
      1. CAP (f)

4. Refer to table 15-1 on page 308 of your text book. Use it to determine the amino acid or action coded in the nucleotide sequences below.

   A. mRNA sequence: UGG

   B. mRNA sequence: AUG

   C. mRNA sequence: UAA

   D. DNA sequence: TTC

E. DNA sequence: CTG

LEARNING CHECKLIST

1. How is a code formed from nucleotide sequences in DNA?
2. Explain the exceptions to universality of the genetic code.
3. Relate the processes of transcription and translation to protein synthesis.
4. Differentiate between eukaryotic and prokaryotic protein synthesis.
5. Briefly describe gene regulation and explain its necessity.
6. What are the five regions of the **lac** operon.
7. Explain the regulation of lactose metabolism by the **lac** operon.

MINI EXAM

A. Circle the letter of the one best answer for each question.

1. In the expression of genes
   a. the process is halted when a repressor protein, rather than an activator protein, binds to the promoter.
   b. translation is initiated when the RNA polymerase locates the three nucleotide "stop" codon on the promoter segment
   c. transcription begins when an enzyme called the activator binds to the initiation factor of a ribosome
   d. in eukaryotic cells, the activator protein binds to the operator site of an operon
   e. transcription is initiated when RNA polymerase binds to a six-nucleotide sequence called a promoter site

2. The formation of a polypeptide corresponding to the instructions encoded in RNA is called
   a. transcription   c. replication
   b. transmission   d. translation

3. The "**lac** system" exists in
   a. plants   c. protists
   b. bacteria   d. viruses

4. In eukaryotic protein synthesis,
   a. the existence of introns and exons is less common than prokaryotic cells
   b. introns are removed from the gene transcript before cytoplasmic mRNA is translated into a protein
   c. the process is more commonly carried out by operon activity than it is in prokaryotic cells
   d. regulation is exercised by activator and repressor strands of rRNA in ribosomes
   e. exons are excised by an enzyme and discarded, leaving the intelligence bearing introns to be translated

5. Which is <u>not</u> part of an operon?
   a. structural genes   d. promotor
   b. operator   e. regulator
   c. repressor

6. By using radioactive amino acids, scientists found that proteins are synthesized on
   a. nuclear RNA
   b. cytoplasmic ribosomes
   c. nuclear DNA
   d. nuclear ribosomes
   e. previously unknown nuclear organelle

7. The assembly of a protein by a ribosome
   a. is initiated by the formation of an initiation complex comprised of the large subunit of the ribosome and the initiating codon
   b. proceeds as the elongation factors are translocated along the mRNA
   c. requires that the reading frame be established by a set of regulatory proteins called operators
   d. is terminated when ribosome's terminal complex recognizes the release factor encoded in the mRNA
   e. begins with the binding of met-tRNA to the small subunit of the ribosome, guided by proteins called initiation factors.

   e

8. As compared to eukaryotic protein synthesis, all of the following are true prokaryotic protein synthesis except
   a. prokaryotic mRNA is shorter than that of eukaryotic cells and cannot code for more than one protein
   b. translation may begin in prokaryotic cells before transcription is completed
   c. prokaryotic translation begins with an AUG codon followed by a special nucleotide sequence
   d. most prokaryotic genes lack introns and exons
   e. prokaryotic ribosomes are smaller than eukaryotic ribosomes

   a

9. Between the transcription unit and the promotor is the
   a. operon
   b. CAP site
   c. operator
   d. leader region
   e. ribosome recognition site

   c

10. In the **lac** system of <u>Escherichia coli</u>
    a. the presence of the repressor protein on the operator blocks the path of the polymerase attempting to reach the promoter
    b. RNA polymerase binds to the promoter which is otherwise known as CAP
    c. a transcription unit consists of a leader
    d. the operon consists of three structural genes that code for lactose digesting enzymes and their regulator sites
    e. a coding sequence and its promoter and operator sections make up each of the three transcription units

    c

11. A site of negative gene regulation is a(n)
    a. operon
    b. negator
    c. anticodon
    d. operator
    e. suppressor

    d

12. In protein synthesis, amino acids are transported by
    a. aRNA
    b. mRNA
    c. rRNA
    d. tRNA

    d

13. The **lac** repressor protein blocks the binding of
    a. CAP
    b. RNA polymerase
    c. RNA transcriptase
    d. cAMP

    b

14. In the regulation of the **lac** system
    a. lactose causes a conformation change in the promoter that allows the activating enzyme to bind to it
    b. the activity of the RNA polymerase, called the operator, is stimulated by low energy in the cell
    c. the stimulus for activation of the transcription process is presence of lactose
    d. the operator site is not available when lactose is present because lactose molecules bind with the operator
    e. lactose binds to the repressor, disabling it

    e

15. The binding with the CAP site by activator protein is blocked by
    a. cMAP
    b. cATP
    c. cADP
    d. cAMP

    d

16. DNA segments between those that specify polypeptides are
    a. axons
    b. exons
    c. introns
    d. noncoms
    e. zircons

17. Initiating factors position _____ on the mRNA molecule.
    a. try-tRNA
    b. met-tRNA
    c. gly-RNA
    d. ade-tRNA
    e. phe-tRNA

18. The site for polypeptide synthesis is provided by
    a. aRNA
    b. mRNA
    c. rRNA
    d. tRNA
    e. sRNA

19. The second genetic code involves the coupling of
    a. DNA and mRNA
    b. mRNA and ribosomes
    c. amino acids to each other
    d. tRNA and amino acids

20. The formation of a strand of RNA corresponding to DNA is called
    a. transcription
    b. replication
    c. transmission
    d. translation
    e. translocation

B. Provide the appropriate term to complete each statement.

1. The word, _Complementary_ describes the relationship of the two strands of a DNA molecule.

2. _rRNA_ are where proteins are synthesized.

3. A three-nucleotide block of mRNA is called a(n) _codon_.

4. A three-nucleotide block of DNA is called a(n) _triplet_.

5. A three-nucleotide block of the tRNA molecule that is complementary to an mRNA triplet is called a(n) _anticodon_.

6. The process of forming a mRNA complement of DNA is called _transcript_.

7. The process of forming a protein for which mRNA codes is _translat_.

8. The placement of an amino acid on a molecule of tRNA is done by _activating enzymes_.

9. Segments of eukaryotic DNA that specify a polypeptide is called a(n) _exons_.

10. The portions of eukaryotic DNA **between** segments that specify polypeptides are called _introns_.

C. Briefly answer each of the following questions.

1. Describe the structure and state the function of each kind of RNA.

2. Explain the process of transcription and describe its product.

3. What are the steps of the protein synthesis process?

CHAPTER ANSWERS

TOPIC EXERCISES

1. A. Provides a site for polypeptide assembly.
   B. Transports amino acids to ribosome.
   C. Carries code for a polypeptide and directs its assembly.
   D. The process of transferring code for the amino acid sequence of a polypeptide from DNA to mRNA.
   E. The formation of a polypeptide based on the code on mRNA.

2. A. Positioning a molecule of met-tRNA on the ribosomal surface.
   B. Beginning just behind the first met-tRNA, each tRNA is positioned on the mRNA molecule based on the appropriate anticodon.
   C. Amino acids are joined by a peptide bond.
   D. The ribosome moves to the next codon on mRNA.
   E. The amino acids forming the polypeptide are released from their tRNA molecules.

3. A. One or more structural genes are their associated operator and promoter.
   B. 1. Untranslated portion of mRNA ahead of three coding sequences.
      2. The leader region plus three coding sequences.
   C. DNA nucleotide sequence to which RNA polymerase binds.
   D. Provides binding site for repressor proteins between the promoter site and transcription unit.
   E. Provides a binding site for activator proteins.

4. A. Tryptophan
   B. (start): Methionine
   C. Stop
   D. Lysine*
   E. Aspartate*

   * Note that the RNA sequence for which the table is intended is the complement of the DNA sequence.

LEARNING CHECKLIST

1. In DNA, the code for a polypeptide consists of a series of nucleotides in sequences of three nucleotides. Each three nucleotide sequence codes for one amino acid or for assembly instructions such as "stop." (pp. 303-305)

2. The exceptions to the universality of the genetic code occur primarily in organisms after they become incorporated symbiotically by eukaryotes. Such examples are mitochondria and chloroplasts. In these organelles and some protists, the variations occur in the reading of "stop" sequences as well as some amino acid codons. (p. 308)

3. Transcription is the encoding of a mRNA molecule with the complement to the code for a polypeptide in DNA. Translation is the formation of the polypeptide corresponding to the code in the mRNA (pp. 302-303)

4. See table 15-2 on page 311 of the text.

5. Uncontrolled gene activity would result in the chaotic combination substance production at the wrong time and in the wrong amount. Genes are regulated by both negative and positive controls. Gene function is repressed by the binding of a repressor protein to its regulatory site. Positive control is exercised by the binding of an activator protein to its regulatory site. (pp. 313-314)

6. The five regions of the **lac** operon are: coding sequence, ribosome recognition site, RNA polymerase binding site, regulatory protein binding site, and the CAP site. See figure 15-17 on page 314.

7. The activator protein CAP (catabolite activator protein) stimulates the transcription of the **lac** operon when the cell energy is low. The **lac** operon activation results in the production of enzymes to metabolize lactose. In the absence of lactose to metabolize, a repressor protein will block the binding of the RNA polymerase. If lactose is available, it will bind to the repressor protein disabling its recognition of the operator sequence. (p. 316)

MINI EXAM

A.

1. e	2. d	3. b	4. b	5. c	6. b
7. e	8. a	9. c	10. c	11. d	12. d
13. b	14. e	15. d	16. c	17. b	18. c
19. d	20. a				

B.

1. complementarity	2. ribosomes	3. codon
4. triplet	5. anticodon	6. transcription
7. translation	8. activating enzymes	9. exons
10. introns		

C. 1. (a) Messenger RNA (mRNA) is a single strand of nucleotides built around the five carbon sugar ribose and containing the bases adenine, guanine, cytosine, and uracil. It is built as a complement to a segment of one strand of DNA and codes for the same amino acid sequence as the complementary DNA segment. It serves as a prescription in the synthesis of a polypeptide.
(b) Ribosomal RNA (tRNA) makes up a family of specific molecules, each with a specific code at one location that matches it with its complementary code on mRNA. At an other location, is a binding site for that specific amino acid specified by the complementary code on mRNA. See figure 15-8 in the text. (p. 307)

2. Transcription is the process of forming a strand of mRNA with a nucleotide code complementary to that of a segment of DNA. See figure 15-4 of the text. Transcription is initiated by an enzyme called RNA polymerase. The polymerase binds to a nucleotide sequence at the beginning of a gene on the "sense" strand in an open segment of DNA. Since the two strands of DNA are complementary to each other, one strand contains the code for the desired polypeptide and is called the "sense" strand. Once bound to the DNA, at the beginning of the gene, the polymerase proceeds to use the DNA as a template and forms a complementary strand of mRNA until it reaches a "stop" sequence of nucleotides. (pp. 302-303)

3. The steps of protein synthesis are:
(a) initiation complex formation. (See figure 15-10 in the text, p. 309)
(b) codon is exposed
(c) tRNA with appropriate anticodon is positioned at the codon by an elongation factor
(d) newly arrived amino acid is combined with another are in the polypeptide being synthesized
(e) tRNA separates from the mRNA and drifts away
(f) next codon is exposed
(g) process repeats. (pp. 303-304)

16: MUTATION

IN THE GRAND SCHEME

Mutations have an affect, be it small or large, on biological processes. Mutations may occur spontaneously within the cell or may result from some form of intervention. Genes or chromosome segments may migrate. Nucleotides may alter their conformation. Errors occur in otherwise normal chromosome behavior. Mistakes occur in replication. All of the possibilities are simply imperfections in normal events.

Chromosomes may be altered by the outside factors called mutagens. Replication failures may be caused by chemical agents. Chromosomes may be broken by free ions caused by ionizing radiations. Ultraviolet light may cause adjacent nucleotides to pair and interface with replication.

Cancer is a very important consequence of somatic mutation. Cancer is a cell or group of cells multiplying in an invasive manner outside the control of the organisms regulatory mechanisms. The study of a chicken virus has led to the oncogene theory. Oncogenes escape the cells regulatory mechanisms and cause excessive production of some cellular substance. It appears that most organisms have one or more oncogenes.

Cancer appears to require the interaction of two or more oncogenes. Mutagens activate previously inactive oncogenes or alter normal genes into oncogenes. Such interactions, are improbable. However, the improbable occurs when given enough time and opportunity. There is no certainty of being able to avoid cancer. It is, however, prudent to maintain a life style and behavior that minimizes the mutagenic insult upon one's genes.

FOR REVIEW

Synaptonemal complex: A synaptonemal complex is a homologous pair of chromosomes held together by a lattice of protein. The complex is formed in prophase I of meiosis.

Triplet reading frames: Amino acids are specified by a triplet of nucleotides. Additions of deletions to the strand of nucleotides would cause a change in the set of nucleotides that are read as a triplet.

Repression of gene transcription: Gene transcription can be blocked or "repressed" by the presence of a repressor regulator protein that blocks the movement of RNA polymerase.

Codon: a codon is a set of three nucleotides in mRNA that specifies an amino acid.

CHAPTER OUTLINE

KEY TERMS

p. 321: mutation, point mutations, transposition

p. 322: chromosomal rearrangement, mutagens, free radical, ionizing radiation, double-stranded break, pyrimidine dimer

p. 323: xeroderma pigmentosum

p. 324: isomers, slipped mispairing, deletion, frameshift mutations

p. 325: germline cells, somatic cells, somatic mutation, tumor, sarcoma, carcinoma, metastases

p. 326: Rous avian sarcoma virus (RSV), retrovirus

p. 328: oncogene theory

p. 329: tyrosine kinase, epidermal growth factor, transfection

TOPIC EXERCISES

1. Listed below are the three major causes of DNA damage. Beside each, state the kind of damage that tends to result.

   A. Ionizing radiation

   B. Ultraviolet radiation

   C. Chemical mutagens (there are three kinds of actions)
      1.

      2.

      3.

2. In addition to mutations caused by outside agents, mutations may occur spontaneously. Two types of spontaneous events are listed below. For each, list the nature of the resulting mutation.

   A. Shift of nucleotide bases producing isomers.

   B. Slipped mispairings in chromosome alignment forming loops.

3. In a brief statement, explain how each of the following causes cancer.

   A. Viruses

   B. Smoking

LEARNING CHECKLIST

1. Describe the three kinds of genetic mutation.
2. Discuss the biological significance of mutation.
3. Define (a) cancer, (b) tumor, (c) carcinoma, (d) sarcoma, and (e) metastases.
4. What have we learned about cancer from the study of the Rous avian sarcoma virus?
5. Why is cancer usually very slow to develop and why is it more common in older individuals?
6. How can you minimize your chances of developing cancer?

MINI EXAM

A. Circle the letter of the one best answer for each question.

1. The **src** gene of RVS
    a. though lethal to mankind, is controlled in chickens by their regulatory system.
    b. is a gene acquired a long time ago by a bacterium known as <u>Carcinia</u>
    c. codes for an enzyme that makes people vulnerable to sunlight
    d. is actually a chicken gene acquired by the virus
    e. causes a metastatic carcinoma in chickens

2. A slopped mispairing
    a. results from more than one copy of a sequence on a chromosome which can be deleted without ever affecting the chromosome's function
    b. occurs spontaneously because of a frameshift mutation
    c. is of no consequence since the cell's regulatory mechanism will excise it
    d. results from the failure of a chromosome to pair with its homologue in mitosis
    e. may result in a deletion of a loop in the chromosome

3. A double-strand break is thought to be repaired by using
    a. syncytial mechanism
    b. microtubules
    c. synaptonemal complex
    d. extrinsic protein
    e. initiating complex

4. Because RNA viruses make a DNA copy of their genome, they are called
    a. parvoviruses
    b. phages
    c. retroviruses
    d. oncoviruses

5. The process of gene transposition
    a. causes a mutation usually resulting in insertional activation
    b. is spontaneous and normal and merely increases the opportunity for variation
    c. is entirely a prokaryotic phenomenon
    d. is the unfortunate consequence of infection by a retrovirus
    e. is often referred to by molecular geneticists as gene conversion

6. A tumor forming a connective tissue is called a
    a. carcinoma
    b. lymphoma
    c. melanoma
    d. sarcoma
    e. teratoma

7. The production of free radicals
   a. caused by chemical mutagens such as cigarette smoke induce the metastatic mechanism
   b. results from excision of portions of a gene causing it to be unregulated by cellular mechanisms
   c. is caused by ultraviolet radiation and is more common in tropical regions
   d. occurs as a result of exposure to ionizing radiation
   e. is the direct result of solar infrared radiation

8. Chemical mutagens may act by
   a. deletion of carboxyl groups from amino acids causing dimer formation
   b. breaking both strands of DNA which results in the deletion of one or more genes
   c. resembling nucleotides that have no appropriate base pair
   d. adding hydrocarbons to the nucleotide base causing single nucleotide substitution
   e. adding nonsense nucleotides that disrupt transcription

9. Cells leaving a tumor and spreading throughout the body to new sites are called
   a. carcinomas   d. sarcomas
   b. metastases   e. translocations
   c. phlebomas

10. A change in gene locations on a chromosome is called
    a. retroposition   c. point mutation
    b. transposition   d. translation

11. The hereditary disorder called xeroderma pigmentosum makes one very vulnerable to
    a. IR radiation   c. UV radiation
    b. ionizing radiation   d. atomic radiation

12. An attempt to correct a slipped mispairing usually results in a(n)
    a. isomer   c. heteromer
    b. deletion   d. inclusion

13. According to naming procedure for tumors,
    a. cancerous tumors of epithelial tissue must be called a melanoma
    b. tumors caused by genetically transmitted oncogenes are called unclassified cancer tumors
    c. benign tumors such as ovarian cysts are considered sarcomas because of the tissue they infect
    d. the carcinoma category includes melanomas, sarcomas and lymphomas
    e. all cancer tumors involving connective tissue anywhere in the body are called carcinomas

14. The movement of a large segment of a chromosome to a new location in eukaryotic organisms
    a. is referred to as transposition
    b. is usually attributed to chemical mutagens
    c. is called chromosomal rearrangement
    d. is triggered by the insertion of retrovirus DNA
    e. has no effect since there is a great deal of repetition of sequences in eukaryotic DNA

15. Life insurance companies have calculated that each cigarette smoked reduces one's life expectancy by about
    a. 10 hours   c. 10 days
    b. 10 minutes   d. 1 minute

16. Nucleotide bases that spontaneously shift to alternative conformations produce
    a. isomers   d. interdictions
    b. deletions   e. dimers
    c. insertions

17. An example of an oncogene is the _____ gene.
    a. src
    b. rvs
    c. sar
    d. rvp
    e. mmr

18. Transfection is
    a. a relocation of genes on a chromosome
    b. substitution of a viral gene into another organisms genome
    c. one of the greatest sources of cancer not induced by viruses
    d. the transfer of DNA by a phage virus into the host bacterium
    e. a technique for studying tumors

19. It is thought that meiosis may have evolved as a means of repairing
    a. deletions
    b. point mutation
    c. double-strand breaks
    d. frameshift mutations

20. Cross-links between adjacent bases of the DNA strand are called
    a. pyrimidine dimer
    b. isomers
    c. base pairings
    d. purine dimer
    e. polymers

B. Provide the appropriate term to complete each statement.

1. A tumor in connective tissue is called a _____.

2. A tumor in epithelial tissue is called a _____.

3. A mutation in cells <u>other than</u> germline cells is called a _____ mutation.

4. Mutations are hereditary only if they occur in _____ cells.

5. A chemical causing DNA damage is called a _____.

6. Mutations affecting one or just a few nucleotides is called a _____.

7. Radiation producing free radicals is called _____ radiation.

8. One of the few tyrosine kinases known in animals is _____.

9. Cancer causing genes have been designated _____ genes.

10. Cancer cells that spread through the body causing tumors are called _____.

C. Briefly answer each of the following questions.

1. How do mutations and various forms of radiation damage DNA?

2. What are the events in spontaneous mispairing?

3. Ionizing radiation tends to act primarily upon water molecules rather than DNA. Why then does it cause mutations?

CHAPTER ANSWERS

TOPIC EXERCISES

1. A. DNA breakage by free radicals
   B. Formation of pyrimidine dimers that (a) block DNA replications, or (b) result in faulty repair.
   C. 1. Formation of "look alike" nucleotides that pair incorrectly.
      2. Removal of amino groups from nucleotide bases.
      3. Addition of hydrocarbon groups to nucleotide bases.

2. A. Errors in nucleotide pairings
   B. Deletions caused by excisions of loops

3. A. Viruses insert viral DNA into the genome of the host resulting in <u>onc</u> genes that escape regulation.
   B. Increased exposure to chemical mutagens increases the frequency of <u>onc</u> gene mutations.

LEARNING CHECKLIST

1. Genetic mutations may be point mutations that involve only one or a few nucleotides. They may result from gene movements from one place to another, called transposition. Genetic mutations may also result from segments of a chromosome larger than a single gene becoming relocated. (pp. 321-325)

2. Mutations usually degrade the performance of the system within which it occurs. The degradation may be trivial or disastrous. If the mutation occurs in somatic cells, the mutation affects only the individual in which it occurs. If the mutation occurs in a gametic cell, it will alter the heredity of one or many generations. (p. 325)

3. (a) Cancer is a growth disorder in which cells begin to grow in an uncontrolled and invasive manner.
   (b) A tumor is an expanding ball of cells resulting from cancerous growth.
   (c) A sarcoma is a growth forming a hard tumor in connective tissue.
   (d) Carcinoma is the term given to a tumor of epithelial tissue such as skin. (pp. 325-326)

4. From the Rous avian sarcoma virus, we have learned that a gene of such a virus causes cancer in organisms that incorporate it into their genome. The gene, called and **onc** gene, is free of controls that govern the host's genome and cause cancer by producing excessive amounts of a protein. (pp. 326-329)

5. Initiation of cancer usually involves the interaction of various genes. Such interactions have a low probability. However, given enough time and opportunity, the improbable can occur. Cancer tends to be more common in older individuals simply because they have given the improbable time and opportunity. (pp. 329-331)

6. Cancer risks can be minimized by a lifestyle that reduces exposure to mutagens. One can become informed of known behaviors that correlate with cancer and avoid them. (pp. 332-333)

MINI EXAM

A.
1. d	2. e	3. c	4. c	5. a	6. e
7. d	8. d	9. b	10. b	11. e	12. b
13. e	14. c	15. b	16. a	17. a	18. e
19. c	20. a				

B.
1. sarcoma	2. carcinoma	3. somatic
4. germline	5. mutagens	6. point mutations
7. ionizing	8. epidermal growth factor	9. **onc**
10. metastases		

C. 1. Free radicals resulting from ionizing radiation may cause a double-strand break in DNA. Ultraviolet radiation tends to cause the joining of two adjacent pyrimidines into a pyrimidine dimer. Such a dimer, would block DNA replication if it were not for the cell's repair processes. Often the dimer forming bond is cleaned or it is excised and repaired. However, if no such repair is made, a gap in replication occurs. The filling of the gap may be flawed, resulting in a mutation. Mutagenic chemicals may mimic nucleotides and be incorporated into DNA. Some mutagens remove amino groups from amino acids or may add hydrocarbons to nucleotide bases. (Table 16-1, pp. 321, 322-324)

2. Spontaneous mispairings are of two major kinds. A nucleotide base may change its conformation to that of a different isomer, causing the DNA polymerase to pair it incorrectly with another base. Chromosomes may misalign when pairing. such a slipped mispairing forms a loop, Such errors, usually revert to a correct pairing. If not, the loop ma;y be excised and a deletion results. Should such a deletion occur in a nucleotide triplet rather than between triplets, it would cause a shift in the reading frame for the triplets. (pp. 324-325)

3. When ionizing radiation acts upon water it produces free radicals. The free radicals damage the DNA. (p. 322)

17: RECOMBINATION

IN THE GRAND SCHEME

We tend to assume that once a genome is acquired from our parents, one's genome is ours for life as stable strings of nucleotides. While this is true for a large number of genes, alteration of genomes occurs in both prokaryotic and eukaryotic organisms. Bacteria produce fragments of chromosomes that may remain separate from the source chromosome, rejoin with it or even be transferred to another bacterium. Bacteria can, in fact, transfer a copy of their own chromosome.

Eukaryotic organisms, too have migratory segments of DNA that may spontaneously relocate. Many errors in chromosome behavior are corrected in eukaryotic organisms. Some attempts to correct errors result in alterations. Pairing of homologues may be imprecise and cause errors of commission or omission. That is, errors may result from attempts to correct the imprecision or errors may result from a failure to correct the flow. Normal crossing-over or errors in crossing-over in gametic cell lives result in alteration of the genome for future generations. Some of the many kinds of genome modification have small affects or no affects. Others are catastrophic. Somewhere between the extremes are enough functional variances to fuel the engine of evolution.

FOR REVIEW

Heterochromatin: Heterochromatin is DNA that remains coiled and does not code for hereditary traits.

Crossing-over: In prophase I of meiosis, homologues pair tightly and exchange portions of chromosomes. Thus, genes "cross over" to the other homologue.

Double-stranded break repair theory: This theory holds that the synaptonemal complex used in the crossing-over process was evolved as a mechanism for repairing double-strand breaks in DNA.

Independent assortment: In mitosis and meiosis, the destination pole for each chromosome is determined randomly. Thus, genes located on different chromosomes from each other are assorted randomly and independently.

CHAPTER OUTLINE

AN OVERVIEW OF RECOMBINATION (p. 337)
GENE TRANSFER (pp. 337-341)
    Plasmids
    Gene Transfer Among Bacteria
    Transposition
    The Impact of Transposition
RECIPROCAL RECOMBINATION (pp. 341-343)
    Crossing-Over
    Gene Conversion
    Unequal Crossing-Over
THE EVOLUTION OF GENE ORGANIZATION (pp. 343-347)
    Satellite DNA
    Transposition Elements
        ALU elements
    Tandem Clusters
    Multigene Families
    Dispersed Pseudogenes

Single-Copy Genes
CHROMOSOMAL REARRANGEMENTS (pp. 347-348)
THE IMPORTANCE OF GENETIC CHANGE (p. 348)

KEY TERMS

p. 337: genetic recombination, gene transfer, reciprocal recombination, chromosome assortment, plasmids, transposons
p. 338: reciprocal exchange
p. 339: recognition site, integrated, Pilus, conjugation bridge, rolling-circle replication, conjugation
p. 340: transposase
p. 341: insertional inactivation, gene mobilization, resistance transfer factor
p. 342: mismatch pair, gene conversion, unequal crossing-over
p. 344: satellite DNA,
p. 345: nuclear organizer regions, tandem clusters, multigene families
p. 346: pseudogenes, dispersed pseudogenes
p. 347: translocations, inversions
p. 348: aneuploid, polyploid

TOPIC EXERCISES

1. Two genetic units leave form and return to chromosomes. A major difference is the degree of restriction of reentry locations. Beside each transfer unit listed below, state the degree of specificity of reentry locations.

    A. Plasmids   _____

    B. Transposons   _____

2. In the various recombination processes, there may be merely a redistribution of genes, or there is an alteration of gene expression. Beside each recombination process, indicate "redistribution" or "expression change" as appropriate.

    A. Crossing-over   _____

    B. Gene conversion   _____

    C. Unequal crossing-over   _____

3. In the evolution of gene organization, various gene groupings have arisen. Beside each grouping listed below, state the composition of the group.

    A. Satellite DNA   _____

    B. Transposition elements   _____

    C. Tandem clusters   _____

    D. Multigene families   _____

    E. Dispersed pseudogenes   _____

    F. Single-copy genes   _____

LEARNING CHECKLIST

1. How does recombination affect genetic variation?
2. List and give examples of the three main kinds of genetic recombination.
3. Compare transposons and plasmids.
4. What is the role of plasmids in genetic recombination?
5. What are the six classes of eukaryotic genes? Compare them with respect to amount of sequence duplication.
6. How does proximity of a heterochromatin region affect a gene's transcription?
7. Why do most genes maintain relatively stable positions over a long period of time?

MINI EXAM

A. Circle the letter of the one best answer for each question.

1. Plasmids may be integrated into a chromosome at any point of a
   a. shared sequence
   b. single-strand break
   c. double-strand break
   d. conjugation

2. Variance from the normal diploid number of chromosomes in somatic cells does occur.
   a. One who gains a full set becomes 4N, a condition otherwise known as quadraploid.
   b. The loss of a single chromosome would leave the individual with only one homologue of that chromosome, so they would be haploid
   c. The gain of a full set causes one to be 4N, a condition to which the term polyploid is properly applied.
   d. If one gains a full set of chromosomes, the condition is lethal, but they would be regarded as diploid when they die.
   e. Such variances occur normally, frequently, and without effect, thus no special term is applied to the condition.

3. Gene expression is unaffected by
   a. inversion
   b. translocation
   c. mutation
   d. reading frame shift

4. Fragments of bacterial DNA exist that may be integrated into the bacterium's chromosome, but only at specific locations.
   a. Such a fragment, called a pilus, is used in bacterial conjugation.
   b. The position of the recognition unit on the fragment results in inversion of the fragment when incorporated in the chromosome.
   c. Because of the condition that results from the described behavior, the fragment is called an aneuploid unit.
   d. The fragments are called satellite DNA because of their movement.
   e. Such specificity is characteristic of plasmids.

5. Unequal crossing-over in reciprocal recombination
   a. is responsible for the formation of satellite DNA
   b. tends to occur as a result of mispairing with identical duplicated gene sequences
   c. is very common and has only a slightly different effect than simple crossing-over
   d. will be corrected by excision of the excess chromosome length which will return the chromosome to a normal condition
   e. cannot affect future generations because it occurs only in somatic cells

6. Short nucleotide sequences are sometimes repeated several million times in genomes of eukaryotic organisms.
   a. Their frequency and their locations on the chromosome increases the probability that they will be involved in reciprocal exchange.
   b. The sequences are believed to have been acquired from viral DNA since they do not code for eukaryotic traits.
   c. Because all such segments share the same sequence, they are called shared sequence DNA.
   d. Such sequences, are called satellite DNA.
   e. The function of such sequences is believed to be gene repair.

7. In order to provide substances that a cell requires in large amounts,
   a. copies of very similar genes called dispersed pseudogenes are widely dispersed throughout the genome.
   b. the amount of heterochromatin in the nucleolar organizer is increased to provide more ribosomes.
   c. the cell resorts to sequences of identical genes called multigene families
   d. transcription occurs on both DNA strands, but in opposite directions, by the enzyme reverse transcriptase
   e. the cell encodes repeated sequences called tandem clusters

8. An example of gene conversion would be the conversion of
   a. euchromatin to heterochromatin
   b. viral DNA to human DNA
   c. one nucleotide sequence to another
   d. DNA to RNA

9. In some cases, a bacterial recombination enzyme causes a duplex to exchange strands.
   a. The requirement of an enzyme to bring about the change indicates that the exchange is a transposition
   b. The result is gene inversion, common in prokaryotic cells.
   c. Such an exchange is a typical technique for insertion of viral DNA utilizing the host cell's enzyme.
   d. The loop formed results in a plasmid.
   e. The enzyme, found both in prokaryotic and eukaryotic cells, is called the reciprocity factor.

10. Through accumulated mutations, a pseudogene becomes
    a. a transposon   c. a satellite DNA
    b. a single-copy gene   d. heterochromatin

11. Chromosome fragments may spontaneously move to new sites in a purely random manner.
    a. The randomness results from rolling-circle replication.
    b. The enzyme is unable to place these mobile elements within a gene, therefore the insertion will not affect gene function.
    c. It is estimated that nearly 50% of all Drosophila DNA is made of such fragments.
    d. The entry of the mobile unit into a chromosome may alter a specific gene, thus the term gene conversion.
    e. The randomness of the movement indicates that the fragments are transposons which gain insertion by use of the enzyme transposase.

12. The phenomenon in which the inclusion of a mobile element within a gene destroys its function is called
    a. gene mobilization   c. destructive inclusion
    b. insertional inactivation   d. insertional interference

13. An individual may lose or gain a single whole chromosome rather than a set.
    a. The individual is called aneuploid if the chromosome is lost, or polyploid if the chromosome is gained.
    b. In either case, the term aneuploid is correct.
    c. The term aneuploid is applied to the homologous chromosome only, not the individual.
    d. The correct term is aneuploid if the chromosome is gained or haploid if lost.
    e. There is no special term for the condition, but the consequences is unequal crossing-over.

14. Products required in large amounts are often encoded in thousands to copies of genes that occur together in
    a. tandem clusters
    b. satellite sequences
    c. contiguous pseudogenes
    d. multigene families

15. Because paired homologues are not identical, some nucleotides are not complementary and form mismatch pairs.
    a. Where the mismatch occurs, the nucleotides that fail to find a match will form a bridge with an adjacent nucleotide, preventing transcription.
    b. The DNA will form a loop of the mismatches until a successful pairing occurs.
    c. The cell's attempts to repair may result in gene conversion.
    d. The failed pairing will be excised and a splice formed altering the reading frame.
    e. An attempt by the cell to correct the problem by inserting a nucleotide will result in insertional activation.

16. Viral DNA incorporated into an organism's genome adds one or more new genes to that genome.
    a. Since genes are also sometimes acquired by the virus, the case stated above is considered reciprocal recombination.
    b. The gene inserted into the host genome is not recognized by the enzymes of the host and results in insertional inactivation.
    c. This is a classical example of gene mobilization.
    d. Such a merging of genomes or parts there of is conjugation.
    e. This type of gene acquisition is called gene transfer.

17. Plasmids can be donated only by bacteria possessing
    a. T plasmids
    b. C plasmids
    c. R plasmids
    d. F plasmids

18. Multigene families are thought to result from
    a. transposition
    b. conjugation
    c. inversion
    d. unequal crossing-over

19. Some bacteria form a tubular bridge to another bacterium and are able to transfer a chromosome to the other bacterium.
    a. This transfer is accomplished by replicating the donor's DNA at a point near the opening of the bridge in a process called rolling-circle replication.
    b. The chromosome transferred is always a fraction of the donor's chromosome called a plasmid.
    c. This transfer between the two bacteria is referred to as reciprocal exchange.
    d. Plasmids are usually transferred in this manner, but since a full chromosome is involved, the process can occur in bacteria that do not have plasmids.
    e. The chromosome transferred is a full complimentary copy of the donor's chromosome called a pilus.

20. A conjugation bridge is formed from a
    a. transposon
    b. conjugon
    c. plasmid
    d. pilus

B. Provide the appropriate term to complete each statement.

1. _____ is the bringing together of genes usually located at different positions on the chromosome.

2. The repair of mismatched pairs often results in alteration of the nucleotide sequences in a process called _____.

3. If deletion is used to correct slipped mispairing and crossing-over occurs in the repair region, the process is called _____.

4. Bacteria have small auxiliary chromosomes called _____.

5. Small fragments of a chromosome that migrate from one part of a chromosome to another are _____.

6. Some bacteria can transfer bits of DNA from one to another via a structure called a _____.

7. The region of a chromosome coding for rRNA is called the _____.

8. Genes that are related but distinctly different and occur together in a cluster constitute a(n) _____.

9. Silent genes, inactivated by mutation, are called _____.

10. When a portion of a chromosome becomes oriented in a reversed position, the process is called _____.

C. Briefly answer each of the following questions.

1. What are the impacts of (a) transposition, (b) insertional inactivation, and (c) gene mobilization?

2. Discuss the evolutionary potential of the reciprocal recombination examples (a) simple crossing-over, (b) gene conversion, and (c) unequal crossing-over.

3. Compare translocation and inversion.

CHAPTER ANSWERS

TOPIC EXERCISES

1. A. Specific locations
   B. Random locations

2. A. Redistribution
   B. Expression change
   C. Redistribution

3. A. Short nucleotide sequences repeated millions of times.
   B. Nucleotide sequences, longer than satellite DNA, repeated often and randomly scattered.
   C. Many duplicated genes in tandem array that code for substances in large amounts.
   D. Groups of related, yet different, genes clustered together.
   E. Genes, silenced by mutation, scattered from each other.
   F. A newly mutated active gene without a duplicate.

LEARNING CHECKLIST

1. Recombination is responsible for most of the differences between individuals. (p. 326)

2. (a) Gene transfer. Viral genes added to human chromosomes.
   (b) Reciprocal combination. Crossing-over of genes in meiosis I prophase.
   (c) Chromosomal assortment. The Mendelian ratio of 9:3:3:1. (p. 337)

3. Plasmids are axillary genes that can leave a chromosome and reenter at points on a chromosome with DNA sequences that are the same as those of the plasmid. Transpons are chromosome segments that can migrate to new location in a chromosome randomly. (pp. 337-339)

4. The F plasmid is capable of transferring copies of itself or an entire bacterial genome to another bacterium. (p. 339)

5. See table 17-2 on page 347.

6. The tight condensation of heterochromatin nearby may prevent the transcription of a gene that would be transcribed if located elsewhere. (p. 347)

7. Proximity to tightly coiled portions of chromosomes, such as those of heterochromatin, reduces the probability of a gene being relocated. Those at greatest risk are farthest from a condensed region. (p. 347)

MINI EXAM

A.
1. a	2. c	3. b	4. e	5. b	6. d
7. e	8. c	9. d	10. b	11. e	12. b
13. b	14. a	15. c	16. e	17. d	18. d
19. a	20. d				

B.
1. gene mobilization	2. gene conversion	3. unequal crossing-over
4. plasmids	5. transposons	6. pilus
7. nucleolar organizer region	8. multigene family	9. pseudogenes
10. inversion		

C. 1. (a) The transposition of elements has had a profound impact on evolution, causing both insertional inactivation and gene mobilization.
(b) Insertional inactivation deprives an organism of the function of a gene. A significant fraction of spontaneous mutations are believed to have resulted from this mode.
(c) Gene mobilization could bring together several fortuitous genes in a single plasmid or move a gene from plasmid to another. Plasmids that contain genes for resistance to several antibiotics simultaneously are called resistance transfer factors. (pp. 340-341)

2. (a) Simple crossing-over as seen in meiosis prophase I has already been shown to provide genetic variation. Since the event occurs in gametic cells, there is the potential for passing mutational changes to future generations.
(b) Gene conversions result from the "correction" of mismatched pairs. The correction of the mismatch results in gene alteration, termed gene conversion.
(c) Duplicate copies of various sequences in chromosomes may result in misalignment between homologues. A misaligned segment may be of a different length than the one with which it pairs. If such segments of

different length cross-over, the result will be unequal crossing-over. Though the two chromosomes whose segments crossed-over were homologues, the segments that misalign are not homologous. This action rapidly expands the number of copies of genes. (pp. 341-343)

3. Translocations are chromosome segments moved to a different chromosome but retaining the original gene order. Translocations have effects similar to those of transpositions. Inversions reverse the gene order. If this occurs in gametic cells and recombination occurs in the inverted area, neither gamete will have a complete set of genes. (pp. 347-348)

18: GENE TECHNOLOGY

IN THE GRAND SCHEME

Genetic engineering is a rapidly growing science. The title, "genetic engineering," often evokes negative reactions. The uninformed person usually reacts with alarm, fearing the creation of monsters, plagues, etc. Dire potentials certainly exist. However, safeguards exercised by researchers minimize the risks.

Ingenious scientists, discovering and utilizing little known and seemingly insignificant properties of bacterial and viral genetics, evolved techniques for using microbes to serve the needs of mankind. DNA can be cut with surprising precision and spliced into new combinations that enables the organism to develop products and assume characteristics that fill our needs. The use of bacterial plasmids and enzymes and selected viruses enables scientists to manipulate DNA to achieve specific goals. It is probable that many of the greatest impacts on biological sciences, industry and public health will arise from this remarkable science.

FOR REVIEW

Enzymes: Enzymes are proteins that catalyze specific reactions. Since active sites are limited by the configuration of the substrate, the range of reactions and substrates is quite limited.

DNA: DNA, deoxyribonucleic acid, is a double-stranded, helical molecule consisting of purine and pyrimidine nucleotides linked by phosphate groups. The two strands are linked by hydrogen bonds between the bases of the nucleotides. DNA contains the hereditary information of the cell and controls its form and function.

Point mutations: Point mutations are alterations in the coding sequences of nucleotides of DNA. They are called point mutations because they have very local effects.

Plasmids: Plasmids are segments of bacterial DNA that may leave and reenter the chromosome at specific points. They may be transferred to other bacteria via pili.

CHAPTER OUTLINE

Virus resistance
    tobacco mosaic virus (TMV)
    T$_i$ plasmid-transfer system
Immunity to insects
Nitrogen fixation
Farm animals
Probing the Human Genome
Piggyback Vaccines
    sub-unit vaccines

KEY TERMS

p. 351: interferon, cloning, genetic engineering, restriction endonuclease
p. 352: methylases, twofold rotational symmetry
p. 353: ligase, chimera, pSC101
p. 354: recombinant DNA, vector, vehicle
p. 355: library
p. 357: Southern blot, hybridize
p. 358: tissue plasminogen activator, atrial peptides, T$_i$ plasmids,
p. 359: glyphosphate
p. 365: sub-unit vaccines, outer surface

TOPIC EXERCISES

1. When people ask, "What good is genetic engineering?" What will you say? For each area of research listed below, cite at least three benefits produced or under study.

    A. Pharmaceuticals _____

    _____

    _____

    B. Agriculture _____

    _____

    _____

2. In this chapter, you have learned of a myriad of substances utilized in genetic engineering. Sorting them out is a challenge. In this exercise, the four steps of genetic engineering are listed on the right and the substances are listed on the left. Place the number of the step in the blank in front of the substance.

    A. _____ restriction endonuclease   1. cleaving

    B. _____ T$_i$ plasmids   2. producing recombinant DNA

    C. _____ virus coat genes   3. cloning

    D. _____ ligase   4. screening

E. _____ probe

F. _____ vector

G. _____ antibiotic resistance

3. Fear or mistrust are common reactions to genetic engineering by the general public. What are two safeguards against harmful outcomes of genetic engineering?

A. _____

B. _____

LEARNING CHECKLIST

1. What is the natural function of restriction endonucleases and how do normal bacterial cells protect their DNA from their activity?
2. How are "sticky ends" formed and what is their importance to gene technology?
3. How is chimeric genome constructed?
4. What are the four steps of genetic engineering?
5. What are some commercial applications of gene technology?
6. How can the location of a cloned gene in a chromosome be determined?

MINI EXAM

A. Circle the letter of the one best answer for each question.

1. A useful technique in screening is the incorporation of _____ in the introduced gene set of the vehicle.
   a. antibiotic resistance
   b. marker carbohydrates
   c. punctuation nucleotide sequences
   d. heavy metals

2. A chimera is formed by
   a. inserting genes for antimicrobial resistance into a DNA fragment
   b. splicing together portions of genomes from different organisms
   c. excising a portion of a genome and rejoining the remaining ends
   d. utilizing a genetic library
   e. using a bacterial vector as a vehicle

3. The most useful restriction endonuclease in genetic engineering.
   a. type II
   b. type IV
   c. type III
   d. type I
   e. r type

4. Genetically engineered tissue plasminogen activator is expected to
   a. reduce hypertension
   b. prevent kidney failure
   c. help hemophiliacs
   d. reduce cholesterol
   e. prevent strokes

5. The final stage in any genetic engineering experiment is
   a. cloning
   b. cleaving
   c. screening
   d. producing recombinant DNA
   e. hybridizing

6 Reassociation of cleaved units is prevented, in genetic engineering, by using restriction endonucleases that cleave _____ special 4 to 6 nucleotide sequences.
   a. at the beginning
   b. in the center of
   c. just following
   d. into groups of

7. Researchers in genetic engineering use safeguards such as
   a. plasminogen enzyme activators
   b. restriction endonucleases
   c. shotgun techniques
   d. self-destructive enzymes such as glyphosphatase
   e. anaerobic bacteria

8. The insecticidal protein produced by Bacillus thuringiensis is not harmful to us because we
   a. have a certain enzyme
   b. don't eat what it is in
   c. excrete it
   d. metabolize it
   e. lack a certain enzyme

9. One of the most useful procedures for identifying specific genes has been the
   a. western blot
   b. southern blot
   c. eastern blot
   d. northern blot

10. Bacteria infected by viruses attack the viral DNA with
    a. methylases
    b. ligases
    c. restriction endonucleases
    d. diribonucleases
    e. lysozymes

11. The T_i plasmid-transfer system was used to introduce the
    a. TMV gene
    b. influenza gene
    c. HILVI gene
    d. pSC101 gene
    e. HVA gene

12. Bacterial recognition sites are no longer recognizable to restriction enzymes if they are modified by the addition of _____ by the bacterium.
    a. ethyl groups
    b. methyl groups
    c. EDTA groups
    d. propyl groups
    e. pBR322 groups

13. The vaccine conferring immunity to hepatitis B is an example of a
    a. sub-unit vaccine
    b. passive vaccine
    c. retroviral vaccine
    d. pi-unit vaccine
    e. ß vaccine

14. In an important experiment, Cohen and Boyer combined pSC101 with
    a. toad DNA
    b. E. coli DNA
    c. cowpox organism
    d. TMV DNA
    e. vaccinia virus

15. Ligase reforms
    a. base-to-base hydrogen bonds
    b. purine-pyrimidine bonds
    c. phosphodiester bonds
    d. dipeptide bonds
    e. complimentary co-bonds

16. In any genetic engineering experiment, the first step is
    a. cloning
    b. cleaving
    c. screening
    d. producing recombinant DNA
    e. hybridizing

17. Glyphosphate acts to suppress production of
    a. T_i plasmids
    b. somatotropin
    c. EPSP synthetase
    d. interferon
    e. plasminogen activator

18. Specific DNA fragments produced by cleaving are called
    a. plasmids
    b. vectors
    c. transfer sets
    d. inserts
    e. libraries

19. A substance commonly used as a "probe" is purified
    a. cAMP
    b. mDNA
    c. cDNA
    d. cRNA
    e. mDTA

20. The infective genome that carries foreign DNA into an organism is called a
    a. ligon
    b. vector
    c. probe
    d. sub-unit

B. Provide the appropriate term to complete each.

1. The protein _____ increases human resistance to viral infections.

2. The sealing enzyme _____ is used to rejoin two DNA strands.

3. One of the most useful procedures in identifying a specific gene is the _____ .

4. A DNA fragment that binds by complementary base pairing is said to _____.

5. The tobacco mosaic virus gene is introduced to a tobacco cell chromosome by using the
   _____.

6. The need for adding nitrogen fertilizers to crops may be eliminated by engineering plants capable of
   _____.

7. The manufacture of _____ through genetic engineering may help farm animals to grow larger and now helps human dwarfism.

8. Plants engineered to produce more _____ would be resistant to the herbicide, glyphosphate (Roundup).

9. A protein found in the bacterium <u>Bacillus thruingiensis</u> may enable plants to become
   _____ resistant.

10. A virus used to produce a "piggyback" vaccine against hepatitis B is the virus that causes the mild disease
    _____.

C. Briefly answer each of the following questions.

   1. What are the screening techniques and of what importance are they?

   2. How are piggyback vaccines constructed and why are they effective?

   3. Discuss the ethical implications of genetic engineering?

CHAPTER ANSWERS

TOPIC EXERCISES

   1. A. Interferon, tissue plasminogen activator, atrial peptides, insulin, somatotropin, malaria vaccine, hepatitis B vaccine, herpes simplex vaccine.
      B. Herbicide resistance, virus resistance, insect tolerance, nitrogen fixation, frost resistance, animal growth.

   2. A. 1
      B. 2
      C. 2
      D. 2
      E. 4
      F. 2
      G. 4

   3. A. Dangerous experiments are prohibited.
      B. Most experimental organisms are unable to live outside the laboratory (such as obligate anaerobes.)

LEARNING CHECKLIST

   1. Restriction endonucleases are used by bacteria to cut up the DNA of invading phage viruses. The bacteria alter their own DNA so that the enzyme does not recognize it as DNA. (pp. 351-353)

   2. "Sticky ends" are formed by the cutting of DNA by a restriction endonuclease. The two strands are not cut at the same place. Thus, one strand extends beyond the other. "Sticky ends" produced by a particular restriction nuclease are complementary and can be paired and rejoined. Any two DNA molecules cleaved by the same restriction endonuclease can be spliced together. (pp. 352-353)

   3. Chimeric genomes are those that do not exist in nature. They are formed by using the same restriction endonuclease to cut up DNA from two different genomes and splicing them together. (pp. 353-355)

4. (a) Cleavage
   (b) producing recombinant DNA
   (c) cloning
   (d) screening. (pp. 355-356)

5. There are many commercial applications of gene technology in pharmaceuticals and agriculture and the list continues to grow. (pp. 357-366)

6. A cloned gene can be localized in a chromosome by inserting a radioactive probe at the location of that gene. (pp. 356-357)

MINI EXAM

A.
1. a	2. b	3. a	4. e	5. c	6. b
7. e	8. d	9. b	10. c	11. a	12. b
13. a	14. a	15. c	16. b	17. c	18. e
19. c	20. b				

B.
1. interferon	2. ligase	3. Southern blot
4. hybridize	5. T_i plasmid-transfer system	6. nitrogen fixation
7. somatotropin	8. EPSP synthetase	9. insect
10. cowpox		

C. 1. (a) To eliminate bacteria not containing a vehicle (inserted DNA), the vehicle is made to include a gene giving resistance to an antibiotic. The culture is then treated with the antibiotic. Only those containing the desired vehicle survive.
   (b) To eliminate bacteria not containing a fragment of the original library as well as the vehicle, a vehicle is used that contains only on restriction site for the endonuclease used. That site is located in a gene conferring resistance to a different antibiotic than the one used for the screening described above. The selected gene is one contained in the fragment of the original library. (p. 356)

2. Piggy back vaccines are formed by splicing the surface antigen specifying gene of a disease causing virus into the genome of a benign virus. When the altered benign virus is injected into an individual, the recipient's immune system makes antibodies against the disease causing viruses antigens carried by the benign virus. Thus the recipient of the altered virus becomes immune to the disease. (pp. 356-357)

3. Gene technology provides great opportunity to produce results good for individuals and society. The potential also exists to make changes in genomes, human and otherwise, that one might question as to the ethics of some endeavors. (pp. 353-355)

19: GENES WITHIN POPULATIONS

IN THE GRAND SCHEME

Only identical twins and clones have identical genetic makeups. Most members of a population have unique genotypes and therefore also exhibit unique phenotypes. The suite of characteristics that one individual has may make it more or less likely to survive and reproduce than other members of its population. Individuals that are better adapted to their environment tend to live longer and produce more and better offspring than more poorly adapted individuals. Thus the next generation contains more genes contributed by the better-adapted individuals than by the more poorly adapted individuals. These changes in gene frequencies within a population are called microevolution, and over many generations can lead to such significant changes in the genetic makeup of the population that a whole new species is created. This second process of change is macroevolution. All the species that have ever lived on earth, including the ones alive today, are the result of such selection, adaptation, and evolution. Natural selection tends to make populations better adapted to their environments over time, and as a result, evolution occurs. If there were no mutation, migration into or out of populations, genetic drift, nonrandom mating, or selection, there would be no changes in allele frequencies over time and thus no evolution. But these factors do affect populations, and evolution does occur.

FOR REVIEW

Natural selection: Darwin proposed natural selection as the mechanism behind evolutionary change. Darwin's theory has been called "survival of the fittest"--that is, the best adapted or most fit individuals survive. The real key to understanding evolutionary mechanisms, however, is realizing that differential reproduction, not just survival, is the answer. Better adapted individuals reproduce more and pass their traits on to future generations. Because of the reproductive success of these individuals and their offspring, their genes become more and more common in future generations.

Mechanism of heredity: Gregor Mendel was the first person to quantify the patterns of inheritance. He discovered that inherited traits are determined in an individual by two discrete factors that assort independently during the formation of gametes. New combinations of factors are formed when two gametes come together at fertilization. Today we know that these factors are alleles, forms of genes, and that the genes are located on chromosomes. During meiosis, each gamete receives one of the two alleles for each gene; thus when two gametes fuse at fertilization, the new offspring receives one allele for each gene from each parent. Meiosis produces haploid gametes from diploid parent cells, and fertilization brings together two haploid gametes to form a diploid zygote.

Alleles: Alleles are the alternative forms of a gene, a specific location and sequence of DNA nucleotides on a chromosome. Red and white, for example, are alleles or alternative forms of the gene for flower color in pea plants.

Heterozygosity and homozygosity: When an individual has two copies of the same allele, the individual is homozygous for that allele or trait. If the two alleles for a particular gene are not the same, the individual is heterozygous for that trait. If, for example, a pea plant has an allele for red flowers and an allele for white flowers, the plant is heterozygous for flower color. But if both alleles are for red flowers or both alleles are for white flowers, the plant is homozygous for flower color.

Mutation and recombination: A mutation is a change in the genetic composition of an organism. Mutations can be induced by many different factors. Mutation is the ultimate source of all genetic variability; mutations create alleles, alternative forms of a gene. Recombination shuffles the genetic changes and is the driving force behind individual variation. Sexual reproduction results in extensive recombination because of chromosome assortment and crossing-over. Other forms of chromosome alteration also contribute to recombination.

CHAPTER OUTLINE

KEY TERMS

p. 371: macroevolution, microevolution, adaptation
p. 372: electrophoresis
p. 373: genetic polymorphism, population genetics, Hardy-Weinberg equilibrium, binomial expansion, frequency
p. 375: mutation, migration, genetic drift, nonrandom mating, selection
p. 376: gene pool, gene flow
p. 377: founder principle, bottleneck effect, inbreeding
p. 378: outcrossing, artificial selection, natural selection
p. 380: eugenics, directional selection
p. 382: stabilizing selection, disruptive selection
p. 383: fitness

TOPIC EXERCISES

1. Feral animals are animals that used to be domesticated, but have reverted back to the wild. Populations of feral goats exist on many islands around the world, left by previous settlers or sailors who wanted to establish a source of fresh meat for future visits. Consider a population of 100 feral goats in which 75 individuals are solid black and 25 individuals are black and white spotted, the recessive phenotype. Calculate the frequency of the black allele (B) and the spotted alele (b) in the population, as well as the frequency of each genotype (BB, Bb, and bb) in the population. Show your work.

2. Consider the effect of selection on the length of ears in a population of feral goats. For each graph below draw what the shape of the curve would look like after many generations of the type of selection indicated. The dotted curve shows the starting position of the population. Draw your curve over it.

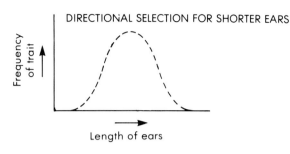

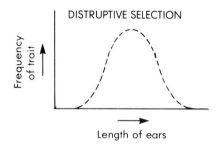

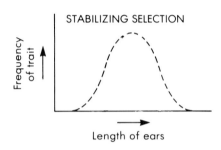

LEARNING CHECKLIST

1. Define and distinguish between microevolution andmacroevolution.
2. If a gene is polymorphic, how many alleles does it have?
3. The binomial expansion of $(p + q)^2$ is $p^2 + 2pq + q^2$. What do each of the three terms in the expansion stand for (with regard to population genetics and the Hardy-Weinberg principle)? What do p and q stand for?
4. What five factors disrupt the Hardy-Weinberg equilibrium and cause allele frequencies to change in populations? Which one regularly produces adaptive evolutionary change?
5. What single factor is responsible for altering allele frequencies when genetic drift occurs? In what size population would you expect this to occur? List two specific situations that result in populations with few individuals and thus enhance genetic drift.
6. What is the guiding or determining force behind artificial selection? Behind natural selection?
7. What two factors limit what can be accomplished by selection?
8. List the three forms of selection.

MINI EXAM

A. Circle the letter of the one best answer for each question.

1. Mating with relatives is called
   a. inbreeding
   b. outcrossing
   c. random mating
   d. eugenics
   e. fitness

2. The random loss of alleles in a population is called
   a. mutation
   b. selection
   c. genetic drift
   d. electrophoresis
   e. gene flow

3. Which of the following factors is most likely to contribute to gene flow between populations?
   a. random mating
   b. migration
   c. mutation
   d. genetic drift
   e. inbreeding

4. In the Hardy-Weinberg equation, the term 2pq represents the frequency of the
   a. dominant homozygotes
   b. recessive homozygotes
   c. dominant allele
   d. recessive allele
   e. heterozygotes

5. A scientist measures the circumference of acorns in a population of oak trees and discovers that the most common circumference is 2 cm. What would you expect the most common circumference(s) to be after 10 generations of stabilizing selection?
   a. 2 cm
   b. greater than 2 cm or less than 2 cm
   c. greater than 2 cm and less than 2 cm
   d. can't tell from the information given

6. Refer to question 5, but this time answer what you would expect after 10 generations of disruptive selection.
   a. 2 cm
   b. greater than 2 cm or less than 2 cm
   c. greater than 2 cm and less than 2 cm
   d. can't tell from the information given

7. Refer to question 5, but this time answer what you would expect after 10 generations of directional selection.
   a. 2 cm
   b. greater than 2 cm or less than 2 cm
   c. greater than 2 cm and less than 2 cm
   d. can't tell from the information given

8. Progressive changes in gene frequencies within a population is called
   a. gene flow
   b. macroevolution
   c. eugenics
   d. microevolution
   e. binomal expansion

9. How common is genetic polymorphism in natural populations?
   a. essentially all loci are polymorphic
   b. essentially no loci are polymorphic
   c. depending on the species, all loci are polymorphic or none are
   d. depending on the species, more or less than half the loci are polymorphic

10. What percent of a typical human's loci are heterozygous?
    a. 2%
    b. 5%
    c. 37%
    c. 55%
    d. 76%

11. Why is genetic polymorphism important to evolution?
    a. Individual variability provides the raw material for natural selection to act on.
    b. Genes cannot mutate unless they are polymorphic.
    c. Only heterozygous individuals are selected for in natural populations.
    d. The Hardy-Weinberg equilibrium is less likely to be disturbed in polymorphic populations.
    e. None of the above; genetic polymorphism is <u>not</u> important to evolution

12. In a population of wildflowers, the frequency of the allele for red flowers was .8. What was the frequency of the other allele for flower color, the white allele?
    a. .8   d. .2
    b. .4   e. .1
    c. .6

13. Referring to question 12, what is the frequency of homozygous red flower plants in the population?
    a. .04   d. .48
    b. .16   e. .64
    c. .32

14. Referring to question 12, what is the frequency of homozygous white flower plants in the population?
    a. .04   d. .48
    b. .16   e. .64
    c. .32

15. Referring to question 12, what is the frequency of plants in the population that are heterozygous for flower color?
    a. .04   d. .48
    b. .16   e. .64
    c. .32

16. An individual of which of the following species is likely to have the highest level of heterozygous genes?
    a. fish   d. bird
    b. land snail   e. mammal
    c. self-pollinating plant

17. What is the <u>ultimate</u> source of genetic variability?
    a. mutation   d. nonrandom mating
    b. migration   e. none of the above
    c. genetic drift

18. The movement of new genes into a population as a result of migration or hybridization is called
    a. founder principle   d. bottleneck effect
    b. selection   e. adaptation
    c. gene flow

19. A virus killed most of the seals in the North Sea (e.g., dropped the population from 8000 to 800 individuals). In an effort to help preserve the species, scientists caught 20 individuals and used them to start a new population in the northwest Pacific Ocean. Which of the following factors would most likely have the <u>least</u> impact in this new population?
    a. founder principle   c. genetic drift
    b. random mating   d. bottleneck effect

20. Inbreeding
    a. increases the rate of mutation
    b. increases the proportion of homozygous individuals in a population
    c. never occurs in plants
    d. all of the above
    e. none of the above

21. What term describes the contribution of an individual to the gene pool of future generations, relative to the contribution of other members of the population?
    a. eugenics
    b. selection
    c. adaptation
    d. allozymes
    e. fitness

B. Provide the appropriate term to complete each statement.

1. Darwin proposed that the mechanism behind evolutionary change was _____.

2. The kind of evolution that deals with the origin of new species is called _____.

3. _____ refers to features that promote the likelihood of survival and reproduction by an organism in a particular environment.

4. The study of the properties of genes in populations is called _____.

5. The puzzle of why genetic variation persists in populations was solved in 1908 by _____ and _____.

6. All the alleles present in a particular population is referred to as the populations's _____.

7. When a population has been drastically reduced in size and has restricted genetic variability, it has experienced a(n) _____.

8. Selection acts only on the _____ of an individual.

9. Migration of individuals out of a population is called _____.

C. Briefly answer each of the following questions.

1. Research has shown that adult male deer with large antlers tend to have more mating opportunities and produce more offspring than adult males with smaller antlers. Why hasn't natural selection produced male deer with huge antlers?

2. Does selection act more efficiently on dominant or recessive alleles? Beneficial or deleterious alleles? Explain.

CHAPTER 19 ANSWERS

TOPIC EXERCISES

1. If 25 of 100 individuals are spotted, and spotted is the recessive phenotype, the frequency of bb = .25 (=25%). From the Hardy-Weinberg principle we know that if bb = .25 that's the same as saying q^2 = .25, so q = .5. We also know that p + q must equal 1.0, so if q = .5 than p = .5 too. Now we can calculate the number of BB individuals in the population: BB = p^2 = .25, and similarly, the number of heterozygotes (Bb) = 2pq = 2 x .5 x .5 = .50

2.

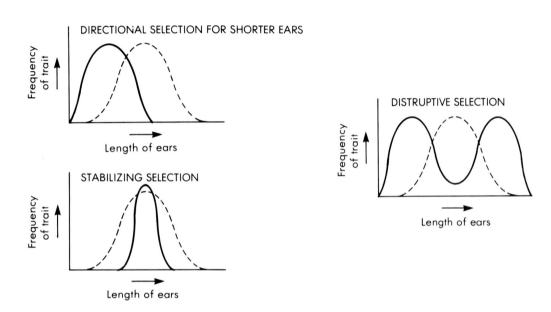

LEARNING CHECKLIST

1. Microevolution = the progressive change in gene frequencies that occurs over time in a population; macroevolution = what happens after lots of microevolution -- enough changes accumulate to result in the formation of new types of organisms (new species) (p. 371)

2. more than one (p. 373)

3. p^2 = the frequency of homozygous dominant genotypes in the population, 2pq = the frequency of heterozygotes, and q^2 = the frequency of homozygous recessive genotypes. p = the frequency of the dominant allele, q = the frequency of the recessive allele (pp. 373-374)

4. mutation, migration, genetic drift, nonrandom mating, and selection (p. 375); selection (pp. 378-380)

5. chance (p. 376); small (p. 376); founder principle and bottleneck effect (pp. 376-377)

6. humans (the breeders); the environment (p. 378)

7. interactions between genes and the fact that selection acts only on phenotypes (pp. 379-380)

8. directional selection, stabilizing selection, disruptive   selection (pp. 380-383)

MINI EXAM

A.
1. a	2. c	3. b	4. e	5. a	6. c
7. b	8. d	9. d	10. b	11. a	12. d
13. e	14. a	15. c	16. b	17. a	18. c
19. b	20. b	21. e			

B.
1. natural selection
2. macroevolution
3. Adaptation
4. population genetics
5. G.H. Hardy, G. Weinberg
6. gene pool
7. bottleneck effect
8. phenotype
9. emigration

C. 1. There are limits to what selection can accomplish. Selection is acting on the entire phenotypic makeup of the deer, not just the trait of antler size. Genes tend to interact, not operate in isolation. As the antlers get bigger, interactions may lead to other selection pressures that are negative. For example, the antlers may be so big and heavy that it is difficult for the buck to move through the woods, or feed, or detect and flee from predators. Or it may take so much energy and calcium to make such large antlers that the buck is weak and his bones break easily. (pp. 379-380)

2. Selection acts more efficiently on dominant alleles than on recessive alleles because selection acts only on phenotypes. Selection can act on an allele only if it is physically expressed, and dominant alleles are physically expressed in both the homozygous and heterozygous conditions. Recessive alleles on the other hand are expressed phenotypically only in the homozygous condition. Recessive alleles can be carried in the heterozygous condition and never be acted on by selection. It doesn't matter if an allele is beneficial or deleterious. Selection can act for or against the trait. The greater the benefit or harm caused by the trait, the stronger (more efficient) the selection will be, and the more quickly the frequency of the allele will be increased or decreased in future generations. (pp. 378-380)

20: THE EVIDENCE FOR EVOLUTION

IN THE GRAND SCHEME

Nature documentaries and stories about "Mother Nature" are filled with examples of remarkable adaptations exhibited by plants and animals. The adaptations help the organisms survive in harsh and unusual environments, such as polar bears in the arctic or cacti in the desert. These adaptations are the result of natural selection and evolutionary change. We are surrounded by evidence that evolution has occurred in the past and is continuing to occur. The diversity of life that exists on earth today, plus all the vast and minute specializations that it displays, is the result of the action of natural selection and evolution. As discussed in this chapter, in some cases we have even been able to identify particular selection forces and observe their impacts on populations. Despite the overwhelming evidence supporting evolutionary theory, some people continue to confuse science and religion, and try to promote religious beliefs as scientific theory. Although there may be debate among scientists about specific details of the theory (e.g., about the rates of evolutionary change), there is virtually no disagreement that evolution is the best scientific theory explaining the origin of species.

FOR REVIEW

Radioactive carbon dating: Carbon-14 is an isotope of carbon that is rare in nature and also unstable. It tends to break down and emit particles in a process called radio-active decay. The decay rate is constant. For carbon-14 the half-life (the amount of time it takes for 50% of the molecules in a sample to decay) is about 5600 years. By knowing the decay rate and the proportion of carbon-14 left in a fossil or rock or some other sample, it is possible for scientists to determine the approximate age of the item.

Natural selection: Natural selection is the mechanism responsible for evolutionary change. It is the process by which microevolution occurs. Organisms that have traits that make them better adapted to their environment will be selected for. They will tend to reproduce more than other individuals in the population and pass on more of their genes. Gradually, over generations, the advantageous traits become more common in the population because of differential survival and reproduction (i.e., because of natural selection). Thus, over generations, the genetic makeup of the population changes (i.e., microevolution occurs).

Mutation and recombination: Mutations are changes in the genetic composition of an organism and are the ultimate source of genetic variability. Recombination shuffles the genetic material and produces individual variability. Chromosome assortment and crossing-over during meiosis, as well as other chromosome alterations, contribute to recombination.

Hardy-Weinberg principle: G.H. Hardy and G. Weinberg discovered that the proportion of different alleles at a particular locus and genotype frequencies do not change from generation to generation unless certain factors are in effect. The five major factors that can cause changes in allele and genotype frequencies are mutation, migration, genetic drift, nonrandom mating, and selection.

CHAPTER OUTLINE

THE EVIDENCE THAT NATURAL SELECTION EXPLAINS MICROEVOLUTION (pp. 386-390)
    Sickle Cell Anemia
        malaria resistance
    Peppered Moths and Industrial Melanism
    Lead Tolerance
        bent grass

KEY TERMS

p. 388: industrial melanism
p. 390: fossils
p. 391: titanotheres, Early Eocene Epoch, Early Oligocene Epoch
p. 393: phylogenetic tree
p. 396: coccyx, lanugo, vestigial
p. 397: vermiform appendix, appendicitis, placental mammals, marsupials
p. 399: punctuated equilibria, stasis, gradualism
p. 400: scientific creationism
p. 402: melanic

TOPIC EXERCISES

1. Industrial melanism in the peppered moth is good evidence of natural selection and microevolutionary change. Listed below in alphabetical order are eight statements that explain what conditions were like before and after pollution occurred in the peppered moths' habitat. Indicate whether each condition occurred before or after pollution by placing its letter in the appropriate column of the chart below.
    Conditions:
    a. dark color more common in population
    b. dark color selected for, light color selected against
    c. dark moths seen and eaten by birds more than light moths
    d. light color more common in population
    e. light color selected for, dark color selected against
    f. light moths seen and eaten by birds more than dark moths
    g. tree trunks dark colored
    h. tree trunks light colored

    Before Pollution   After Pollution

2. Consider the phylogenetic tree diagrammed below and answer the following questions.

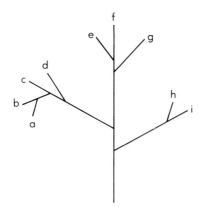

i. What species is most closely related to "a"?

ii. Which group of species is mostclosely related to the group e,f,g?

iii. Would you expect any similarities between species d and h? Why or why not?

3. Try constructing a simplified phylogenetic tree yourself. Consider the five species (A-E) with the number of genetic differences among them indicated in the table below. Fill in the letter for each species in the appropriate spot on the tree based on the degrees of relatedness.

Species	Number of Genetic Differences Between
A and B	4
A and C	2
A and D	2
B and C	4
B and E	3
C and D	2
C and E	3
D and E	3

Species 3

Species 4

Species 2

Species 5

Species 1

PHYLOGENETIC TREE

WHO'S WHO

Complete the following chart.

Scientist	Contribution to Biology
a._____	first to describe sickle cell anemia
Kettlewell	b. _____

c. _____   demonstrated natural selection, adaptation, and evolutionary change in bent grass

Simpson   d. _____

Eldredge and Gould   e. _____

f. _____   has studied giant pandas extensively in the wild

g. _____   determined the evolutionary relationships and relatives of pandas by using molecular techniques

LEARNING CHECKLIST

1. List three case histories that are documented cases of adaptation and provide clear evidence of microevolution.
2. What phenotypic traits are associated with each of the following genotypes: (a) homozygous for the sickle cell allele, (b) heterozygous for the sickle cell allele, (c) homozygous for the normal hemoglobin allele?
3. Why does the color of a peppered moth influence the moth's fitness?
4. List seven sources of evidence for macroevolution and progressive change.
5. What are two ways to determine the age of rocks and fossils?
6. List three features found in human embryos that are evidence of our evolutionary relationship to our ancestors.
7. What type or group of mammals is most common in Australia?
8. What are the names of the two major theories on the rate at which evolution occurs?
9. List three major reasons why scientific creationism is not a science.

MINI EXAM

A. Circle the letter of the one best answer for each question.

1. As adults, humans have a vestige of a tail. It is called the
   a. lanugo
   b. vermiform
   c. placenta
   d. coccyx
   e. stasis

2. Nearly all scientists agree that the earth is approximately
   a. 4.5 thousand years old
   b. 4.5 million years old
   c. 4.5 billion years old
   d. 20 billion years old
   e. 20 million years old

3. Biston betularia is the scientific name for
   a. the peppered moth
   b. the appendix
   c. bent grass
   d. baleen whales
   e. the Galapagos tortoise

4. The fossil record indicates that the average life span of a mammalian species is approximately
   a. 1 million years
   b. 150 million years
   c. 2000 years
   d. 35,000 years
   e. 200,000 years

5. The fossil record indicates that the average life span of a mammalian genus is approximately
   a. several hundred years
   b. several thousand years
   c. several million years
   d. at least 150 million years
   e. the fossil record provides no clue

6. The theory that evolutionary change occurs at a slow steady pace is called
   a. stasis
   b. gradualism
   c. punctuated equilibria
   d. scientific creationism
   e. melanism

7. An adaptation for lead tolerance has been demonstrated to exist in
   a. Agrostis tenuis
   b. titanotheres
   c. Biston betularia
   d. all of the above
   e. none of the above

8. Molecular research techniques have shown that the giant panda is most closely related to
   a. the racoon
   b. the red or lesser panda
   c. humans
   d. the dog
   e. the bear

9. Which of the following is not an example of a vestigial structure in humans?
   a. coccyx
   b. pelvis
   c. appendix
   d. lanugo
   e. all of the above are vestigial

10. During their early stages of development, the embryos of reptiles, birds, and mammals look very similar. This suggests that reptiles, birds, and mammals
    a. have a common ancestor
    b. live in the same types of environments
    c. have undergone parallel adaptation
    d. are no longer undergoing evolution
    e. have gotten rid of all their vestigial structures

11. In what type of environment would you expect melanic moths to be common?
    a. in an unpolluted forest
    b. in a polluted forest
    c. in a formerly polluted forest that had been cleaned up
    d. none of the above; melanic moths are never common

12. Which of the following presents evidence of progressive evolutionary change?
    a. the fossil record of titanotheres
    b. the fossil record of coiled oysters
    c. the molecular record of nucleotide substitutions in the globin gene
    d. all of the above
    e. none of the above

13. Which group of vertebrates has changed very little during the past 150 million years?
    a. humans
    b. giant pandas
    c. lungfish
    d. titanotheres
    e. all of the above have changed a lot

14. The similarities between marsupials in Australia and placental mammals elsewhere are an example of
    a. industrial melanism
    b. stasis
    c. genetic drift
    d. parallel adaptation
    e. punctuated equilibria

15. Using the molecular record to determine phylogenetic relationships is based on the assumption that
    a. nucleotide sequences do not change over time
    b. nucleotide sequences change at a fairly constant rate over time
    c. nucleotide sequences change randomly and erratically over time
    d. evolutionary changes occur in phenotypes but not in genotypes
    e. all mutations are harmful

16. Who demonstrated that industrial melanism had occurred in England?
    a. Eldredge and Gould
    b. Herrick
    c. Darwin
    d. Bradshaw
    e. Kettlewell

17. For a black woman living in central Africa, which genotype would be the most advantageous to have?
    a. homozygous for the sickle cell allele
    b. heterozygous for the sickle cell allele
    c. homozygous for the normal hemoglobin allele
    d. it doesn't matter; all are equally advantageous

18. For a black woman living in the United States, which genotype would be the most advantageous to have?
    a. homozygous for the sickle cell allele
    b. heterozygous for the sickle cell allele
    c. homozygous for the normal hemoglobin allele
    d. it doesn't matter; all are equally advantageous

19. If pollution is cleaned up, what should happen to the color of moths living in the woods?
    a. Color patterns shouldn't change
    b. Dark-colored moths should change to light-colored
    c. Light-colored moths should change to dark-colored
    d. Dark-colored moths should become more common
    e. Light-colored moths should become more common

20. Which of the following is an example of a nonscientific theory or concept?
    a. scientific creationism
    b. gradualism
    c. punctuated equilibria
    d. industrial melanism
    e. all of the above are scientific theories

B. Provide the appropriate term to complete each statement.

1. The first report of sickle cell anemia in 1910 mentioned the abnormal appearance of the patient's _____.

2. _____ describes the evolutionary process in which initially light-colored populations become dark as a result of pollution and natural selection.

3. Bent grass growing on mine tailings shows an unusual tolerance to _____.

4. When organisms are buried in sediment, are mineralized, and the sediments are converted to rock, the organisms become _____.

5. Rocks can be aged by measuring the degree of decay of _____ in the rocks.

6. The pattern of descent or diagram of the evolutionary relationships among organisms is called a _____ tree.

7. The pelvis of baleen whales is an example of a _____ structure.

8. _____ mammals are not common in or native to Australia.

9. The theory that evolution proceeds in spurts is called the _____ theory.

10. The direction and extent of microevolutionary change in a population is determined by the _____.

C. Briefly answer the following question.

1. When the environment changes or organisms move into a new environment, where do the "new" organisms, the ones with the better adapted traits, come from? For example, where did the first dark moths come from in the polluted woods in England and where did the lead-tolerant bent grass come from in Wales?

CHAPTER 20 ANSWERS

TOPIC EXERCISES

1. <u>Before Pollution</u>   <u>After Pollution</u>
      h,c,e,d   g,f,b,a

2. i.   b
   ii. a,b,c,d
   iii. yes; they share a common ancestor - they are both evolving from the same stock so should show similarities as well as differences

3. Species 1 = B
           2 = E
           3, 4, and 5 = A, C, and D (any order)

WHO'S WHO
  a. Herrick
  b. demonstrated natural selection, adaptation and evolutionary change in peppered moths (industrial melanism)
  c. Bradshaw
  d. noted that lungfish are evolving much more slowly than mammals
  e. proposed the idea of punctuated equilibria for evolutionary rates
  f. Schaller
  g. O'Brien

LEARNING CHECKLIST

1. sickle cell anemia, industrial melanism in peppered moths, lead tolerance in bent grass (pp. 386-389)

2. (a) sickle cell anemia, usually fatal
    (b) resistance to malaria, increased fertility in women
    (c) susceptible to malaria (pp. 387-388)

3. If moths do not blend in with their background (i.e., match the color of the tree trunk they are sitting on), they are more susceptible to predation by birds. (p. 388)

4. the fossil record, the molecular record, homologies, development patterns, vestigial structures, parallel adaptations, and patterns of distribution on oceanic islands and mainlands (pp. 390-398)

5. by their position or depth relative to other rocks and fossils; by measuring radioactive isotope decay (pp. 390-391)

6. gill slits, a tail, lanugo (p. 396)

7. marsupials (p. 397)

8. punctuated equilibria, gradualism (p. 399)

9. (a) it is not supported by any empirical observations
    (b) it does not infer its principles from observation as does all true science
    (c) its assumptions lead to no testable or falsifiable hypotheses (p. 401)

MINI EXAM

A.
1. d	2. c	3. a	4. e	5. c	6. b
7. a	8. e	9. b	10. a	11. b	12. d
13. c	14. d	15. b	16. e	17. b	18. c
19. e	20. a				

B.
1. red blood cells	2. Industrial melanism	3. lead
4. fossils	5. radioactive isotopes (radioisotopes)	6. phylogenetic
7. vestigial	8. Placental	9. punctuated equilibria
10. environment		

C. 1. The first dark moths and the initial lead-tolerant bent grass were already present in the populations of moths in unpolluted woods and bent grass in regular pasture lands. They were present, however, in very low numbers because they were not well adapted to their environment and therefore did not survive and reproduce well. Dark moths in unpolluted woods were not camouflaged as well as light moths and so were eaten more by bird predators. Lead-tolerant plants were smaller and grew more slowly than regular plants in pastures. But in the new environments (polluted woods and mine tailings), these phenotypes were strongly selected for. Dark moths were now camouflaged, and lead-tolerant grasses were able to grow well. They reproduced more and became more common in each succeeding generation. They existed in the initial populations because of the genetic variability that is inherent in sexually reproducing populations. It took a change in the environment for them to be selected for. Ultimately, the presence of an allele for dark color and an allele for lead tolerance can be traced back to mutations at those gene loci at some point in time. (pp. 388-390)

21: THE ORIGIN OF SPECIES

IN THE GRAND SCHEME

Where do species come from? A simple answer to this question is that microevolution gives rise to macroevolution. Populations continually undergo changes in allele frequencies and adaptive change. Eventually, populations that used to be similar diverge enough to be classified as no longer belonging to the same species. There are many mechanisms that prevent hybridization between divergent populations and species, and thus help keep them separate. The greater the differences in the habitats of the populations and their selection pressures, the greater the rate of the divergence. We intuitively recognize the concept of species: no one would argue that a giraffe and an oak tree belong to the same species, and the distinction between an oak tree and a maple tree is also clear. A precise definition of species is more difficult, however. We define species on the basis of shared characteristics and degree of interbreeding, but there are many gray areas. It is impossible to say precisely at what point two divergent populations become two separate species. The process is a continuum. When we look at the millions of species with which we share this planet, we see the result of billions of years of populations diverging under different selection pressures in new and changing environments.

FOR REVIEW

Natural selection: Evolutionary change occurs because of natural selection. Differential survival and reproduction of individuals within a population is the driving force behind microevolution, and over time microevolution leads to macroevolution.

Fitness: An individual's fitness is a measure of its genetic contribution to future generations relative to the contributions of other individuals in the population. The more fit an individual is, the greater its relative contribution to the future gene pool.

Microevolution: Microevolution is progressive change in gene frequencies in a population over time. These changes occur because of natural selection. Traits that make an individual more fit are selected for; traits that make an individual less fit are selected against. As a result of natural selection and microevolution, populations are adapted to their environment.

Change in populations: Over time, populations change on both a microevolutionary and a macroevolutionary scale. Via natural selection, populations adapt to their environments and undergo the changes in allele and gene frequencies that represent microevolution. Clear evidence of such changes can be seen in the sickle cell allele, industrial melanism, and lead tolerance in bent grass. Eventually, enough microevolution occurs that populations are no longer considered to be members of the same species. At that point, macroevolution has occurred, the origin of a new species. Again, there is much evidence to support the theory of macroevolution, just as there is for microevolution.

CHAPTER OUTLINE

KEY TERMS

TOPIC EXERCISES

1. In discussing speciation, this chapter presents many examples identifying particular species and genera. Match the following genera discussed in this chapter with the proper common name of organisms belonging to that genus.

   a. <u>Drosophila</u>   i.   frogs
   b. <u>Geospiza</u>   ii. oaks
   c. <u>Lactuca</u>   iii. lions and tigers
   d. <u>Panthera</u>   iv. Darwin's finches
   e. <u>Quercus</u>   v.   flies
   f. <u>Rana</u>   vi. wild lettuce

2. For each of the following examples, indicate what type of hybridization barrier is in effect.
   a. Two species of fireflies that live in the same area and are active at the same time of night and year use different flash patterns to attract their mates.
   b. Mules are sterile.
   c. One species of pine tree in California sheds its pollen in February; another species of pine growing in the same parts of California sheds its pollen in April.
   d. Franklin's ground squirrels live in areas of North Dakota with vegetation that is at least 0.5 meters tall;

Richardson's ground squirrels live in grazed pastureland and short grasses in North Dakota.

   e.   Pollen from one species of tobacco plant cannot form a pollen tube to reach the egg of a different species of tobacco even if the pollen lands on the stigma (the receptive female flower part).

   f.   In the wild, Asian elephants are found only in Asia and African elephants are found only in Africa.

   g.   The male copulatory organs of one species of <u>Drosophila</u> will not physically fit the female organs of another <u>Drosophila</u> species.

3.   How would you go about proving that the differences between two ecological races of animals were genetically determined and not just environmentally induced?

WHO'S WHO

Complete the following chart.

<u>Scientist</u>	<u>Contribution to Biology</u>
Ray	a. _____
b. _____	Stated definition of species in the 1900s, based on reproductive isolation
Turesson	c. _____
d. _____	Has studied reproductively isolated local populations of butterflies in California
Steadman	e. _____

LEARNING CHECKLIST

1.   List two scientists who have contributed to the concept and definition of species. Is the modern definition of species always clear-cut and easy to apply? Define "species" in one sentence.
2.   List five reasons why local populations tend to diverge from each other over time.
3.   List four different names used for subsets or smaller divisions of a species.
4.   Do most of the differences between plant ecotypes have a genetic or strictly environmental basis?
5.   What are the two major types of barriers that prevent hybridization between species?
6.   List the six types of prezygotic isolating mechanisms.
7.   List four ways that postzygotic isolating mechanisms can work.
8.   State two reasons why multiple isolating mechanisms often arise between species.
9.   Give two examples of genera that exhibit clusters of species as a result of adaptive radiation and tell where these clusters occur.
10.   Name three environmental conditions that promote rapid evolution.
11.   Hybridization between species does occur sometimes in nature and may produce sterile hybrids. List three ways that terile hybrids may actually reproduce.

MINI EXAM

A. Circle the letter of the one best answer for each question.

1. Which of the following is <u>not</u> a prezygotic isolating mechanism?
    a. prevention of gamete fusion
    b. temporal isolation
    c. production of sterile hybrids
    d. geographical isolation
    e. all of the above <u>are</u> prezygotic isolating mechanisms

2. Approximately how many species are there in the cluster of <u>Drosophila</u> and <u>Scaptomyza</u> species in Hawaii?
    a. 2
    b. 14
    e. 56
    d. 200
    e. 800

3. John Ray and others of his time believed that species
    a. did not change
    b. rarely occurred in nature
    c. could undergo adaptive radiation
    d. frequently hybridized in nature
    e. all of the above

4. Which of the following terms is analogous to races?
    a. subspecies
    b. varieties
    c. both of the above
    d. neither of the above

5. How many species of finches did Darwin find on the Galapagos Islands?
    a. 3
    b. 13
    c. 23
    d. 300
    e. 800

6. Which of the following is <u>not</u> one of the main groups into which the species of Darwin's finches can be placed?
    a. warbler finch
    b. ground finches
    c. tree finches
    d. all of the above <u>are</u> groups of Darwin's finches
    e. none of the above are groups of Darwin's finches

7. Behavioral isolating mechanisms may occur when two species have different
    a. sized and shaped copulatory organs
    b. courtship displays
    c. times of the day that they are sexually active
    d. habitat ranges
    e. chemical compatibilities of their gametes

8. Genetically identical organisms derived from a single genetic source are called
    a. populations
    b. varieties
    c. sibling species
    d. ecotypes
    e. clones

9. Sterile hybrids may reproduce if they undergo
   a. sexual selection
   b. parthenogenesis
   c. both of the above
   d. neither of the above

10. Which of the following is typical of local populations?
    a. large number of interbreeding individuals
    b. selection pressures identical to other populations
    c. some geographical isolation
    d. all of the above
    e. none of the above

11. Two species of wild lettuce grow in the same areas, but one flowers in early spring and the other flowers in summer. This is an example of a
    a. postzygotic isolating mechanism
    b. geographical isolating mechanism
    c. behavioral isolating mechanism
    d. mechanical isolating mechanism
    e. temporal isolating mechanism

12. Which of the following statements is most likely to be true about two species?
    a. they occupy different niches
    b. they can never hybridize
    c. they will intergrade extensively if they occur in the same area
    d. none of the above is true

13. Under which of the following conditions would you expect rapid evolution of species to occur?
    a. among populations in similar habitats
    b. in large, randomly breeding populations
    c. in populations with few reproductive isolating mechanisms
    d. among populations exposed to climatic and other environmental changes
    e. under all of the above conditions

14. Which of the following statements about species and speciation is true?
    a. hybrids are always selected against in nature
    b. polyploidy is very rare in plants
    c. reproductive isolating mechanisms are usually selected against in nature
    d. a single species can undergo adaptive radiation and produce a cluster of species
    e. species usually have only one type of reproductive isolating mechanism

15. The ancestor of Darwin's finches most likely came from
    a. South America
    b. Hawaii
    c. Cocos Island
    d. North America
    e. England

16. Drosophila species
    a. are an example of a cluster of species
    b. are closely related to Scaptomyza species
    c. exhibit behavioral isolating mechanisms
    d. all of the above
    e. none of the above

17. The sperm of species A dies when it comes in contact with the female reproductive tract of species B. This is an example of
    a. sexual selection
    b. a prezygotic isolating mechanism
    c. a postzygotic isolating mechanism
    d. parthenogenesis
    e. polyploidy

18. Which of the following species would you be most likely to find in the chaparral habitat?
    a. Panthera tigris
    b. Geospiza conirostris
    c. Quercus dumosa
    d. Lactuca graminifolia

19. Male bighorn sheep fight each other to determine which male will mate with females. They fight by charging each other, rearing up and clashing their horns together. The male with the bigger set of horns usually wins. From this description, you would expect male bighorn sheep to be affected by
    a. sexual selection
    b. mechanical isolating mechanisms
    c. adaptive radiation
    d. ecological races
    e. parthenogenesis

B. Provide the appropriate term to complete each statement.

1. The Latin word for "kind" or "type" is _____.

2. An organism's role in nature (e.g., the habitat it lives in, the food it eats, the way it behaves) is all summed up by the term _____.

3. Races of a species usually intergrade with one another when they occur in the same area, but different _____ usually do not.

4. Thirteen species of Darwin's finches live on the Galapagos Islands, and one species lives on _____ Island.

5. _____ are ecological races of plants that have been shown to have a genetic basis to their differences.

6. _____ isolating mechanisms prevent the proper functioning of a hybrid zygote once it has formed.

7. Clusters of closely related species occur in areas where a common ancestor underwent _____ as it spread into new habitats in the area.

8. _____ results from competition between members of the same sex in a population or species, competing for mates.

9. In the process called _____, egg cells may give rise directly to new individuals without being fertilized, or other somatic cells may produce embryos.

10. A _____ cell has more than two sets of chromosomes.

11. Closely related species that can be distinguished only behaviorally or by other not easily discerned characteristics are called _____ species.

12. The _____ finch uses a twig or cactus spine as a tool to help it obtain food.

CHAPTER 21 ANSWERS

TOPIC EXERCISES

1. a. v   b. iv   c. vi   d. iii   e. ii   f. i

2. a. behavioral isolation   b. postzygotic isolation
    c. temporal isolation   d. ecological isolation
    e. prevention of gamete fusion   f. geographical isolation
    g. mechanical isolation

3. Set up an experiment similar to the ones done to demonstrate that ecotypes in plants had genetically determined differences (see pp. 409-410). That is, collect members of the ecological races, raise members of each race under each of the different environmental conditions the races are found in, and see if each race still exhibits its normal traits. If it does, this is evidence that there is a genetic basis to its particular traits; the traits are not just environmentally induced.

WHO'S WHO

a. defined concept of species in 1700
b. Mayr
c. experimentally demonstrated the existence of plant ecotypes
d. Ehrlich
e. has studied the origin, adaptive radiation and classification of Darwin's finches

LEARNING CHECKLIST

1. John Ray, Ernst Mayr; no; species are groups of organisms that differ from each other in one or more characteristics and do not intergrade extensively if they occur together in nature. (pp. 405-407)

2. Local populations usually separated geographically to some extent; environmental conditions and thus selection pressures not identical; number of interbreeding individuals often small and exchange of individuals limited, therefore gene flow low and genetic drift high; gene interactions make development and phenotypic expression complex; each population begins with its own unique gene pool. (pp. 407-408)

3. Populations, races, subspecies, varieties (p. 407)

4. Genetic (pp. 409-410)

5. Prezygotic isolating mechanisms; postzygotic isolating mechanisms (p. 410)

6. Geographical isolation; ecological isolation; temporal isolation; behavioral isolation; mechanical isolation; prevention of gamete fusion (pp. 410-413)

7. Hybrid zygotes fail to develop (i.e. die); hybrid zygotes develop abnormally and are selected against; hybrids are less fit than parents and are selected against; hybrids are incapable of reproducing (p. 414)

8. The isolating factors arise primarily as byproducts of adaptive changes and several can emerge simultaneously; natural selection may strengthen isolating mechanisms that are already present. (pp. 415-416)

9. Darwin's finches in the Galapagos Islands; _Drosophila_ flies in Hawaii. (pp. 416,418)

10. Varied habitats, habitats located near each other, rapid climatic change (p. 419)

11. Vegetative reproduction; parthenogenesis; polyploidy (p. 420)

MINI-EXAM

A.

1. c	2. e	3. a	4. c	5. b	6. d
7. b	8. e	9. b	10. c	11. e	12. a
13. d	14. d	15. a	16. d	17. b	18. c
19. a					

B.

1. species	2. niche	3. species
4. Cocos	5. Ecotypes	6. Postzygotic
7. adaptive radiation	8. Sexual selection	9. parthenogenesis
10. polyploid	11. sibling	12. woodpecker

22: EVOLUTIONARY HISTORY OF THE EARTH

IN THE GRAND SCHEME

The life that we see around us on our planet is the result of 3.5 billion years of natural selection and evolution. The earth formed approximately 4.5 billion years ago and bacterial life appeared within 1 billion years of the earth's formation. Over the eons, evolutionary changes accumulated in populations and new species arose. Eukaryotic cells evolved from prokaryotic ones and later, multicellular life forms appeared. This chapter presents the evolutionary history of life on earth. It explains how we humans and all other forms of life came into being. It outlines our evolutionary roots and reminds us that the evolution of species did not and does not occur in a vacuum, but under particular environmental and geographical conditions. Over the eons, continents have moved and major climatic changes have occurred, both having direct impact on the evolution of species. Having come this far in the text, you have learned about the chemistry of life, cellular biology, energetics, cell reproduction, genetics, and evolution. This chapter stands as a summary to all those preceding it; life on earth not only evolves, it carries out all the fundamental processes you have learned about. This chapter is also an overview of things to come. In the remaining chapters you will examine in more detail the history and biology of each of the groups of organisms introduced here.

FOR REVIEW

Isotopes: Isotopes are atoms of the same element that have different numbers of neutrons. In nature, most elements exist as mixtures of different isotopes. Some isotopes are unstable and undergo radioactive decay. Each radioactive isotope has its own constant rate of decay, called its half-life. By knowing the decay rate of a particular isotope and by determining the proportion of that isotope in the rock or fossil being studied, the approximate age of the rock or fossil can be determined.

The origin of life: The earth formed approximately 4.5 billion years ago. By 3.5 billion years ago, life existed on earth. It apparently evolved spontaneously through a gradual process of chemical evolution. Inorganic molecules gave rise to organic molecules that gradually became more complex and eventually formed aggregates with more and more cell-like characteristics. At some point approximately 3.5 billion years ago, the first true cells, and thus life itself, were formed. These first life forms were prokaryotic.

Punctuated equilibrium: Punctuated equilibria is the name given to the theory formulated by Niles Eldredge and Steven Jay Gould which states that evolution occurs in spurts rather than gradually. Between the spurts of rapid evolutionary change are long periods of stasis or little evolution. The spurts would be expected when populations were relatively small and selection pressures were strong. The rate of macroevolution has not been constant for many species, but the reasons why are not always clear.

Origins of species: Evolutionary change that produces new species is called macroevolution. It occurs as a result of populations undergoing microevolution and accumulating enough genetic changes to diverge into separate species. There are many mechanisms that prevent hybridization between species and help keep species separate. Under suitable environmental conditions, a single species can undergo adaptive radiation and give rise to a cluster of species.

CHAPTER OUTLINE

FOSSILS AND FOSSILIZATION (pp. 424-427)
    Mechanical Problems in Preservation
    Dating Fossils
        Correlations of strata
        Direct age determination
            radioactive isotopes
CONTINENTAL DRIFT AND BIOGEOGRAPHY (pp. 427-429)
    History of Continental Movements
THE EARLY HISTORY OF LIFE ON EARTH (pp. 429-431)
        bacteria
        eukaryotes
        multicellularity
THE PALEOZOIC ERA (pp. 431-434)
    The Invasion of the Land
    Mass Extinctions
THE MESOZOIC ERA (pp. 434-439)
    The History of the Vertebrates
    The History of Plants
    The Extinction of the Dinosaurs
        iridium
THE CENOZOIC ERA: THE WORLD WE KNOW (p. 440)
    The Origin of Contemporary Biogeography
THE EVOLUTION OF PRIMATES (pp. 440-442)
    The Evolution of Hominoids
THE APPEARANCE OF HOMINIDS (pp. 443-446)
    The Australopithecines
    The Use of Tools: Homo habilis
    Homo erectus
        fire
    Modern Humans: Homo sapiens
        Neanderthals
        Cro-Magnons

KEY TERMS

p. 424: paleontologists, fossil, trilobites
p. 425: sedimentary rocks
p. 426: carbon-14 (^{14}C), half-life
p. 428: Pangaea, continental drift, plate tectonics, isthmus, ratite birds, biogeography
p. 429: Hadean, Archaen, Proterozoic, Phanerozoic, stromatolites
p. 430: acritarchs, Cambrian Period, Paleozoic Era, Mesozoic Era, Cenozoic Era, Precambrian, Ediacaran Period, Cnidaria, Annelida, Arthropoda
p. 431: adaptive zones, Burgess Shale
p. 432: Chlorophyta, parapodia
p. 433: chitin, Zygomycetes, Permian Period
p. 434: Cretaceous Period, Triassic Period, Jurassic Period, Chordata
p. 435: pterosaurs, plesiosaurs, Protoavis
p. 436: Archaeopteryx
p. 437: Aves, Carboniferous Period
p. 438: conifers, angiosperms, coevolved, plankton, ammonites

p. 439: iridium, forams
p. 440: Oligocene Epoch, anthropoid primates, nocturnal, diurnal, binocular vision, opposable thumb
p. 441: hominids, hominoids, Early Miocene Epoch, molecular clock
p. 443: bipedalism, Australopithecus, australopithecines
p. 444: Homo habilis, Homo erectus, Homo sapiens
p. 446: Neanderthals, Cro-Magnons, Pleistocene Epoch

TOPIC EXERCISES

1. Many geologic time periods are discussed in this chapter. Alphabetically listed, three of these time divisions are Epochs, Eras, and Periods. What is the proper sequence of these terms, going from largest unit to the smaller subdivisions?

2. Listed alphabetically below are the Phanerozoic geologic time units mentioned in this chapter. Arrange them in proper chronological order from oldest to most recent and show which is a subdivision of which other by filling in the blank outline.

Units:

Cambrian Period
Carboniferous Period
Cenozoic Era
Cretaceous Period
Jurassic Period
Mesozoic Era
Miocene Epoch
Oligocene Epoch
Paleozoic Era
Permian Period
Pleistocene Epoch
Triassic Period

Outline:

I.
   A.
   B.
   C.
II.
   A.
   B.
   C.
III.
      1.
      2.
      3.

3. Match the following organisms with the time that they are believed to have first appeared on earth. (bya = billion years ago, mya = million years ago).

a. plants
b. mammals
c. hominoids
d. angiosperms
e. Homo erectus
f. bacteria
g. reptiles
h. chordates
i. Homo habilis
j. birds (Protoavis)
k. eukaryotes
l. Homo sapiens
m. amphibians
n. Australopithecus
o. multicellular organisms

i. 3.5 bya
ii. 1.5 bya
iii. 630 mya
iv. 540 to 550 mya
v. 410 mya
vi. 360 mya
vii. 300 mya
viii. 225 mya
ix. 200 mya
x. 127 mya
xi. 20 to 25 mya
xii. 5 to 5.5 mya
xiii. 2 mya
xiv. 1.7 mya
xv. 0.5 mya

WHO'S WHO

Complete the following chart.

Scientist	Contribution to Biology
Wegener	a. _____
b. _____	Discovered fossil of earliest known bird, Proavis
Alvarez	c. _____

LEARNING CHECKLIST

1. List four mechanical problems that contribute to the fossil record being incomplete.
2. List two methods of determining the age of fossils.
3. What is the name of the mechanism that explains continental drift?
4. When did Pangaea exist? When did South America and Africa separate? When did the Isthmus of Panama connect North America and South America?
5. What are the four main divisions of earth's history?
6. What are the three eras of the Phanerozoic time and what are their approximate dates?
7. List three phyla that are represented in the fossil record of the Ediacaran Period (Precambrian).
8. What three groups of organisms invaded the land at about the same time? What other group followed within 50 million years? When did the first invasion take place?
9. How many major episodes of mass extinction have there been in the history of life on earth? Which was the largest and when did it occur? In which one did the dinosaurs become extinct and when did it occur?
10. What group of reptiles was dominant during the Mesozoic Era? To what other group of vertebrates did they give rise?
11. What was the weather generally like in the Permian Period? What type of plants evolved then? What type of plant is dominant in terrestrial habitats today (and has been for the last 100 million years)?
12. What four general events or environmental conditions have marked the Cenozoic Era?
13. List four characteristics of anthropoid primates that set them apart from other animals.
14. List the five types of living hominoids.
15. Name the first type of hominid to appear on earth and state when it lived.
16. Name the three species of Homo that have lived on earth and the dates of their existence.

MINI EXAM

A. Circle the letter of the one best answer for each question.

1. The first use of fire by hominids is associated with
   a. Australopithecus
   b. Homo habilis
   c. Homo erectus
   d. Homo sapiens
   e. Cro-Magnons

2. The study of the past and present distributions of organisms and attempts to explain how these distributions originated is called
   a. biogeography
   b. adaptive zones
   c. plate tectonics
   d. paleontology
   e. bipedalism

3. Insects belong to the phylum
   a. Cnidaria
   b. Annelida
   c. Aves
   d. Chordata
   e. Arthropoda

4. Which of the following geologic times is not part of Precambrian times?
   a. Ediacaran
   b. Hadean
   c. Archaen
   d. Phanerozoic

5. The first organisms to colonize land were probably
   a. amphibians
   b. plants
   c. insects
   d. dinosaurs
   e. humans

6. What geological evidence did Alvarez and his group use in formulating their theory on why the dinosaurs went extinct?
   a. large fragments of meteorites found embedded in the earth
   b. a sedimentary layer rich in iridium
   c. many dinosaur fossils with crushed skulls or empty stomachs
   d. cave drawings of dying dinosaurs with large dark clouds over their heads

7. Which of the following periods occurred during the Mesozoic Era?
   a. Ediacaran Period
   b. Carboniferous Period
   c. Permian Period
   d. Cambrian Period
   e. Jurassic Period

8. Which of the following is not an Epoch?
   a. Pleistocene
   b. Oligocene
   c. Miocene
   d. Cretaceous
   e. all of the above are Epochs

9. Which of the following is not part of the Paleozoic Era?
   a. Triassic Period
   b. Carboniferous Period
   c. Permian Period
   d. Cambrian Period

10. What land mass connected South America to Australia approximately 53 million years ago?
    a. Isthmus of Panama
    b. Antarctica
    c. Africa
    d. Pangaea
    e. none of the above

11. The first primate to consistently use tools was
    a. Neanderthals
    b. Australopithecus
    c. Homo habilis
    d. apes
    e. Homo sapiens

12. Which of the following is most modern in its characteristics?
    a. Cro-Magnon
    b. Neanderthal
    c. australopithecines
    d. Homo erectus

13. When did humans first cross Siberia and reach the New World?
    a. at least 2 million years ago
    b. at least 500,000 years ago
    c. at least 150,000 years ago
    d. at least 50,000 years ago
    e. at least 12,000 years ago

14. Which isotope of carbon is commonly used for dating fossils?
    a. ^{14}C d. ^{16}C
    b. ^{12}C e. ^{6}C
    c. $^{1/2}C$

15. An oxygen-containing atmosphere became stabilized during the
    a. Phanerozoic   c. Permian
    b. Proterozoic   d. Paleozoic

16. The greatest period of diversification of multicellular animals occurred during the
    a. Cambrian   c. Cretaceous
    b. Triassic   d. Permian

17. Dinosaurs became extinct about
    a. 2 million years ago
    b. 600 million years ago
    c. 65 million years ago
    d. 100 million years ago
    e. 60 thousand years ago

18. Approximately what percentage of all species of marine animals became extinct at the end of the Permian Period?
    a. 6%   d. 96%
    b. 40%   e. 100%
    c. 73%

19. Reptiles gave rise to
    a. birds
    b. mammals
    c. both of the above
    d. none of the above

20. Archaeopteryx is a fossil
    a. amphibian   d. mammal
    b. reptile   e. fish
    c. bird

21. Great coal deposits were formed from forests during the
    a. Permian Period   d. Ediacaran Period
    b. Carboniferous Period   e. Cretaceous Period
    c. Cambrian Period

22. When dinosaurs dominated the world, hominids
    a. had already become extinct
    b. had not yet evolved
    c. were present but lived in different areas
    d. were present and lived in the same areas

B. Provide the appropriate term to complete each statement.

1. North America is part of the _____ World.

2. Periods, in geologic time units, are subdivisions of _____.

3. The apes, together with humans and their direct ancestors, make up a group called the _____.

4. _____ are people who study and interpret the fossil record.

5. Most fossils are preserved in _____ rocks.

6. About 200 million years ago, the continents were all grouped together in one giant supercontinent called _____.

7. The movement of continents (continental drift) is explained by the theory of _____.

8. Stromatolites are produced by organisms called _____.

9. The first type of eukaryotes to appear in the fossil record are called _____.

10. The substance _____ is found both in the cell walls of fungi and the outer skeletons of arthropods.

11. Flying reptiles are called _____.

12. Flowering plants are called _____.

C. Briefly answer the following question.

1. According to Alvarez and his colleagues, how is the presence of iridium in sedimentary layers related to the extinction of the dinosaurs?

CHAPTER 22 ANSWERS

TOPIC EXERCISES

1. Eras, Periods, Epochs

2. I. Paleozoic Era
    A. Cambrian Period
    B. Carboniferous Period
    C. Permian Period
   II. Mesozoic Era
    A. Triassic Period
    B. Jurassic Period
    C. Cretaceous Period
   III. Cenozoic Era
        1. Oligocene Epoch
        2. Miocene Epoch
        3. Pleistocene Epoch

3.
a. v	b. ix	c. xi	d. x	e. xiv	f. i	g. vii
h. iv	i. xiii	j. viii	k. ii	l. xv	m. vi	n. xii
o. iii						

WHO'S WHO

a. first to propose that continents move
b. Chaterjee
c. based on presence of iridium layer, proposed that large meteorite collided with the earth and led to extinction of the dinosaurs as the result of the formation of a dense cloud and decreased photosynthesis

LEARNING CHECKLIST

1. Organisms may not live in place where they are likely to be preserved in sedimentary rock; fossils may not be in place accessible to us; fossils disintegrate quickly when exposed; soft body parts do not preserve well (pp. 425-426)

2. Correlating strata; radioactive isotope dating (pp. 426-427)

3. Plate tectonics (p. 428)

4. About 200 million years ago (during the Jurassic Period) (p. 428); about 125 to 130 million years ago; about 3.1 to 3.6 million years ago (pp. 428-429)

5. Hadean, Archean, Proterozoic, and Phanerozoic (p. 429)

6. Paleozoic Era, 590 to 248 million years ago; Mesozoic Era, 248 to 65 million years ago; Cenozoic Era, 65 million years ago to present (p. 430)

7. Cnidaria, Annelida, Arthropoda (p. 430)

8. Plants, arthropods (insects), and fungi; amphibians; 410 million years ago (pp. 432-433)

9. Five; fourth, end of Permian Period; fifth, end of Cretaceous Period (pp. 433-434)

10. Dinosaurs; birds (p. 435)

11. Cool and dry; the seed-bearing conifers; angiosperms (pp. 437-438)

12. Forests have receded; extensive desert barriers have formed; climate has deteriorated; regional evolution and distribution of organisms have occurred (p. 440)

13. Larger brain; binocular vision and short snouts; opposable thumbs and dexterous fingers; complex and extensive social behavior (pp. 440-441)

14. Chimpanzees, gorillas, orangutans, gibbons, and humans (p. 441)

15. Australopithecus, 5.0 to 1.3 million years ago (p. 443)

16. Homo habilis, 2.0 to 1.5 million years ago; Homo erectus, 1.7 to 0.25 million years ago; Homo sapiens, 0.5 million years ago to present (pp. 444-446)

MINI EXAM

A.
1. c	2. a	3. e	4. d	5. b	6. b
7. e	8. d	9. a	10. b	11. c	12. a
13. e	14. a	15. b	16. a	17. c	18. d
19. c	20. c	21. b	22. b		

B.
1. New	2. Eras	3. hominoids
4. Paleontologists	5. sedimentary	6. Pangaea
7. plate tectonics	8. cyanobacteria	9. acritarchs
10. chitin	11. pterosaurs	12. angiosperms

C. Iridium is an element much more common in meteorites than on earth in general. A sedimentary layer rich in iridium has been found in many places around the world, marking the end of the Cretaceous Period and Mesozoic Era (about 65 million years ago). This is the time when dinosaurs went extinct after being the dominant vertebrates of the Mesozoic Era. Alvarez proposed that the iridium was deposited as fall-out from a large iridium-rich dust cloud that was thrown up after a large meteorite hit the earth. This cloud would have darkened the earth and prevented photosynthesis for several months, causing the extinction of the dinosaurs as well as many other species. (pp. 438-439)

23: POPULATION DYNAMICS

IN THE GRAND SCHEME

With this chapter, we begin our study of ecology, a study of the relationships among organisms and their environments. You have already learned about the chemistry of life, the biology of cells, patterns of heredity, molecular genetics, and how evolution occurs and creates species diversity. Now it is time to see how species actually act in the real world, how they interact with each other and with their environments. Organisms can be grouped into tiered levels of organization: populations, communities, ecosystems, and biomes. We start with populations (the first tier), all the individuals of a particular species living in a particular area. As the title of this chapter implies, populations are not static. Individuals in the population reproduce, move to new areas or die, and the population changes size. The size and growth of a population is influenced by interactions with other populations in the form of competition, predation and parasitism. Populations are also influenced by environmental factors, such as carrying capacity and catastrophic climatic events. All these complex interactions result in each population having a characteristic size, dispersion pattern, growth rate, mortality rate, and survivorship curve. While we talk about populations, however, do not forget that each population is made up of individuals and that each individual has its own particular genetic endowment, which determines its phenotype. Natural selection acts on the individual phenotype.

FOR REVIEW

Adaptation: An adaptation is a feature that promotes the likelihood of survival and reproduction by an organism in a particular environment. It results from natural selection and microevolution. The better adapted individuals are more fit (have greater fitness) and produce more offspring than more poorly adapted individuals in the population. When we look at a population today, we see the results of a long, long history of natural selection and evolution. Thus the population and its individual members seem well adapted to the surrounding environment, both the nonliving environment and other populations of other organisms.

How species originate: New species are formed when enough microevolution has occurred to cause populations to diverge into separate species. Such a process is called macroevolution. Hybridization barriers help keep species separate. Strong selection pressure and available habitats can result in rapid speciation.

Major features of evolution: Life first appeared on earth about 3.5 billion years ago, within a billion years of the formation of the earth. By about 1.5 billion years ago eukaryotic cells appeared, and multicellular organisms had appeared by 600 million years ago. The evolution of the organisms that inhabit the earth today continued, all via micro- and macroevolution. For example, terrestrial plants and insects evolved approximately 410 million years ago, amphibians about 360 million years ago, and mammals about 200 million years ago. Our genus, Homo, appeared only 2 million years ago and our species, Homo sapiens is very much a newcomer, appearing only about half a million years ago. While all these evolutionary changes were occurring, plate tectonics caused the continents to move, greatly affecting the biogeography of species.

CHAPTER OUTLINE

KEY TERMS

p. 451: ecology, communities, ecosystem, biomes, population, niche
p. 452: population density, dispersion, randomly spaced, evenly spaced, clumped
p. 453: biotic potential
p. 454: carrying capacity
p. 456: sigmoid curve, density-dependent effects, density-independent effects
p. 457: optimal yield, K strategists, r strategists
p. 459: age distribution, generation time, survivorship, mortality, demography, stable population
p. 460: population pyramid, cohorts, interspecific competition, intraspecific competition
p. 461: competitive exclusion
p. 462: predation, parasitism
p. 464: chestnut blight, myxomatosis
p. 466: habitat, realized niche, fundamental niche

TOPIC EXERCISES

1. Shown below are the dispersion patterns of three different species of trees. Each dot represents an individual tree's location; the box represents the study area where the trees were studied. Name the type of dispersion pattern each species exhibits.

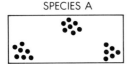

SPECIES A

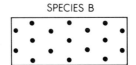

SPECIES B

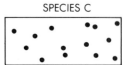

SPECIES C

2. Draw an example of an exponential growth curve and a sigmoid growth curve on the blank graphs below. Be sure to label the axes on both graphs, and on the sigmoid curve, indicate where the carrying capacity (K) is.

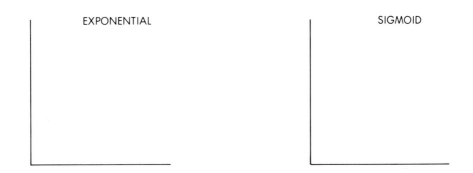

3. Draw a Type I survivorship curve, a Type II curve, and a Type III curve on the graph below.

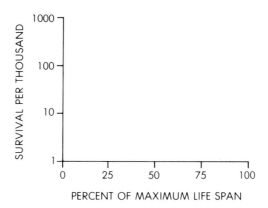

WHO'S WHO

Complete the following chart.

Scientist	Contribution to Biology
a. _____	Has studied whales extensively
Gause	b. _____
c. _____	Performed experiments on competitive exclusion with flour beetle species
Harper	d. _____
Connell	e. _____
f. _____	Studied competition in warbler species and helped develop theories on island biogeography

LEARNING CHECKLIST

1. Briefly define these four levels of organization that ecologists use in their studies: population, community, ecosystem, biome.
2. List two features of a population that measure the way it is spatially distributed or arranged.
3. What are the three dispersion patterns seen in populations? Which one is the most common in nature?
4. What are the two types of curves associated with population growth? Briefly explain the conditions under which each type of growth curve would occur.
5. What two types of effects limit population growth?
6. Describe the differences between K strategists and r strategists with regard to age of first reproduction, size of broods, number of offspring, amount of parental care, and generation time.
7. What are the three types of survivorship curves? Briefly describe what each means.
8. Name three types of interspecific interactions that limit population size.
9. List and briefly define the two types of niches.
10. State Gause's competitive exclusion principle in terms of niches.

MINI EXAM

A. Circle the letter of the one best answer for each question.

1. The statistical study of populations is called
   a. density
   b. parasitism
   c. dispersion
   d. mortality
   e. demography

2. The myxomatosis virus was introduced into Australia and New Zealand to
   a. prevent chestnut blight
   b. kill prickly pear cactus
   c. increase the carrying capacity for sheep
   d. limit intraspecific competition
   e. control rabbit populations

3. What type of survivorship curve do humans have?
   a. Type I
   b. Type II
   c. Type III
   d. Type IV
   e. none of the above

4. Which dispersion pattern is most common in nature?
   a. randomly spaced
   b. evenly spaced
   c. clumped
   d. all are equally common
   e. none of these are found in nature

5. r strategists have
   a. few offspring
   b. little parental care
   c. sigmoid growth curves
   d. all of the above
   e. none of the above

6. The number of individuals that a particular place can support indefinitely is called the
   a. biotic potential
   b. survivorship
   c. niche
   d. carrying capacity
   e. community

7. To obtain optimal yield, populations should be harvested at what part of the sigmoid growth curve?
   a. the very beginning
   b. the steep part
   c. where it levels off
   d. it doesn't make any difference
   e. populations should never be harvested

8. A community plus the nonliving factors with which it interacts is called a(n)
   a. ecosystem
   b. niche
   c. biome
   d. population
   e. cohort

9. Which of the following populations is most likely to go extinct?
   a. a very small population in an unstable environment
   b. a moderate-sized population of r-strategists
   c. a large population with lots of genetic variability
   d. all would be equally likely to go extinct

10. The number of individuals per unit area determines the population's
    a. survivorship
    b. mortality
    c. age distribution
    d. density
    e. fundamental niche

11. In the formula for biotic potential (dN over dt equals r_iN), what does N stand for?
    a. the carrying capacity of the environment
    b. the change in time
    c. the number of individuals in the population
    d. the intrinsic rate of natural increase of the population
    e. the age distribution of the population

12. Which of the following factors will affect population growth rates?
    a. net emigration
    b. net immigration
    c. birth rate
    d. all of the above
    e. none of the above

13. During exponential growth,
    a. the number of individuals in a population increases rapidly
    b. the rate of increase remains constant
    c. the curve on the graph levels off
    d. all of the above
    e. none of the above

14. When members of a population move out of a given area, it is called
    a. survivorship
    b. immigration
    c. mortality
    d. demography
    e. emigration

15. What causes a sigmoid growth curve to level off?
    a. The population stops reproducing
    b. Mortality decreases in the population
    c. The population shifts from a clumped to an evenly spaced dispersion
    d. The population reaches the environmental carrying capacity
    e. Sigmoid growth curves never level off

16. What type of effect has an increasing impact as the population size increases?
    a. density-independent effect
    b. cohort effect
    c. competitive exclusion effect
    d. fundamental niche effect
    e. density-dependent effect

17. What is the size of the human population today?
    a. over 10 billion
    b. over 5 billion
    c. less than 2 billion
    d. just under 1 bilion
    e. less than 4 million

18. What type of population would be associated with a population pyramid that had an extremely broad base?
    a. a rapidly expanding population
    b. a stable population
    c. a population where the birth rate equaled the death rate
    d. a population where there were more old individuals than young individuals
    e. a population with more males than females

19. Interspecific competition has been demonstrated experimentally in
    a. barnacles
    b. flour beetles
    c. clover
    d. all of the above
    e. none of the above

20. Which of the following statements about predator-prey interactions or parasitism is true?
    a. The most fit parasites kill their hosts
    b. As the size of the prey population increases, the size of the predator population is likely to decrease
    c. The presence of predators can prevent or reduce competitive exclusion among prey species
    d. All of the above are true
    e. None of the above is true

B. Provide the appropriate term to complete each statement.

1. The study of the relationships of organisms with one another and their environments is called _____.

2. The individuals of a given species that occur together at one place and time make up a(n) _____.

3. The intrinsic rate of increase of a population is also called its _____.

4. A late spring blizzard that kills a flock of birds that have returned to their northern breeding grounds is an example of a density-_____ effect.

5. The maximum sustainable catch or harvest from a population is called the _____.

6. Whales are examples of _____ strategists.

7. The percentage of an original population that survives to a given age is defined as the _____.

8. A _____ population maintains the same size and age distribution over time.

9. Competition between members of the same species is called _____ competition.

10. The actual role that an organism plays in a particular ecosystem is called its _____ niche.

C. Briefly answer each of the following questions.

1. Do you think it is possible that in nature an organism's realized niche might equal its fundamental niche?

2. Back in the days of sailing ships and long sea voyages, sailors would often drop off goats on isolated islands so that there would be a source of fresh meat available when they next passed by. In many cases, the goat population skyrocketed, with disastrous consequences for the native flora and fauna of the islands. Explain why these results probably occurred.

3. Giant land tortoises weighing up to 150 kilograms live on a large tropical atoll in the western Indian Ocean. The population is quite large, more than 150,000 individuals. The tortoises graze during the early morning and late afternoon, but spend midday resting in any available shade. If they do not get out of the hot, tropical noonday sun they overheat and die. Trees and bushes are scarce in many parts of the atoll, so shade is often scarce too. Are the sun and shade density-dependent or density-independent limiting factors for the tortoises?

CHAPTER 23 ANSWERS

TOPIC EXERCISES

1. Species A = clumped dispersion
   Species B = evenly spaced dispersion
   Species C = randomly spaced dispersion

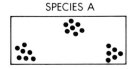
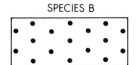
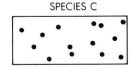

2.

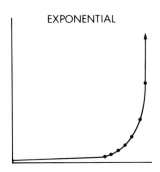
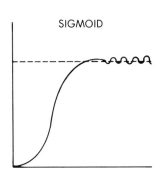

3.

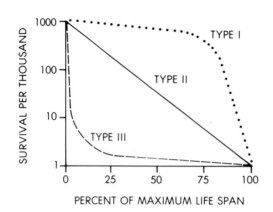

WHO'S WHO

    a. Payne

    b. developed principle of competitive exclusion

    c. Park

    d. performed experiments on competitive exclusion with clover species

    e. studied competition between barnacle species in nature

    f. MacArthur

LEARNING CHECKLIST

1.   Population = all the individuals of one species that occur together at one place and one time; community = all the different populations of different species that occur together in an area; ecosystem = a community plus the nonliving (environmental) factors with which it interacts; biome = an assemblage of terrestrial organisms that has a characteristic appearance and occurs over a wide geographical area (p. 451)

2.   Population density, population dispersion (p. 452)

3.   Randomly spaced, evenly spaced, clumped; clumped is most common (pp. 452-453)

4.   Exponential growth curve, sigmoid growth curve. Exponential growth occurs when there are no limits on the population; it is the intrinsic rate of increase or biotic potential. A sigmoid curve results when there are limits to the population's growth and ability to increase. The limits cause the number of individuals to level off at, or fluctuate around, the carrying capacity (pp. 453-456)

5.   Density-dependent effects, density-independent effects (pp. 456-457)

6.   K strategists = delayed reproduction, small broods, few offspring, extended parental care, long generation time; r strategists = early reproduction, large broods, numerous offspring, little or no parental care, short generation time (pp. 457-458)

7.   Type I: highest mortality occurs later in life; Type II: equal probability of dying at any time in life; Type III: high mortality early in life but then low mortality (p. 459)

8.   Competition, predation, parasitism (pp. 460-466)

9. Fundamental niche = niche an organism would occupy if competitors were not present; realized niche = niche that an organism actually occupies under natural circumstances (p. 466)

10. No two species can occupy the same niche indefinitely (p. 466)

MINI EXAM

A.
1. e	2. e	3. a	4. c	5. b	6. d
7. b	8. a	9. a	10. d	11. c	12. d
13. a	14. e	15. d	16. e	17. b	18. a
19. d	20. c				

B.
1. ecology	2. population	3. biotic potential
4. independent	5. optimal yield	6. $\underline{K}$
7. survivorship	8. stable	9. intraspecific
10. realized		

C. 1. Only under unusual circumstances would there be no competition, allowing the realized niche to equal the fundamental niche. Such a situation might arise in a super-rich environment in which resources were not limiting (not too realistic), or if an organism was the first to colonize an area and had no competitors. (pp. 466-467)

2. There were most likely no predators on the islands to help limit the goats. If the islands were small and far from other land, there were probably not many, if any, other large herbivores present either, so there would be little competition for the goats. The plants would probably not have evolved strong defenses against herbivory (e.g., thorns, tall height, toxic compounds), so they would be more susceptible to damage. (pp. 460-466)

3. The sun is density-independent because the size of the tortoise population does not influence how brightly or hotly the sun shines or whether there is cloud cover. The availability of shade, however, is density-dependent. The more tortoises there are in an area, the harder it is for all of them to find shade. There is a limit to how many tortoises can pile under the few available trees and bushes. The greater the density of tortoises, the greater the number that are going to die from overheating on sunny days. (pp. 456-457)

24: COEVOLUTION AND SYMBIOSIS: INTERACTIONS WITHIN COMMUNITIES

IN THE GRAND SCHEME

The last chapter dealt with populations, the first tier of ecological organization. We examined how populations grow and how various biotic and abiotic factors influence population growth and size. Now we turn our attention to the second tier of organization, the community. Instead of focusing on the characteristics of a single population and what helps determine them, we now look at the way populations interact. A community is defined by the set of populations that coexist in a given area. Communities are no more static than are individual populations. Populations interact in complex ways, from predator-prey interactions and parasitism, to mutually beneficial interactions. Over evolutionary time, many populations have adapted and adjusted to each other. This coevolution has led to remarkable chemical and morphological defenses and countering predatory strategies, to warning and mimicry colorations, morphologies and behaviors, and to symbiotic relationships. Just as "no man is an island," no population is an island, existing in isolation. Each population is part of a community and interacts with other populations.

FOR REVIEW

Natural selection: Evolutionary change occurs in populations because of natural selection. Individuals that have traits that make them better adapted to their environment will be selected for. These more fit individuals will be more likely to survive and produce more offspring than the less fit members of the population. Over time, the advantageous traits become more and more common in the population as a result of the differential survival and reproduction of individuals. The end result is populations that are highly adapted to their environments, both the abiotic factors and the other populations with which they must interact.

Adaptation: Adaptations increase the likelihood of survival and reproduction of an individual in its environment. We see populations with remarkable adaptations, because over time natural selection has favored the better adapted individuals and selected against the poorly adapted members of the population. As a result, adaptations become more and more common in the population.

Demography: Demography is the statistical study of populations. It includes the study of such population characteristics as size, growth rate, mortality, and age distribution. To understand why a population has the demographic characteristics that it does, you must also understand the factors that influence the population; factors such as the climate, availability of resources, intra- and interspecific competition, predator-prey interactions, parasitism, and other symbiotic relationships.

Competition: When there is not enough of a particular resource available to meet the needs of every individual in a particular area, competition occurs. Individuals compete for the limited resource, and the better adapted individuals usually win and are selected for. The competition may be at the intraspecific or interspecific level. Competition may occur over resources such as food, water, sunlight, nesting sites, mates, and shelter. Individuals have evolved many adaptations for reducing competition or for enhancing their competitive ability.

CHAPTER OUTLINE

COEVOLUTION (p. 471)
PREDATOR-PREY INTERACTIONS (pp. 471-479)
  Plant Defenses

KEY TERMS

p. 471: coevolution, morphological defenses
p. 472: secondary chemical compounds, primary compounds, mustard oils, alkaloids, steroids, cardiac glycosides, urushiol, ricin
p. 475: terpenoids, amphipods
p. 476: warning coloration, cryptically colored, nudibranchs, elatol
p. 477: aposematic coloration
p. 478: Batesian mimicry, models, mimic, Muellerian mimicry
p. 480: symbiosis, commensalism, mutualism, parasitism, mycorrhizae, epiphytes
p. 482: stipules, Beltian bodies

TOPIC EXERCISES

1. Match each of the following organisms with the type of defense it is known to have to deter predators. Choices may be used more than once.

    a. cactus
    b. poison ivy
    c. inchworm caterpillar
    d. milkweed
    e. monarch butterflies
    f. wild potato (Solanum)

    i.   morphological defense
    ii. secondary compounds
    iii. aposematic coloration
    iv. cryptic coloration

2. Complete the following chart on Batesian and Muellarian mimicry by indicating the palatability of the model and the mimic (poisonous or edible) and their relative abundance (common or rare).

	Palatability		Abundance	
	Model	Mimic	Model	Mimic
Batesian	a.	b.	c.	d.
Muellerian	e.	f.	g.	h.

3. Complete the following chart on symbiotic relationships by placing a "+" or a "-" or a "0" sign in the appropriate spot to indicate whether the organism is helped, harmed, or unaffected by the relationship.

	Species 1	Species 2
mutualism	+	a. ____
commensalism	b. ____	0
parasitism	+	c. ____

WHO'S WHO

Complete the following chart.

Scientist	Contribution to Biology
Bates	a. _____
b. _____	First to describe Muellerian mimicry
c. _____	First to write about Beltian bodies in plants
d. _____	Studied mutualism in ants and <u>Acacia</u> trees

LEARNING CHECKLIST

1. Of what type of ecological entity are communities made?
2. Do all populations found in a particular community have the same geographic distributions?
3. How many species are involved in a coevolutionary relationship?
4. What are two general categories of defense employed by plants against herbivores?
5. What are the main functions of plant primary and secondary compounds?
6. What are two strategies that some herbivores have evolved to deal with plant secondary compounds?
7. What two types of coloration are used by animals as a defense against predation?
8. What are the two types of mimicry systems found among species?
9. What are the three major types of symbiotic relationships that exist between species? Are they always clear-cut and easy to determine?
10. In general, are more extreme specializations found in internal or external parasites?

MINI EXAM

A. Circle the letter of the one best answer for each question.

1. Which of the following helps a prey species avoid being detected by a predator?
   a. Muellerian mimicry
   b. secondary compounds
   c. aposematic coloration
   d. cryptic coloration
   e. Batesian mimicry

2. Which of the following helps a prey species advertise to predators that it is unpalatable?
   a. Beltian bodies
   b. primary compounds
   c. aposematic coloration
   d. cryptic coloration
   e. epiphytes

3. Which of the following is an example of a plant chemical defense?
   a. primary compound
   b. secondary compound
   c. cactus spine
   d. all of the above
   e. none of the above

4. All the organisms that occur in the redwood community
   a. make up a single population
   b. use the redwoods for food
   c. have identical geographic distributions
   d. have the same evolutionary history
   e. have niches that overlap

5. Which of the following is not an example of symbiosis?
   a. monarch butterflies
   b. lichens
   c. mycorrhizae
   d. hookworms and humans
   e. clownfish and sea anemones

6. Which of the following is not an example of coevolution?
   a. milkweeds and monarchs
   b. Muellerian mimicry
   c. mutualism
   d. all of the above are examples of coevolution
   e. none of the above is an example of coevolution

7. Which of the following is an example of a plant morphological defense?
   a. urushiol
   b. mustard oils
   c. ricin
   d. elatol
   e. silica

8. Milkweeds contain
   a. cardiac glycosides
   b. urushiol
   c. ricin
   d. all of the above
   e. none of the above

9. What is the name of the protein that attacks ribosomes, blocks protein synthesis, and is found in castor beans?
   a. elatol
   b. mustard oil
   c. silica
   d. urushiol
   e. ricin

10. Which of the following statements about plants and herbivores is true?
    a. Each type of plant contains all twenty types of amino acids
    b. Secondary compounds are toxic to all herbivores
    c. Algae also produce toxic chemical compounds
    d. There are many more species of plants than there are species of herbivores

11. Why are monarch butterflies toxic?
    a. They incorporate the toxic chemicals from the milkweed they eat
    b. They produce their own secondary compounds
    c. They break down the toxic chemicals from the milkweed they eat
    d. Monarch butterflies aren't toxic; they only look that way

12. An animal that is cryptically colored probably
    a. contains toxic chemicals
    b. is palatable to predators
    c. eats plants that have secondary compounds
    d. is part of a Batesian mimicry system
    e. is part of a Muellerian mimicry system

13. Sea slugs are also called
    a. epiphytes
    b. stipules
    c. amphipods
    d. nudibranchs
    e. terpenoids

14. For a Batesian mimicry system to work,
    a. the predator must be able to learn to recognize the model
    b. the model must outnumber the mimic
    c. both of the above
    d. none of the above

15. The viceroy butterfly is a
    a. Batesian model
    b. Batesian mimic
    c. Muellerian model
    d. Muellerian mimic

16. A number of nonrelated, different kinds of stinging wasps have black-and-yellow striped abdomens and similar behavior. This is an example of
    a. commensalism
    b. cryptic coloration
    c. parasitism
    d. Batesian mimicry
    e. Muellerian mimicry

17. Both yellowjackets and longhorn beetles have black-and-yellow striped abdomens, but only the yellowjacket stings. This is an example of
    a. Batesian mimicry
    b. Muellarian mimicry
    c. parasitism
    d. mutualism
    e. primary compounds

18. Which of the following statements about symbiotic relationships is true?
    a. In a parasitic relationship, both organisms are harmed
    b. Symbiotic organisms have usually undergone little or no coevolution
    c. A relationship that appears to be commensalistic may in fact be mutualistic or parasitic
    d. The most efficient type of parasite is one that kills its host
    e. None of the above is true

19. What type of relationship do epiphytes have with their hosts?
    a. aposematic
    b. parasitic
    c. mutualistic
    d. commensalistic
    e. cryptic

20. What are Beltian bodies?
    a. A specialized structure for morphological defense found in certain types of <u>Acacia</u> trees
    b. Protein-rich structures found at the tips of leaflets of some types of <u>Acacia</u> trees
    c. Specialized structures that prevent anemone fish from being stung by the anemones with which they associate
    d. Modified body structures commonly found in internal parasites but not in external parasites
    e. Specialized organs in amphipods that break down secondary compounds of algae

B. Provide the appropriate term to complete each statement.

1. The mutual, long-term evolutionary adjustments that populations make toward each other are called _____.

2. Chemicals that a plant produces in the course of normal metabolism, such as photosynthesis and respiration, are called _____.

3. Viceroy and monarch butterflies are examples of _____ mimicry.

4. The type of symbiosis in which one species benefits while the other species is not affected is called _____.

5. An association of interacting populations in a given area is called a(n) _____.

6. Warning coloration is also known as _____ coloration.

7. _____ are plants that grow on the branches of other plants.

8. In Latin America, certain species of ants live in the _____ of certain <u>Acacia</u> trees.

9. The _____ is a parasitic member of the morning glory family.

C. Briefly answer each of the following questions.

1. What type of animals would you expect to be aposematically colored and what type cryptically colored?

2. Cabbage butterflies can feed on mustard plants and monarch butterflies can feed on milkweeds. Why are these considered to be evolutionary "breakthroughs?" What are the implications of such breakthroughs in terms of natural selection and competition?

CHAPTER 24 ANSWERS

TOPIC EXERCISES

1. a. i   b. ii   c. iv   d. ii   e. iii   f. i,ii

2. a. poisonous   b. edible   c. common
    d. rare   e. poisonous   f. poisonous
    g. common   h. common

3. a. +   b. +   c. -

WHO'S WHO

a. discovered Batesian mimicry
b. Mueller
c. Belt
d. Janzen

LEARNING CHECKLIST

1. Interacting populations (pp. 470-471)

2. No (p. 470)

3. Two (p. 471)

4. Morphological defenses, chemical defenses (secondary compounds) (pp. 471-474)

5. Primary compounds = components of major metabolic pathways; secondary compounds = protection against predation, not involved in major metabolic pathways (p. 472)

6. Developed ability to break down (neutralize) the toxins; able to incorporate toxic chemicals into own body without breaking them down, thus becoming toxic themselves (pp. 474-476)

7. Warning (aposematic) coloration; cryptic coloration (p. 476)

8. Batesian mimicry; Muellerian mimicry (pp. 478-479)

9. Commensalism, mutualism, parasitism; no (pp. 480-481)

10. Internal (p. 483)

MINI EXAM

A.

1. d	2. c	3. b	4. e	5. a	6. d
7. e	8. a	9. e	10. c	11. a	12. b
13. d	14. c	15. b	16. e	17. a	18. c
19. d	20. b				

B.

1. coevolution	2. primary compounds	3. Batesian
4. commensalism	5. community	6. aposematic
7. Epiphytes	8. stipules	9. dodder

C. 1. Animals that are toxic to predators or have some other strong defense system such as poisonous stings or bites should be aposematically colored to warn potential predators to leave them alone. Animals that are palatable to predators, however, should be cryptically colored. By being camouflaged with their surroundings, edible prey species may avoid being seen and eaten by predators. (pp. 476-478)

2. The ability of these butterflies to feed on those particular plants is an evolutionary breakthrough because it required the evolution of special systems to cope with the toxic secondary compounds produced by the mustard plants and milkweed. Earlier in evolutionary time, the plants had evolved the ability to produce the secondary compounds, and this was a breakthrough for the plants - it protected them from herbivory. But eventually the cabbage butterflies evolved their own breakthrough - the ability to break down the toxic secondary compounds. Similarly, the monarchs evolved the ability to overcome the toxic effects and actually incorporate the compounds into their own bodies. In both cases, the butterflies gained access to a new source of food and one for which there was little competition since other herbivores still couldn't handle the plant toxins. Such an ability to feed without competition would be selected for strongly. In the case of the monarchs, not only did they gain an undisputed food source, but they also gained a chemical defense system. By incorporating the milkweed's toxins, the monarchs themselves became toxic to their predators. Such a breakthrough, with its double benefits would be selected for even more strongly than the ability to feed on toxic plants by breaking down the toxins. (pp. 474-476)

25: DYNAMICS OF ECOSYSTEMS

IN THE GRAND SCHEME

In order to live, all organisms on earth need to obtain nutrients, water, and energy. The minerals and other chemicals that make up nutrients, as well as water itself, are continually cycled from the nonliving environment to living organisms and back to the environment. The sun is the ultimate source of energy for all living organisms. Autotrophs capture solar energy and convert it to chemical energy. Then the autotrophs and the heterotrophs utilize the autotrophs' chemical energy. We have examined in depth the process of converting solar energy to chemical energy (i.e., photosynthesis) and the process of utilizing the chemical energy (i.e., cellular respiration). Now it is time to look at the bigger picture - how living organisms interact with each other and their surrounding environment while cycling chemicals and transferring energy. This is what ecosystems are all about, and it is not a static proposition. Ecosystems are dynamic and constantly changing, just as populations and communities are. Many of the changes occurring now, unfortunately, are harmful ones brought about by human interference and pollution.

FOR REVIEW

Respiration: Virtually all the work that a living cell or organism performs utilizes ATP. ATP is the universal energy currency. Cellular respiration is the oxidative process that results in the synthesis of ATP. All organisms carry out cellular respiration, either anaerobically or aerobically. Autotrophs obtain the energy-rich organic compounds to be oxidized in respiration by making them. Since heterotrophs cannot do this, heterotrophs obtain their fuels for respiration by eating autotrophs or other heterotrophs.

Nitrogen fixation: The triple bond that holds two nitrogen atoms together to form N_2 must be broken before atmospheric nitrogen can be incorporated into proteins, nucleic acids, and other biologically important molecules. This process is called nitrogen fixation. The development of the ability to fix nitrogen was a major event in the evolution of metabolism. Because oxygen prevents nitrogen fixation, today the process is restricted to anaerobic bacteria and to cyanobacteria with their specialized heterocysts. Without these nitrogen fixers there would be no utilization of atmospheric nitrogen or nitrogen cycle.

Populations: A population is made up of all the individuals of a particular species that occur together in a given place at a given time. Populations have specific characteristics, such as age, dispersion, growth rates, survivorship curves, and age distributions. The members of a population interact with each other and with members of other populations and are influenced by environmental factors. All the populations in a given area, plus the nonliving factors they interact with, make up an ecosystem.

Competition: Individuals compete with each other for limited resources. The competition may be intraspecific or interspecific and may occur over resources such as water, sunlight, food, or physical space. How successfully different organisms compete will influence the flow of materials and energy through ecosystems.

Interactions in communities: Communities are made up of all the different populations in a given area. All these populations of different species interact in numerous and complex ways. They may compete with each other, they may have predator-prey interactions, or they may be part of a symbiotic relationship. Over evolutionary time, many populations have coevolved, interacting with and adjusting to each other. This coevolution has led to remarkable adaptations. All the interactions that occur in a community help define the nature of the ecosystem and help determine the flow of materials and energy.

CHAPTER OUTLINE

BIOGEOCHEMICAL CYCLES (pp. 487-496)
> The Water Cycle
> The Carbon Cycle
> The Nitrogen Cycle
> The Oxygen Cycle
> The Phosphorus Cycle
> Biogeochemical Cycles Illustrated: Recycling in a Forested Ecosystem
>> Hubbard Brook Experimental Forest

THE FLOW OF ENERGY (pp. 496-499)
> autotrophs
>> heterotrophs
> Productivity
> Trophic Levels

ECOLOGICAL SUCCESSION (pp. 499-502)

KEY TERMS

p. 487: biogeochemical cycles
p. 488: water cycle, aquifers, groundwater, water table, transpiration
p. 489: carbon cycle
p. 490: peat, fossil fuels, limestone, nitrogen cycle, ferredoxin, nitrogen reductase, nitrogenase, nitrogen fixation
p. 491: legumes, Rhizobium
p. 492: actinomycetes, Frankia, Anabaena, Nitrosomonas, nitrification
p. 493: Nitrobacter, nitrite ion (NO_2^-), nitrate (NO_3^-), ammonium ions (NH_4^+), ammonification, denitrification, phosphorus cycle, phosphates, guano
p. 494: superphosphate, apatite, mycorrhizae
p. 496: autotrophs, heterotrophs, primary production (primary productivity), gross primary productivity, net primary productivity, biomass
p. 497: primary producers, primary consumers, secondary consumers, decomposers, detritivores, trophic levels, food chain, food web
p. 498: meiofauna
p. 499: pyramids of biomass, pyramids of energy, pyramids of number, succession, plankton
p. 500: secondary succession, primary succession, xerarch succession, hydrarch succession, oligotrophic, eutrophic
p. 501: climax vegetation, climax community, fugitive species

TOPIC EXERCISES

1. Match each of the following substances with its major reservoir(s) for its biogeochemical cycling. An answer may be used more than once.

   a. water   i. rocks
   b. carbon   ii. aquifers
   c. nitrogen   iii. air
   d. phosphorus

2. In the Hubbard Brook experiments, the runoff amounts of various substances were monitored before and after removing all the trees from one area. For each of the substances listed below, indicate whether its runoff quantities increased, decreased, or stayed the same after the clear-cutting.

   a. water   c. phosphorous
   b. calcium   d. nitrogen

3. Label the tiers of the pyramid of energy shown below with the appropriate term for the organisms that are found at each level. Each level should have two labels.

Terms:

autotrophs
carnivores
herbivores
primary consumers
primary producers
secondary consumers

Pyramid:

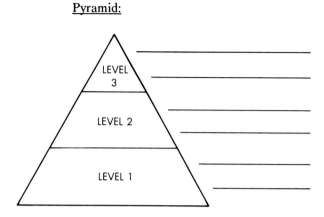

WHO'S WHO

Complete the following chart.

Scientist	Contribution to Biology
a. + b. _____	Conducted experiments on nutrient recycling at Hubbard Brook
c. _____	Studied flow of energy in a freshwater ecosystem
Clements	d. _____

LEARNING CHECKLIST

1. Name the five biogeochemical cycles discussed in this chapter.
2. List four reservoirs (living and nonliving) for water on earth.
3. List four major reservoirs for carbon on earth.
4. What type of organisms carry out nitrogen fixation? Besides nitrogen fixation, what are the names of three other processes involved in the nitrogen cycle?
5. In the Hubbard Brook experiments, which nutrient changed from being accumulated in the system when plants were present to being lost at a rapid rate after the plants were removed?
6. Are autotrophs dependent on heterotrophs or vice versa?
7. What two terms describe the productivity of an ecosystem?
8. Name the four basic trophic levels.
9. Food chains normally consist of how many steps?
10. Name the two types of primary succession.

MINI EXAM

A. Circle the letter of the one best answer for each question.

1. Which type of succession will occur after a forest fire?
   a. xerarch
   b. hydrarch
   c. primary
   d. secondary
   e. eutrophic

2. The major reservoir for phosphorus is
   a. aquifers
   b. soil and rocks
   c. the atmosphere
   d. the sun
   e. clouds

3. When part of the Hubbard Brook Experimental Forest was cut down
   a. water flowed through the system at a greater rate
   b. nitrogen began to accumulate in the system
   c. more phosphorus was lost in stream runoff
   d. all of the above
   e. none of the above

4. Compared with mature systems, early successional stages have
   a. higher total biomass
   b. lower net productivity
   c. a greater ability to regulate biogeochemical cycles
   d. more heterotrophic species
   e. more fugitive species

5. The process of converting nitrate to nitrogen gas and nitrous oxide is called
   a. nitrogen fixation
   b. ammonification
   c. denitrification
   d. nitrification
   e. transpiration

6. Which of the following is a secondary consumer?
   a. a carnivore
   b. an herbivore
   c. a plant
   d. all of the above
   e. none of the above

7. Which of the following pyramids can never be inverted in a natural ecosystem?
   a. pyramid of numbers
   b. pyramid of energy
   c. pyramid of biomass
   d. all can be inverted
   e. none can be inverted

8. Most plants have a symbiotic relationship between their roots and fungi that helps absorb phosphorus from the soil. These root/fungi associations are called
   a. peat
   b. meiofauna
   c. legumes
   d. actinomycetes
   e. mycorrhizae

9. Which of the following contains a lot of carbon?
   a. fossil fuels
   b. limestone rock
   c. peat
   d. all of the above contain a lot of carbon
   e. none of the above contain much carbon

10. On an annual basis, approximately what percentage of all the CO_2 in the atmosphere is fixed by photosynthesis?
    a. 100%
    b. 70%
    c. 36%
    d. 10%
    e. 1%

11. Which of the following organisms is a primary consumer?
    a. an autotroph
    b. a horse parasite
    c. an oak tree parasite
    d. a wolf
    e. a seaweed

12. Of the fresh water in the United States, 96% consists of
    a. streams and rivers
    b. lakes and ponds
    c. oceans
    d. swimming pools
    e. groundwater

13. The earth is an open system with respect to
    a. organisms
    b. chemicals
    c. energy
    d. all of the above
    e. none of the above

14. Which of the following chemicals enters living organisms primarily from the atmosphere rather than from rocks or soil?
    a. calcium
    b. sulfur
    c. sodium
    d. carbon
    e. phosphorus

15. Carbon dioxide makes up approximately what percentage of the atmosphere?
    a. 0.03%
    b. 0.47%
    c. 21.0%
    d. 78.0%
    e. 96.0%

16. The first step in nitrogen fixation involves converting N_2 to
    a. nitrate
    b. nitrite
    c. nitrogenase
    d. amino acids
    e. ammonia

17. The symbol for nitrate is
    a. NO_2^-
    b. NO_3^-
    c. NH_3
    d. NH_4^+
    e. N_2

18. Goats depend on autotrophs for the production of
    a. O_2
    b. glucose
    c. both of the above
    d. none of the above
    e. goats <u>are</u> autotrophs

19. The total amount of energy that is converted to organic compounds in a given area per unit time is called the
    a. biomass
    b. transpiration
    c. net primary productivity
    d. gross primary productivity
    e. succession rate

20. Plants capture approximately _____ of the sun's energy while other trophic levels capture about
_____ of the energy available to them in their food.
   a. 1%, 10%   c. 10%, 1%
   b. 10%, 60%   d. 60%, 10%

B. Provide the appropriate term to complete each statement.

   1. Groundwater is stored in _____.

   2. _____ is a general term that applies to organisms such as scavengers and decomposers that live on the refuse of an ecosystem.

   3. Xerarch succession is a type of _____ succession.

   4. _____ consists of undecomposed organic matter such as cellulose.

   5. _____ is the genus of bacteria that inhabits root nodules of legumes and carries out nitrogen fixation.

   6. Deposits of sea bird feces are rich in phosphorus and are called _____.

   7. Organisms that can capture solar energy and manufacture their own food are called _____ or _____.

   8. The _____ of an ecosystem is the total weight of all the organisms living in the ecosystem.

   9. A lake that is poor in nutrients is said to be _____.

   10. _____ species tend to occur at earlier successional stages and then disappear as succession proceeds.

C. Briefly answer each of the following questions.

   1. What long-term problems can we expect to face with our heavy and increasing utilization of groundwater?

   2. It has been said that meat is a luxury that most of the world's people cannot afford. Considering what you know about energy flow through ecosystems, does this statement make sense?

   3. How do early successional stages differ from late successional stages in an ecosystem?

CHAPTER 25 ANSWERS

TOPIC EXERCISES

   1. a. ii,iii
      b. iii
      c. iii
      d. i

2. a. increased
    b. increased
    c. stayed the same
    d. increased

3. Level 1 = autotrophs, primary producers
    Level 2 = herbivores, primary consumers
    Level 3 = carnivores, secondary consumers

WHO'S WHO

a. + b. Bormann and Likens
c. Cole
d. proposed concept of climax vegetation in ecosystems

LEARNING CHECKLIST

1. water cycle, carbon cycle, nitrogen cycle, oxygen cycle, phosphorus cycle (pp. 488-494)

2. surface waters, groundwaters, atmosphere, and living organisms (pp. 488-489)

3. atmosphere, dissolved in oceans, fossil fuels, and living organisms (pp. 489-490)

4. bacteria (p. 490); nitrification, ammonification, denitrification (pp. 492-493)

5. nitrogen (p. 495)

6. heterotrophs are dependent on autotrophs (p. 496)

7. gross primary productivity, net primary productivity (p. 496)

8. primary producers, primary consumers, secondary consumers, decomposers (detritivores) (p. 497)

9. 3 or 4 (p. 499)

10. xerarch and hydrarch (p. 500)

MINI EXAM

A.

1. d	2. b	3. a	4. e	5. c	6. a
7. b	8. e	9. d	10. d	11. c	12. e
13. c	14. d	15. a	16. e	17. b	18. c
19. d	20. a				

B.

1. aquifers	2. Detritivore	3. primary
4. Peat	5. Rhizobium	6. guano
7. autotrophs, primary producers	8. biomass	9. oligotrophic
10. fugitive		

C. 1.   Aquifers are not only becoming polluted, they are also becoming depleted. In many areas we are removing water from aquifers much faster than the aquifers can recharge or refill. This not only decreases the amount of water available for humans to use for drinking or irrigation, but also lowers the water table and makes it more difficult for plant roots to obtain water. The pollution of groundwater supplies is also serious since it is virtually impossible to clean up aquifers. (pp. 488-489)

2.   Yes; there is an ecological basis to the high cost of meat. The fewer the number of steps in the food chain, the more efficient it is, since available energy decreases drastically with each step. To raise a cow for humans to eat, you must feed it vegetation. The cow can only utilize 10% of the available plant energy; when humans eat the cow they capture only 10% of the cow's available energy. Many more people could be supported by eating plants directly (e.g., cereals, rice). Any ecosystem can support more primary consumers than secondary consumers. Being a carnivore is costly both energetically and economically. (pp. 497-499)

3.   Compared with later successional stages, early successional stages have lower biomass; higher net productivity; fewer total species, especially fewer heterotrophs, but more fugitive species; and less ability to regulate their biogeochemical cycles. (p. 501)

26: ATMOSPHERE, OCEANS, AND BIOMES

IN THE GRAND SCHEME

The organisms that live on the earth are not scattered about the surface of the planet in a random pattern. Each type of organism is found in some places and not in others. The distribution patterns are determined by the environmental conditions existing in different parts of the world and by the ability of organisms to adapt to and survive in those conditions. The pattern of environmental or climatic conditions is not random, either. The location of major climatic types can be traced to the location of the continents and the major circulation patterns that occur in the oceans and the atmosphere. The circulation patterns themselves result from the shape and tilt of the earth, and the unequal distribution of solar energy during the earth's rotations and revolutions. Extremely diverse habitats exist on the earth - for example, oceans, fresh water, and terrestrial habitats. Terrestrial habitats can differ greatly in their climates, having vastly different temperatures, amounts of precipitation, and amounts of sunlight. Each different habitat has its own assemblage of organisms that live in it; the terrestrial assemblages are known as biomes. As we examine the different biomes in this chapter, we are dealing with ecology at a global level, on a much larger scale than individual populations, or communities, or even ecosystems.

FOR REVIEW

Major features of evolution: The earth originated about 4.5 billion years ago, and life arose on it about 3.5 billion years ago. Starting from these simple bacterial beginnings, the diversity of life that exists on earth today has gradually evolved. For example, multicellular organisms evolved at least 630 million years ago, and terrestrial vertebrates evolved about 360 million years ago. The evolution of organisms was influenced greatly by geological events such as continental drift and by drastic climate changes such as glaciation.

Communities: The populations that occur together in a given place at a given time make up a community. These populations interact and influence each other in various ways. Interspecific competition, predator-prey interactions, symbiotic relationships, and coevolution are all examples of how populations within a community may interact. All these interactions help define the community, the ecosystem to which it belongs, and even the biome.

Symbiosis: Symbiosis means living together. Two types of organisms have a symbiotic relationship if they live together consistently. The three major types of symbiotic relationships are mutualism, where both organisms benefit, commensalism, where one organism benefits and the other is not affected, and parasitism, where one organism benefits and the other is harmed. Symbiosis often leads to unique coevolutionary adaptations and helps give different communities and ecosystems their distinct characters. Different examples of symbiotic relationships can be found in all biomes.

Biogeochemical cycles: Biogeochemical cycles describe the movement of substances through ecosystems. Chemicals cycle from nonliving reservoirs such as the atmosphere, oceans, and soil, to living organisms, and back to reservoirs. Water, carbon, nitrogen, and phosphorus are examples of chemicals that are vital to organisms and cycle through ecosystems. Biogeochemical cycles help define the character of an ecosystem and influence the distribution of organisms within different ecosystems.

CHAPTER OUTLINE

THE GENERAL CIRCULATION OF THE ATMOSPHERE (pp. 506-510)

KEY TERMS

TOPIC EXERCISES

1. State where each of the following major atmospheric and oceanic circulation features is located on the earth.

Feature	Location
Doldrums	a.
Trade winds	b.
Prevailing westerlies	c.
Polar front	d.
Gulf Stream	e.
Humboldt Current	f.

2. Listed alphabetically below are nine terms that describe zones in oceans and freshwater lakes. Arrange the terms in their proper orders for ocean depths (going from closest-to-shore to deepest), for lake depth (going from closest-to-shore to deepest), and for lake temperature (going from warmest to coldest).

   Terms: abyssal zone, epilimnion, hypolimnion, limnetic zone, littoral zone, neritic zone, profundal zone, surface zone, thermocline

Ocean Depths	Lake Depths	Lake Temperatures
a.	d.	g.
b.	e.	h
c.	f.	i.

3. Match each of the following biomes with its characteristics or representative flora and fauna.

   a. transitional between tropical rain forest and desert
   b. epiphytes, infertile soil, and high productivity
   c. deep, fertile soil; long, cold winters; prairie
   d. conifers such as spruce, fir, and hemlock; long summer days, short winter days
   e. succulent plants; large daily temperature fluctuations
   f. permafrost; musk-oxen
   g. found only in Northern Hemisphere; warm, rainy summers and cold winters

   i. temperate grasslands
   ii. tundra
   iii. tropical rain forests
   iv. taiga
   v. temperate deciduous forests
   vi. savannas
   vii. desert

LEARNING CHECKLIST

1. Name the two key physical factors that help determine the distribution of biomes.
2. Name four major atmospheric circulation patterns.
3. What is the relationship between air temperature and amount of precipitation?
4. What are the two general locations of the world's great deserts?
5. What direction do gyrals move in the Northern Hemisphere? in the Southern Hemisphere?
6. Name the three major zones or kinds of habitats found in the ocean.
7. Name the three zones found in ponds and lakes.
8. What are the three major temperature zones of a large, temperate lake in the summer?
9. List the seven major biomes.
10. What single factor is having the greatest impact on biomes today?

MINI EXAM

A. Circle the letter of the one best answer for each question.
1. The deep-water areas of the open ocean are called the
   a. abyssal zone
   b. hypolimnion
   c. neritic zone
   d. profundal zone
   e. intertidal zone

2. The climate of a particular region is influenced by its
   a. solar radiation
   b. latitude
   c. both of the above
   d. none of the above

3. Monsoons are characteristic of
   a. the coast of Peru
   b. India and southern Asia
   c. California
   d. North Africa
   e. Antarctica

4. Which of the following regions has a mediterranean climate and is derived from temperate deciduous forests?
   a. North America's taiga
   b. tropical rain forests
   c. northeastern United States
   d. African savannas
   e. California chaparral

5. Where would you find coral reefs?
   a. in the epilimnion
   b. in the abyssal zone
   c. in the profundal zone
   d. in the neritic zone
   e. none of the above

6. Where would you find beardworms?
   a. in the epilimnion
   b. in the littoral zone
   c. in the profundal zone
   d. in the neritic zone
   e. in the abyssal zone

7. Compared with terrestrial habitats, the oceans have _____ species and _____ phyla.
   a. more, more
   b. fewer, fewer
   c. more, fewer
   d. fewer, more
   e. the same, the same

8. At least 40% of all photosynthesis in the world is carried out by
   a. photosynthetic plankton
   b. photosynthetic nekton
   c. epiphytes
   d. tundra
   e. gyrals

9. Which of the following statements is true?
   a. In the temperate zones of the Northern Hemisphere, the eastern edges of continents tend to be warmer than the western edges.
   b. The major circulation pattern in the atmosphere is an east-to-west one; there is very little north or south movement of air.
   c. Geological features, as well as atmospheric and oceanic circulation patterns, help determine which biomes occur where.
   d. Most of the great deserts lie between 60° and 40° north or south latitude.

10. The warmer, upper layer of water in a lake is called the
    a. thermocline   d. neritic zone
    b. hypolimnion   e. epilimnion
    c. nekton

11. The earth radiates heat back to space in the form of
    a. short-wave radiation   d. CO_2
    b. long-wave radiation   e. lightning
    c. ozone

12. Which of the following areas receives little precipitation?
    a. the equator
    b. near 30° north or south latitude
    c. near 60° north or south latitude
    d. all of the above receive a lot of precipitation
    e. all of the above receive very little precipitation

13. What is the name of the event that results in unusual warming of the waters off the coast of Peru and has adverse climatic consequences on a global scale?
    a. the Humboldt Current
    b. the Gulf Stream
    c. estivation
    d. El Niño
    e. the doldrums

14. The deepest parts of the oceans are approximately
    a. three-fourths of a kilometer deep
    b. 3 km deep
    c. 11 km deep
    d. 27 km keep
    e. 90 km deep

15. What type of organisms are the primary producers in the deepsea, warm-water vent ecosystems?
    a. photosynthetic bacteria
    b. crabs and fish
    c. beardworms
    d. chemosynthetic bacteria
    e. there are no primary producers in these ecosystems

16. Approximately what percentage of the earth's surface is covered by inland lakes?
    a. 2%   d. 50%
    b. 10%   e. 75%
    c. 23%

17. Tropical rain forests receive approximately how much rainfall per year?
    a. less than 25 cm   d. 75 to 250 cm
    b. 90 to 150 cm   e. over 400 cm
    c. 200 to 450 cm

18. Which of the following is not characteristic of deserts?
    a. succulent plants
    b. large daily temperature changes
    c. animals that can estivate
    d. all of the above are characteristic of deserts
    e. none of the above is characteristic of deserts

19. Which of the following is not characteristic of the taiga biome?
    a. permafrost
    b. long, cold winters
    c. long days in the summer
    d. conifers
    e. moose

B. Provide the appropriate term to complete each statement.

1. Of all the biomes, _____ have the greatest species diversity.

2. Huge surface currents called _____ dominate ocean circulation patterns.

3. The steadiest winds on earth occur between latitudes 30° north and 30° south, and are called the _____.

4. The rain shadow effect describes the phenomenon where the _____ side of a mountain range receives much more rainfall than the _____ side.

5. Fish and other nonmicroscopic organisms that swim in the surface layers of oceans make up the _____.

6. Light does not penetrate effectively into the _____ zone of a lake.

7. When unrelated groups of organisms evolve to become superficially similar, it is called _____ evolution.

8. The prolonged state of torpor that occurs under hot, dry conditions is called _____.

9. Another name for temperate grasslands is _____.

10. The name for the northern coniferous forest biome is the _____.

C. Briefly answer each of the following questions.

1. In general, do trees or grasses require more water?

2. Why are tropical rain forests particularly vulnerable to human disturbance?

3. Why are there so many phyla but relatively few species that live in the oceans compared with terrestrial habitats?

4. What might happen to the world's biomes if atmospheric circulation stopped?

CHAPTER 26 ANSWERS

TOPIC EXERCISES

1. a. near the equator
   b. between about 30° north and 30° south latitude
   c. between about 30° to 60° north and 30° to 60° south latutide
   d. near 60° north and 60° south latitude
   e. North Atlantic, runs from southwest to northeast
   f. southeast Pacific, runs from south to north along west coast of South America

2. a. neritic zone
   b. surface zone
   c. abyssal zone
   d. littoral zone
   e. limnetic zone
   f. profundal zone
   g. epilimnion
   h. thermocline
   i. hypolimnion

3. a. vi
   b. iii
   c. i
   d. iv
   e. vii
   f. ii
   g. v

LEARNING CHECKLIST

1. a. the amounts of heat from the sun that reach different parts of the earth and the seasonal variations in that heat
   b. global atmospheric circulation and the resulting patterns of oceanic circulation (p. 506)
2. the doldrums, the trade winds, the prevailing westerlies, and the polar front (pp. 507-508)
3. Warmer air can hold more moisture than cooler air, so in areas where air is cooled it tends to lose its moisture (i.e., it rains). Conversely, areas where air is warmed tend to have less precipitation, since the air hangs on to its moisture (p. 508)
4. around 30° north and 30° south latitude on the western sides of continents, or in the interiors of large continents (p. 508)
5. clockwise; counterclockwise (p. 509)
6. the neritic zone; the surface layers; the abyssal zone (p. 512)
7. littoral zone; limnetic zone; profundal zone (p. 516)
8. the epilimnion; the thermocline; the hypolimnion (p. 516)
9. tropical rain forests; savannas; deserts; temperate grasslands; temperate deciduous forests; taiga; tundra (p. 518)
10. the human population (p. 529)

MINI EXAM

A. | 1. a | 2. c | 3. b | 4. e | 5. d | 6. e |
|---|---|---|---|---|---|
| 7. d | 8. a | 9. c | 10. e | 11. b | 12. b13. d |
| 14. c | 15. d | 16. a | 17. c | 18. d | 19. a |

B. | 1. tropical rain forests | 2. gyrals | 3. trade winds |
|---|---|---|
| 4. windward, leeward | 5. nekton | 6. profundal |
| 7. convergent | 8. estivation | 9. prairies |
| 10. taiga | | |

C. 1. Trees. Forest biomes occur only where there is substantial precipitation. Grasslands occur in drier areas. (pp. 519-522, 524-527)

2. They are vulnerable because they occur where human populations are already large and are expanding tremendously. Humans cut the forests for lumber and to clear land for farming. The rain forests are also vulnerable because the soils are relatively infertile; they will not support many years of agriculture, and after they are depleted by the farmers it is almost impossible for the forest to return and reclaim the land. Furthermore, although species diversity is extremely high, the abundance of any one particular species is usually low, thus making the species more vulnerable to extinction. (pp. 519-521)

3. Life arose in the sea and continued to evolve there, so most of the phyla have marine representatives. The oceans represent a relatively stable, amenable environment. Terrestrial habitats are much more diverse and harsher. Not all phyla have been able to colonize the land successfully, but some that have done so have been able to take advantage of the great diversity of habitats. There has been tremendous radiation of species in a few terrestrial phyla. Without a comparable diversity of habitats in the oceans, there has not been a comparable proliferation of species. (pp. 510-512)

4. There would be a drastic change in the distribution and existence of biomes as a result of drastic changes in the climate. Ocean circulation would also be affected, which would further affect biomes. Major changes would occur in regional temperatures and precipitation. As a result, there would be drastic changes in the assemblage of organisms living in the different areas. (pp. 506-510)

27: THE FUTURE OF THE BIOSPHERE

IN THE GRAND SCHEME

The future of the biosphere looks bleak in many ways as the world faces severe problems, the biggest of which is the rapidly increasing human population. More and more people are putting greater and greater demands on finite resources. The global distribution patterns of humans and their production and consumption of food, energy, and minerals are extremely unequal. The disparities will only get larger as the number of people increases; most of the increase will occur in the countries that can least afford it and are the worst off already. The rate of extinction of valuable species will accelerate as humans destroy their environments either directly or via pollution. If societies are currently unable to meet the needs of all their people, what hope is there for meeting those needs in the future (or even maintaining the status quo, much less improving standards of living) when the demands will be even greater? It will take concerted international efforts, and not just by politicians, if these problems are to be solved. Research must be conducted in areas such as improving agricultural productivity, developing new crops, and designing workable renewable energy systems. The results must be implemented on a global scale. Most of all, we must control our population growth. It is encouraging that efforts are already under way in all of these areas. To continue to survive on this planet, humans must understand biology and must implement sound biological principles. We must understand how and why ecosystems and organisms function as they do, and we must take heed of the biological principles that apply to all living organisms.

FOR REVIEW

Overpopulation: The environment limits the size of all populations on this planet. Each habitat or ecosystem has a specific carrying capacity for each of the populations living within it. Humans, however, have been able to minimize environmental controls and expand greatly the carrying capacities of their local environments because of technological achievements in areas such as agriculture, medicine, housing, transportation, and industrial development. As a result, the human population has grown explosively and is continuing to grow at an alarming rate. There is a limit to how much carrying capacities can be increased, and no population can survive successfully if it exceeds the carrying capacity.

Population growth characteristics: Every population has the innate capacity for exponential growth. In nature, however, this rapid growth does not usually continue for long periods because of limiting factors imposed by the environment. These factors may be density-independent (such as a blizzard or fire) and cause the populations to crash. Or the factors may be density-dependent (such as competition and limited resources) and cause the growth rate to slow down as the population gets larger and approaches the carrying capacity of the environment. This results in a typical sigmoid growth curve. The actual growth rate of a population is determined by a complex interaction of factors such as the population's size, age distribution, reproductive strategies, emigration and immigration rates, and interactions with the environment and other species. The human population has been able to overcome many environmental limitations and has increased at a great rate.

Cycling of minerals and flow of energy: Ecosystems regulate the flow of energy through themselves and the cycling of mineral nutrients within themselves. Energy flows from the sun to the photosynthesizers and on to the primary and secondary consumers and the decomposers. The transfer of energy is not particularly efficient. Plants capture only about 1% of the solar energy available to them, and each trophic level captures only about 10% of the energy available from the preceding level. Minerals and other nutrients are continually cycled from abiotic reservoirs (such as the air, oceans, rocks, and soil) to the living organisms of the ecosystem, back to the reservoirs, and so on ad infinitum.

Characteristics of biomes: Each biome is a particular assemblage of organisms that occurs over a large geographical region of the earth. The characteristics of a biome are distinct from those of other biomes. These characteristics are both abiotic (e.g., climate - temperatures, precipitation, solar energy) and biotic (e.g., species diversity, types of species present). The seven major biomes on the earth are tropical rain forests, savannas, deserts, temperate grasslands, temperate deciduous forests, taiga, and tundra.

CHAPTER OUTLINE

KEY TERMS

p. 535:   replacement level fertility, zero population growth rate
p. 538:   guayule, periwinkle, vinblastine, vincristine, jojoba
p. 539:   grain amaranths, winged bean
p. 540:   Green Revolution, monoculture
p. 541:   saline soils
p. 542:   shifting agriculture
p. 543:   manioc (tapioca, cassava)
p. 546:   Chernobyl, uranium dioxide
p. 547:   uranium ore, greenhouse gas, radioactivity, curies, dose, rem units, background radiation, radon gas
p. 548:   incandescent bulbs, global warming, trace gases
p. 549:   threshold effects
p. 550:   plastics, chlorinated hydrocarbons
p. 553:   ozone, chlorofluorocarbons (CFCs), stratosphere
p. 555:   environmental scientists, applied science, meteorology, model
p. 556:   environmental impact

TOPIC EXERCISES

1. Draw the growth curve of the human population on the graph below. Is this an exponential or a sigmoid growth curve?

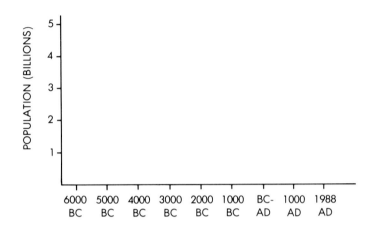

2. The development of agriculture has had a tremendous impact on the human population and the whole biosphere. Complete the chart below by indicating whether each of the agricultural aspects listed can be described as being high or low.

Aspect	High or Low
a. Diversity of crop species	
b. Energy costs of Green Revolution and modern agriculture	
c. Use of chemicals in Green Revolution and modern agriculture	
d. Need for new or modified crops	
e. Fertility of tropical soils	
f. Potential value of currently unknown or untested species	
g. Availability of new lands to cultivate	

LEARNING CHECKLIST

1. State when agriculture was developed, the size of the human population then, and the size now.
2. Has the human birth rate increased or decreased in the last century? Has the human death rate increased or decreased? What were these rates in 1990?
3. Do the majority of people in the world live in developed or developing countries? Is the population of people in developed countries increasing or decreasing? Are more material goods consumed in the developed or developing countries?
4. Name three major trends affecting many people living in or near the tropics.
5. Name the three crops that provide more than half of all human energy requirements.
6. Name the program that helped increase food production in many parts of the world in the 1950s and 1960s. Name seven costs or factors associated with the program.
7. What is the most promising strategy for improving the world food supply? What new technique will help with this? What other avenue exists?
8. What type of agriculture is commonly practiced in tropical forests? What impact will tropical deforestation have on other tropical species?
9. What major advantage does nuclear power have as a source of energy compared to fossil fuels? What problems are associated with nuclear energy?
10. List two major reasons why carbon dioxide levels in the atmosphere are increasing. What major climatic change is associated with the increasing CO_2 levels? What is the name of this phenomenon?
11. List five major pollution problems facing humans and the rest of the world.
12. List the five components that should be part of solving any environmental problem.

MINI EXAM

A. Circle the letter of the one best answer for each question.

1. At the present rate of growth, the human population is expected to double in size in
   a. 2 years
   b. 14 years
   c. 39 years
   d. 78 years
   e. 140 years

2. Villages and towns first became established
   a. after the development of industry
   b. after the development of agriculture
   c. both of the above
   d. none of the above

3. How many children in developing countries starve to death each day?
   a. about 2,000
   b. about 40,000
   c. about 80,000
   d. about 100
   e. about 4

4. If a country has a zero population growth rate, it means that
   a. no one in the country is allowed to have children
   b. the number of deaths is greater than the number of births per year
   c. immigration into the country does not occur
   d. the population size is declining toward zero
   e. there is replacement level fertility of two children per woman

5. If present growth rates continue, which country will have the largest total population by the year 2050?
    a. China
    b. United States
    c. India
    d. Madagascar
    e. Brazil

6. During the next 50 years, the greatest population increase will occur in the
    a. temperate developed countries
    b. temperate developing countries
    c. tropical and subtropical developed countries
    d. tropical and subtropical developing countries
    e. temperate and tropical developed countries

7. How many crop species are responsible for providing almost 50% of the world's food for humans?
    a. 3
    b. 20
    c. 78
    d. 150
    e. 250,000

8. The current growth rate of the human population is about
    a. 1.8% per year
    b. 2.8% per year
    c. 18% per year
    d. 28% per year
    e. 41% per year

9. By 1650, the human population numbered about
    a. 500 thousand
    b. 5 million
    c. 50 million
    d. 500 million
    e. 5 billion

10. Compared with developed countries, developing countries have
    a. higher infant mortality
    b. lower life expectancy
    c. more people living in them
    d. higher birth rates
    e. all of the above

11. In 1990, approximately what percentage of the world's population lived in extreme poverty?
    a. nearly 2%
    b. nearly 10%
    c. nearly 17%
    d. nearly 25%
    e. nearly 43%

12. Which of the following is associated with the Green Revolution?
    a. increased food production
    b. decreased dependence on agricultural chemicals
    c. decreased energy costs to produce crops
    d. all of the above
    e. none of the above

13. Which of the following strategies is least likely to improve the world's food supply?
    a. utilizing new foods
    b. bringing more land under cultivation
    c. using genetic engineering to improve crop species
    d. harvesting fish stocks more intelligently
    e. none of the above will improve world food supplies

14. Approximately what proportion of the people in the world depend on firewood as their primary source of fuel?
    a. 1/8
    b. 1/4
    c. 1/3
    d. 1/2
    e. 5/8

15. By early in the next century, the rate of extinction may easily reach several species per
    a. month
    b. week
    c. day
    d. hour
    e. minute

16. The average global temperature is relatively high because carbon dioxide and other gases trap the longer wavelengths of infrared light (heat) and prevent them from radiating back into space. This is known as
    a. acid precipitation
    b. the ozone effect
    c. the Green Revolution
    d. the slash-and-burn effect
    e. the greenhouse effect

17. Which of the following is <u>not</u> likely to happen as a result of the rising levels of CO_2 in our atmosphere?
    a. increased incidence of skin cancer
    b. rise in sea levels
    c. change in climatic patterns
    d. shifts in locations of deserts and fertile regions
    e. none of the above is likely to happen

18. DDT and chlordane are agricultural chemicals that were once used widely but have now been banned in the United States. They belong to a class of compounds called
    a. chlorofluorocarbons
    b. chlorinated hydrocarbons
    c. fossil fuels
    d. acid precipitation
    e. amaranths

19. What type of plant produces a liquid wax that is similar to sperm whale oil and can be used for fine lubrication?
    a. periwinkle
    b. guayule
    c. winged bean
    d. jojoba
    e. <u>Spirulina</u>

B. Provide the appropriate term to complete each statement.

1. The largest city in the world is _____.
2. The exclusive cultivation of a single crop over wide areas is called _____.
3. An international effort called the _____ allowed many developing countries to increase their food production.
4. In the tropics, _____ is a traditional food crop.
5. In the tropics and subtropics, _____ is the traditional farming technique used.
6. Every year, an area greater than the size of the state of _____ is cut down and destroyed in the tropical forests.
7. Oil, coal, and gas make up the world's supply of _____ fuels.
8. _____ is the raw material used in nuclear power plants.
9. The level of ozone in the upper atmosphere is being decreased by synthetic molecules called _____.

10. Two drugs that are effective in treating certain forms of leukemia have been developed from the _____ plant, native to Madagascar and now cultivated as a garden plant.
11. Radioactivity is measured in units called _____.

C. Briefly answer each of the following questions.

1. Why does acid precipitation kill organisms?

2. Why should we care what happens in the tropics?

3. What do <u>you</u> think is the future of the biosphere, and what do you feel you should or can do about it?

CHAPTER 27 ANSWERS

TOPIC EXERCISES

1.

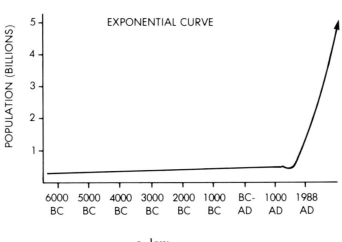

EXPONENTIAL CURVE

2. a. low   e. low
   b. high   f. high
   c. high   g. low
   d. high

LEARNING CHECKLIST

1. agriculture developed about 10,000 years ago when there were approximately 5 million people on the earth; today there are over 5 billion people on earth (p. 533-534)

2. birth rate has remained nearly constant or declined slightly; death rate has decreased steadily; about 27 births per year per 1000 people and about 10 deaths per year per 1000 people (p. 533)

3. majority live in developing countries; proportion in developed countries is decreasing; more goods consumed in developed countries (pp. 534-535)

4. extreme poverty; malnutrition and starvation; massive movement to urban centers (p. 536)

5. rice, wheat, and corn (p. 538)

6. the Green Revolution; costs = increased use of energy, fertilizers, pesticides, herbicides, and machinery; loss of crop diversity and nutrition (p. 540)

7. improve productivity of crops already being grown on lands already under cultivation; genetic engineering; developing new kinds of food (pp. 541-542)

8. shifting agriculture (slash-and-burn); mass extinction of other tropical species (pp. 542-544)

9. raw material is abundant; safe operation of nuclear plants, disposal of radioactive wastes, decommissioning "old" plants, terrorist and sabotage threats (pp. 547-548)

10. burning of fossil fuels; deforestation; increasing temperatures; global warming (the greenhouse effect) (p. 548)

11. water pollution; acid precipitation; ozone depletion; agricultural and industrial pollution (pp. 549-555)

12. assessment, risk analysis, public education, political action, follow through (pp. 555-556)

MINI EXAM

A.
1. c	2. b	3. b	4. e	5. c	6. d
7. a	8. a	9. d	10. e	11. d	12. a
13. b	14. c	15. d	16. e	17. a	18. b
19. d					

B.
1. Mexico City	2. monoculture	3. Green Revolution
4. manioc (tapioca, cassava)	5. shifting agriculture (slash-and-burn)	6. Indiana
7. fossil	8. Uranium ore	9. chlorofluorocarbons (CFCs)
10. periwinkle	11. curies	

C. 1. The increased acidity of soils and water can have direct chemical effects, as well as weakening organisms and making them more susceptible to diseases, predators, and parasites. Remember, all enzymes function optimally within narrow pH ranges. If pH changes, enzyme function can be inhibited or stopped completely. Enzymes are needed to catalyze all the biochemical reactions that take place in living organisms. (pp. 551-553, and chapter 7, pp. 141-144)

2. We are linked to the tropics and to the condition of its people and other species not only on humanitarian grounds, but also on economic and biological grounds. Overpopulation, low standards of living, and destruction of tropical ecosystems will have negative repercussions for us, as well as for the tropics. Destruction of tropical forests will contribute to the increase of CO_2 in our atmosphere and the resulting problems associated with the greenhouse effect. Tropical deforestation will also result in the mass extinction of thousands, even millions, of species that may be of potential use or value to humans. (pp. 532-555)

3. There is no set answer to this question. Think about it though - it is a crucial question, and the ball is in your court. You will help determine the future of the biosphere.

28: THE FIVE KINGDOMS OF LIFE

IN THE GRAND SCHEME

Human beings throughout history -- and probably before recorded history -- have observed the world about them and have tried to arrange what they see in some form of order. As organisms were observed and described, they were first given names that were descriptive. The names grew in length as new and similar organisms were discovered. In this process, additional descriptors were added to the name of the old form and incorporated into the name of the new form. Synonyms for each organism were about as numerous as the people studying them. The need for change and a plan to change to was envisioned by the now famous Carolus Linneaeus. In his system, each organism had just two parts to its name, a binomial, not duplicated for any other organism. Early systems of classification were based upon diverse criteria, and though the binomial system was employed, the grouping of organisms was fairly arbitrary. Since the rise and acceptance of the theory of evolution, efforts have been largely concentrated on a classification reflecting their line of descent. Such a system is called a phylogenetic system, and is considered to represent their natural classification. International organizations now regulate the naming of organisms.

From all of these efforts, a classification system recognizing five major groups called kingdoms has arisen. Within each kingdom there is a hierarchy of subsets, each reflecting closer phylogenetic relationship than shared by members of higher groupings. The ordering of the diversity of the worlds organisms is an enormous task that grows as our knowledge grows.

FOR REVIEW

Prokaryotic verses eukaryotic cells: The word "eukaryotic" means having a true nucleus, whereas the name "prokaryotic" means literally, "before" a nucleus and is understood to mean "without" a nucleus. In addition, prokaryotes lack a membrane bound chloroplast, whereas photosynthetic eukaryotes have such a structure. Prokaryotes have chemically complex cell walls, while those eukaryotes having cell walls have chemically simple cell walls. Eukaryotes also have mitochondria, golgi complexes, and endoplasmic reticula, which are lacking in prokaryotes.

Meiosis: In meiosis, homologous chromosomes exchange genetic information and are segregated into different cells, In the second division of meiosis, the chromosomes are split into single chromatid chromosomes that are randomly distributed into different cells.

Major features of evolution: The Theory of Evolution holds that diversity among organisms exists; that some diverse characteristics equip some organisms better than others to compete in struggle for existence; and that the forces of nature bring about a selection of the organism best fit to survive in its environment. The survivors do not contain the same "mix" as the original population.

Definition of species: Species are groups of organisms that differ in one or more characteristics and do not intergrade extensively if they occur together in nature.

Origin of species: As a result of hereditary adaptive change, populations that are originally identical, eventually become more and more dissimilar. Some populations become different enough that they are recognized as species.

CHAPTER OUTLINE

KEY TERMS

p. 561: genera, genus, taxonomists, systematists, taxonomy, systematics, polynomials
p. 562: binomials, hierarchy, families, taxonomic system, orders, classes, phyla
p. 563: phylum, divisions, kingdoms
p. 564: outcross, asexual reproduction
p. 565: five kingdom system, Animalia, Plantae, Fungi, Protista, Monera, prokaryotes
p. 566: precambrian,
p. 568: endosymbiotic hypothesis
p. 570: syngamy, meiosis, zygotic meiosis, gametic meiosis, sporic meiosis

TOPIC EXERCISES

1. The various levels of taxonomic hierarchy are listed below in alphabetical order. Arrange them in descending order.

    class, division or phylum, family, genus, kingdom, order, species

2. In the spaces provided, briefly state the characteristics of the listed kingdoms.

   A. Animalia

   B. Plantae

   C. Fungi

   D. Protista

   E. Monera

3. Various kinds of organisms are listed on the left. The five kingdoms are listed on the right. Place the number of the kingdom in the blank on the left of the organisms.

   A. ___4___ yeast   1. Animalia

   B. ___2___ orchid   2. Plantae

   C. ___5___ bacteria   3. Protista

   D. ___1___ shark   4. Fungi

   E. ___3___ kelp   5. Monera

LEARNING CHECKLIST

1. What is the nature of and need for the binomial nomenclature system?
2. List the five kingdoms of living organisms.
3. Life cycles of eukaryotes differ in the timing of meiosis. List the three kinds of meiosis that characterize eukaryotic life cycles.
4. What are the two events that must alternate in the life cycle of a sexual organism?
5. Why are we unable to specify the intermediate steps between prokaryotes and eukaryotes?
6. Relate multicellularity to eukaryotic specialization.
7. Critique sexual reproduction versus asexual reproduction.

MINI EXAM

A. Circle the letter of the one best answer for each question.

1. Viruses are thought to be
   a. nonliving fragments of nucleic acid derived from eukaryotes or prokaryotes
   b. chromosome segments lost in unequal crossing-over
   c. the oldest living ancestors of prokaryotes
   d. plasmids that remain after a bacterium is destroyed
   e. fragments of nucleic acid that retain all of the properties of life despite their simplicity

2. Several prokaryotes and protists produce chains or clusters of cells that remain attached. They are not regarded as truly multicellular because
   a. the number of cells formed by prokaryotes and protists is too small to qualify
   b. neither groups has cells in the right arrangement
   c. the term multicellular is reserved for eukaryotic organisms
   d. protistic cells are very small and prokaryotic cells are even smaller
   e. they fail to meet the criterion of integration of specialization

3. The smallest number of species that a genus can contain is
   a. 2   d. 1
   b. 3   e. none of the above
   c. 0

4. The level of classification immediately below class is
   a. order   d. genus
   b. species   e. phylum
   c. family

5. Most animals exhibit
   a. zygotic meiosis   c. somatic meiosis
   b. sporic meiosis   d. gametic meiosis

6. Mitochondria are thought to have been derived from
   a. sulfur bacteria   c. bluish green algae
   b. viruses   d. nonsulfur purple bacteria

7. The plant classification, division, is
   a. unscientific
   b. no longer accepted since it fails to fit into current hierarchy
   c. another name for kingdom
   d. an example of cladistics
   e. equivalent of animal phyla

8. Single-celled eukaryotic heterotrophs are placed in the kingdom
   a. Fungi   c. Protista
   b. Animalia   d. Monera

9. The name for heterotrophic protists is
   a. bacteria   c. algae
   b. protozoa   d. fungi

10. In plants that have an alternation of generations
    a. spores give rise to the diploid phase
    b. spores are produced by the haploid phase
    c. spores give rise to the haploid phase
    d. spores are the only cell of the diploid phase
    e. spores are of gametic origin

11. The taxonomic level into which phyla are grouped is
    a. kingdom   d. class
    b. family   e. order
    c. division

12. An organism is said to have sporic meiosis if meiosis occurs
    a. immediately after spore formation
    b. during spore formation
    c. before spore formation
    d. in lieu of spore formation
    e. irregularly

13. The taxonomic level into which species are grouped is
    a. family   d. genus
    b. order   e. phylum
    c. class

14. When printing scientific names, which following convention is observed?
    a. all letters of both names are capitalized
    b. both names are italicized
    c. the first letters of both names are capitalized
    d. the first letters of both names are capitalized and both names are underlined.

15. Chloroplasts appear to have evolved from
    a. mitochondria
    b. necessity
    c. the purple sulfur bacteria
    d. chlorophyll-bearing pollen
    e. different ancestors for different organisms

16. As compared to sexual reproduction, asexual reproduction
    a. is much more sensitive to environmental conditions, thus less reliable
    b. might benefit a well adjusted stable population by maintaining stability
    c. accelerates evolutionary processes
    d. is more prone to genetic errors
    e. is unaffected by mutagens

17. It is generally estimated that the total number of species in the world is
    a. 10 million   d. 10 billion
    b. 100 million   e. 100 thousand
    c. 1 billion

18. Most biologists accept a classification system based on _____ kingdoms.
    a. 3   c. 4
    b. 5   d. 6

19. Single-celled photosynthetic eukaryotes are placed in the kingdom
    a. Monera   c. Fungi
    b. Plantae   d. Protista

20. Photosynthetic protists are called
    a. plants   d. bacteria
    b. fungi   e. animals
    c. algae

B. Provide the appropriate term to complete each statement.

1. A classification system in which each level is made up of lower levels is called a(n) ___hierarchical___ system.

2. The kingdom, Protista, contains both plant-like and animal-like organisms because of the common characteristic of ___Unicellular___.

3. The term for union of male and female gametes is ___Syngamy___.

4. The ___endosymbiotic hypothesis___ suggests that mitochondria, chloroplasts, etc. descended from free-living bacteria captured by pre-eukaryotic cells.

5. Algae belongs to the kingdom, ___Protista___.

6. Slime molds belong to the kingdom, ___Protista___.

7. The person generally credited with establishing two part (binomial) names as the standard for classification was ___Linnaeus___.

8. Another name for a taxonomist is ___systematist___.

9. If two species have many features in common, these features are said to be ___correlated___.

10. Animals belong to the kingdom, ___Animalie___.

C. Briefly answer each of the following questions.

1. Explain the modern classification of eukaryotic organisms as described in the text including the rationales for such placement.

2. Describe the theory of symbiotic origin of some eukaryotic organelles.

3. Discuss the place of viruses in evolution.

CHAPTER ANSWERS

TOPIC EXERCISES

1. kingdom, division or phylum, class, order, family, genus, species

2. a. multicellular most of its life, ingests food.
    b. multicellular most of its life, manufactures food.
    c. unicellular, secretes enzymes to digest food externally and absorbs digested food.
    d. unicellular in important stages of their lives. Manufactures or ingests food, and are all eukaryotes.
    e. unicellular, all prokaryotes.

3. A. 4   B. 2   C. 5   D. 1   E. 3

LEARNING CHECKLIST

1. Before the advent of the binomial system of nomenclature scientific names of living things were actually lengthy descriptions of the organism. As new organisms were found, more terms had to be added to both the new and the old so that they would be distinguishable. Actual relationships between organisms were not clear and not of great concern. Naming of organisms is greatly simplified by the binomial system. Each organism has two names. The first name is the genus to which it belonges. The second name is a distinctive name of the species. There cannot be two species of the same name within a genus. International organizations of biologists have created rules for naming organisms and arbitrate conflicts in names and/or rules. (pp. 538-39)

2. Monera, Protista, Fungi, Plantae, Animalia (p. 541)

3. zygotic meiosis, gametic meiosis and sporic meiosis (p. 570)

4. syngamy and meiosis (p. 570)

5. Absence of Precambrian fossils. (p. 566)

6. True multicellularity includes integration and specialization of cells. These characteristics allow multicellular organisms to develop complex bodies. Many protists and prokaryotes remain attached in a thread or some other shaped mass, but never achieve integration and specialization. (pp. 568-570)

7. Sexuality is believed to have evolved as a means of supplying a template for the repair of double-strand breaks in DNA. Sexuality also imposes a process of chromosome number adjustment in the form of meiosis following syngamy. The variability resulting from sexuality supports evolutionary development.
    Although lacking some of the benefits of sexuality, there are some merits in asexual reproduction. In times of declining population, the need for finding a mate is eliminated. Stability may be important to successful, well adjusted organisms. (p. 570)

MINI EXAM

A.
1. a	2. a	3. d	4. a	5. d	6. d
7. c	8. c	9. b	10. c	11. a	12. b
13. d	14. b	15. c	16. b	17. a	18. b
19. d	20. c				

B.
1. hierarchical	2. unicellularity	3. syngamy
4. endosymbiotic hypothesis	5. Protista	6. Protista
7. Linnaeus	8. systematist	9. correlated
10. Animalia		

C. 1. Prokaryotic organisms, being quite distinctive, are placed in, and are the sole members of the kingdom Monera. The diverse array of primarily unicellular eukaryotes are assigned to the kingdom Protista. The multicellular eukaryotes are divided into the three kingdoms, Animalia, Plantae and Fungi. Evidence indicates that each of these three groups of organisms evolved from different ancestral protists. Some protists are multicellular and photosynthetic and are treated as plants by some taxonomists. Differences between such multicellular protists and members of the plant kingdom are sufficient to cause them to be classified with the other protists. (pp. 568-570)

2. Mitochondria and chloroplasts bear strong resemblances to ancient bacteria. They also contain DNA and divide separately from chromosome DNA in eukaryotes. These observations and others have led to the

theory that both organelles were acquired by eukaryotes as endosymbiotic prokaryotes. (p. 568)

3. Viruses are not actually organisms. They lack the ability to reproduce themselves, a characteristic that fails to meet the criterion for life. The relationship of viral DNA to that of bacterial DNA suggests a bacterial origin. Some also show eukaryotic affinities. (pp. 570-571)

29: VIRUSES

IN THE GRAND SCHEME

We have examined the nature and classification of organisms. In this chapter, we examine the nature and classification of a nonorganism. Viruses fail to meet the criteria for an organism. Viruses cannot reproduce themselves. Despite this flaw, they are reproduced and spread over the world. Viruses get organisms to do the viruses' work of reproducing their genome and its container. The AIDS virus is so efficient in dealing with our immune system that it would appear to have been educated in a biology course.

The diversity of viruses is remarkable! They are basically a genome of some nucleic acid which is usually contained in a protein shell called a capsid, and less frequently, surrounded by a fatty capsule. The phage virus that preys upon bacteria is still more complex. Geometrically, viruses tend to be helical or isometric. The most common shape is that of an icosahedron formed from twenty triangles fitted as in a geodesic dome. The genome may be of RNA or DNA. If the genome is RNA, it may be plus-stranded, minus-stranded or two-stranded or even circular. The RNA can be collected in one place or divided into separate sets. The DNA may be long or short and one-stranded or two-stranded.

What ever their shape or composition, there is a commonality. They all gain entry into a living cell and induce it to replicate its genome and manufacture containers for the genome. They then may thanklessly destroy their benefactor cell upon exiting. The list of diseases caused by viruses is long and frightening. It is highly improbable that anyone reading this book has entirely avoided viral diseases or will in the future. As of this writing, it is a fair generalization that our technology has failed to produce a cure for viral diseases -- but it will. An irony in which one might derive some satisfaction is that viruses, as a result of genetic engineering, will help us develop a cure for viral diseases and make many other contributions to the science of medicine.

FOR REVIEW

Definition of organism: All organisms have a cellular organization, are capable of growth and metabolism, and are capable of reproducing themselves.

TMV and T2 viruses: The TMV (tobacco mosaic virus) is a virus commonly used in "piggy back" vaccines. The T2 virus is a bacteriophage used by Hershey and Walker in their experiments.

Lambda virus integration: Lambda viruses contain a gene coding for the enzyme integrase, which recognizes sequences of bacterial DNA and inserts the lambda viral DNA in the proper location.

Retroviruses and cancer: Retroviruses are often linked to cancer. Their carcinogenic properties come from possession of RNA that is a transcript of a portion of eukaryotic DNA. The result is a gene inappropriately placed in the host genome. The result is incorrect cell duplication - cancer.

Vaccinia viruses and vaccination: The vaccinia virus has been used to make "piggy back" vaccines against such diseases as hepatitis B and herpes simplex.

CHAPTER OUTLINE

THE DISCOVERY OF VIRUSES (pp. 574-576)
THE NATURE OF VIRUSES (p. 576)
THE STRUCTURE OF VIRUSES (pp. 576-577)
VIRUS REPLICATION (pp. 578-580)
     spikes
     T4 cells

CD4
DIVERSITY AMONG THE VIRUSES (pp. 580-587)
   Unenveloped Plus-Strand RNA Viruses
   Enveloped Plus-Strand RNA Viruses
   Minus-Strand RNA Viruses
        rhabdoviurses
        paramyxoviruses
   Viroids
   Double-Stranded RNA Viruses
   Small-Genome DNA Viruses
   Medium-Genome DNA Viruses
      Herpesviruses
      Poxviruses
   Bacteriophages
VIRUSES: PARTICLES OF GENOMES (p. 587)

KEY TERMS

p. 574: viruses, variolation
p. 575: vaccination
p. 576: capsid, envelope, lyses, virulent viruses, temperate viruses, prions
p. 577: helical, isometric, icosahedron, bacteriophages
p. 579: reverse transcriptase, latent prophage, lysogenic
p. 581: divided-genome viruses, mosaics, stunt diseases, rhinoviruses
p. 582: arboviruses, rhabdoviruses
p. 583: viroids, hemagglutinin (HA), neuraminidase (NA)
p. 584: reoviruses, rotaviruses, parvoviruses, papiloma viruses
p. 585: herpesviruses

TOPIC EXERCISES

1. Herpesviruses comprise a medically important group. Beside each of the herpesviruses listed below, list one disease or ailment caused by that virus.

    A. Herpesvirus 1 (herpes simplex 1)

    B. Herpesvirus 2 (herpes simplex 2)

    C. Herpesvirus 3

    D. Herpesvirus 4 (Epstein-Barr virus)

    E. Herpesvirus 5 (cytomegaloviruses)

2. Viruses are quite diverse with respect to their nucleic acids and coatings. For each type listed, identify a kind of virus (such as bacteriophage or one disease caused by each.

   A. Unenveloped plus-strand RNA viruses

   B. Enveloped plus-strand RNA viruses

   C. Minus-stranded RNA viruses

   D. Viroids

   E. Double-stranded RNA viruses

   F. Small genome DNA viruses

   G. Medium-genome and large-genome viruses

3. Though not alone, the flu virus is a good example of a virus difficult to combat with vaccines.
   Explain briefly how the behavior of the flu nucleic acids makes the immunization against that virus difficult.

LEARNING CHECKLIST

   1. Why are viruses not considered living organisms?

   2. Discuss host specificity of viruses.

   3. Describe the structure of (a) viruses in general and (b) the phage virus in particular.

   4. (a) How do animals combat viral infections? (b) What evasive practices have viruses evolved for animal defenses?

   5. With the AIDS virus as a model, explain the process of viral infection.

MINI EXAM

A. Circle the letter of the one best answer for each question.

   1. The protein sheath around the viral nucleic acid core is the
   a. capsule   d. capsid
   b. corpuscle   e. envelope
   c. chitin

   2. The retrovirus causing AIDS is a member of the viral type
   a. enveloped plus-strand RNA viruses
   b. unenveloped plus-strand RNA viruses
   c. minus-strand viruses
   d. double-stranded RNA viruses
   e. DNA viruses

3. The primary target of the AIDS virus is the _____ cell.
   a. T1 lymphocyte   d. T5 lymphocyte
   b. T6 lymphocyte   e. T4 lymphocyte
   c. T2 lymphocyte

4. A serious to fatal diarrhea in young children is caused by
   a. rhinovirus   d. rhabdovirus
   b. rotavirus   e. rheovirus
   c. arbovirus

5. The cure for smallpox is attributed to
   a. the Chinese
   b. Walter Reed
   c. Wendell Stanley
   d. Edward Jenner
   e. Jonas Salk

6. Insect borne viral diseases are caused by the viral group
   a. rhinovirus   c. viroid
   b. arbovirus   d. paramyxovirus

7. The ancient chinese practice of exposing people to skin scabs of smallpox survivors is called
   a. variolation   c. vacillation
   b. scabation   d. vaccination

8. The Epstein-Barr virus causes
   a. hepatitis B   c. infectious mononucleosis
   b. cold sores   d. chickenpox

9. A latent bacteriophage is called a(n)
   a. lysogenic cell   c. viroid
   b. prion   d. prophage

10. The icosahedron shape is a structural shape within the broader category
    a. asymmetric   c. isometric
    b. helical   d. articulated

11. The spikes on the flu virus
    a. are composed of the enzyme lysin, enabling them to enter the host cell
    b. contain the toxin, hemagglutinin, which destroys the polymorphonuclear leucocytes manufactured in lymph nodes
    c. are almost entirely carbohydrate surface identity markers
    d. are metabolized in the liver, releasing bilirubin and causing flu related hepatitis
    e. contain neuraminidase enabling them to exit the host cell.

12. The viral group whose genome can act directly as mRNA is the group that has
    a. minus-stranded RNA
    b. plus-stranded RNA
    c. double-stranded RNA
    d. single-stranded DNA

13. Infectious mononucleosis is caused by a member of
    a. papillomavirus   c. reovirus
    b. arbovirus   d. herpesvirus

14. Viruses are <u>not</u> regarded as organisms because they lack the ability to
    a. form a true nucleus
    b. propel themselves
    c. replicate on their own
    d. form a phospholipid membrane

15. Herpesviruses are members of the viral group
    a. large-genome DNA viruses
    b. double-stranded RNA viruses
    c. small-genome DNA viruses
    d. retroviruses
    e. poxviruses

16. So far as is known, viroids infect only
    a. ducks
    b. plants
    c. people
    c. rodents
    d. bacteria

17. Warts on humans and other animals may be caused by a member of the virus group
    a. papillomarvirus
    b. rotavirus
    c. parvovirus
    d. rhabdovirus
    e. rhinovirus

18. In addition to DNA polymerase, the hepatitis B virus encodes two proteins
    a. capsule and surface proteins
    b. capsule and core proteins
    c. core and surface proteins
    d. RNA polymerase and surface proteins

19. Polio is caused by a virus of the viral group
    a. enveloped plus-strand RNA
    b. unenveloped plus-strand RNA
    c. minus-strand RNA virus
    d. double-stranded DNA

20. Rhabdoviruses are so named because of
    a. their shape
    b. their nucleic acid
    c. their capsid protein
    d. their core protein
    e. Rh blood specificity

B. Provide the appropriate term to complete each statement.

1. It is said that a cell _____ if it ruptures as a result of viral infection.

2. Viruses that cause the host cell to rupture are called a(n) _____.

3. The structure of protein coats of viruses hat have 20 equilateral sides is called a(n) _____.

4. Viruses that attack bacteria are called _____.

5. Viruses that become established as a stable part of the host's genome are called _____ viruses.

6. The enzyme that enables retroviruse to make DNA copies of the RNA is _____.

7. The common cold is caused by one of many kinds of viruses of a group called _____.

8. HA is the acronym for the viral spike component, _____.

9. Viruses lacking a capsid or other associated proteins are called _____.

10. Jenner inoculated people with a virus causing the mild disease _____ which confers immunity to smallpox to the recipients.

C. Briefly answer each of the following questions.

1. Briefly describe the biological history of the discovery and characterization of viruses.

2. Characterize and give examples of (a) enveloped and unenveloped plus-strand viruses, (b) minus-strand viruses, (c) viroids, (d) double-stranded RNA viruses, (e) small genome viruses and DNA viruses.

CHAPTER ANSWERS

TOPIC EXERCISES

1. A. cold sores and fever blisters
   B. sexually transmitted diseases (lesions)
   C. chickenpox and shingles
   D. infectious mononucleosis and certain human cancers
   E. fatal systemic infections in newborn babies

2. A. bacteriophages, infect plants
   B. arboviruses, encephalitis, dengue, yellow fever
   C. rhabdovirus, rabies, paramyxovirus, measles, mumps, poultry newcastle disease, flu
   D. plant infections
   E. reoviruses, colorado tick fever, rotavirus, serious to fatal infantile diarrhea
   F. parvoviruses, commonly fatal animal disease; papillomaviruses, warts

3. Recombination of the RNA commonly changes the chemical structure of the spikes by which immune systems recognize the virus. Thus, new vaccines must be developed to cope with the changes presented to the immune system.

LEARNING CHECKLIST

1. Viruses are not regarded as living organisms because they cannot reproduce themselves, but rely upon the mechanisms of living organisms to reproduce them. (p. 574)

2. Viruses are very host specific. There may well be as many kinds of viruses as there are infected organisms. (p. 576)

3. The center of the viruses consists of one or several molecules of either RNA or DNA, sometimes accompanied by protein. A protein container, called the capsid, appears to characterize viruses. A lipid-rich envelope surrounds the capsid of some viruses. The capsid of most viruses is usually helical or isometric. The isometric capsids tend to form an icosahedron. The bacteriophage viruses are more complex than most others, having an isometric head, a neck, tail, base plate and tail fibers. (pp. 576-577)

4. (a) Animal hosts of viruses generate chemical antibodies that attach to the virus capsid surface markers, identifying the viruses for phagocytes. (b) Viruses modify their surface markers which are unidentified. (p. 578)

5. See figure 29-8 of your text on page 579.

MINI EXAM

A.
1. d	2. a	3. e	4. b	5. d	6. b
7. a	8. c	9. d	10. c	11. e	12. b
13. d	14. c	15. a	16. b	17. a	18. c
19. b	20. a				

B.
1. lyses	2. virulent	3. icosahedron
4. bacteriophages	5. temperate	6. reverse transcriptase
7. rhinoviruses	8. hemagglutinin	9. viroids
10. cowpox		

C. 1. Viruses were used long before they were discovered. The Chinese a thousand years ago with variolation and Jenner much later with the vaccination used viruses to produce immunity without knowing the identity of the agent. Later the tobacco mosaic virus was purified and, still later, photographed. The virus was shown to be a nucleic acid contained in a protein shell. (pp. 574-576)

2. Most of the information is in table 29-1 on page 581 of your text. Other interesting points from the text are given here. (a) The unenveloped plus-strand viruses act directly as mRNA. This group includes the rhinoviruses. The divided-genome viruses are also plus-stranded but internally subdivide their strands of RNA into separate sets. The enveloped plus-strand RNA viruses includes the arboviruses, many of which are arthropod borne. The retroviruses are also enveloped plus-strand RNA virus but are unique in their use of the enzyme reverse transcriptase to code DNA from their RNA. The AIDS virus is in this group. (b) Minus-strand viruses have the host cell form mRNA complementary to their RNA. This group includes the viruses that are bullet-shaped, for which they are named rhabdoviruses, and the influenza virus. (c) Viroids have a unique ring RNA that seems to code for no polypeptide. (d) Double-stranded RNA viruses have and RNA dependent RN polymerase. This group includes reoviruses and rotaviruses. (e) Small-genome viruses have one or two-stranded DNA. They include parvoviruses and papillomaviruses. The DNA viruses include two major groups, the herpesviruses and poxviruses. Herpesviruses are particularly notable for two habits displayed by some of them as well as for the list of disease caused. One habit some herpesviruses display is the "boomerang" habit. They hit you once and come back to hit you again. Some of these include the "shingles" experienced later in life by chickenpox victims, the recurring cold sores and genital lesions. The second habit makes the first possible. Some herpesviruses retreat to and remain dormant in nerve ganglia, such as the trigeminal nerve ganglia for cold cores and spinal ganglia for chickenpox, alias shingles, alias zoster. The complete list of herpesviruses diseases will not be repeated here, but one surely is well known to the college student who has too many wicks in their candle and has them all lighted -- infectious mononucleosis, caused by the Epstein-Barr member of the herpesviruses. Poxviruses are well remembered for the smallpox disease that now is believed to be nonexistent, though the virus continues to be cultured in laboratories of the World Health Organization. Some poxviruses, have proven useful in making vaccines and in genetic engineering. (pp. 580-587)

30: BACTERIA

IN THE GRAND SCHEME

The sole member of the kingdom Monera, bacteria represent the oldest known group of organisms. They are responsible for much of the earth's atmospheric oxygen, in prehistoric time and today. They have altered soils through nitrogen fixation and mineral utilization. They have been a source of organelles and photosynthetic pigments through endosymbiosis. Bacteria make a high cellulose diet feasible for cattle, reduce the worlds litter through decomposition and manufacture methane fuel. They are used in the manufacture of cheeses and antibiotics. Through genetic engineering, bacteria are increasingly becoming mankind's microscopic manufactures of greatly needed chemicals. Alas, they also are responsible for much suffering and death of a wide range of eukaryotes including ourselves. These simple spheres, rods and spirals lack nuclei, endomembranes, and many organelles common to eukaryotes. They reproduce by binary fission, but achieve genetic diversity through mutation at a rate frustrating to medical practitioners. They are simple but versatile organisms.

FOR REVIEW

Transduction and bacterial conjugation: Bacteria are capable of transferring genetic material from one to another through tubular projection called a pilus. This process enables one population to transfer pathogenic characteristics to a previously non-virile population. Such an alteration of characteristics is called transduction.

Geochemical cycles: All substances utilized by organisms are drawn from their environment. Eventually the substances are returned to the environment through an organism's metabolic processes, including metabolism and decay. This cycling of substances between organisms and environment makes up geochemical cycles.

Prokaryotic cell structure: Prokaryotes have a chemically complex cell wall. They have chromosomes of double-stranded DNA in a closed ring, but the chromosomes are not contained in a nucleus. Prokaryotes lack internal compartmentalization and though some have chlorophyll, they lack chloroplasts. Prokaryotes also lack other typical eukaryotic structures such as a golgi complex, mitochondria, and endoplasmic reticulum. Prokaryotes reproduce only by binary fission.

Bacterial flagella: The flagella of bacteria consists only of the protein flagellin and lack the structure of eukaryotes. The bacterial flagella rotate like a propeller.

Bacterial cell division: Before cell division, the bacterium replicates its genome and collects both copies near a structure called a mesosome. Soon thereafter, the cell is cleaved by the ingrowth of the cell wall dividing the cell into two cells, each with a duplicate genome.

Bacterial metabolism and chemoautotrophy: The world in which bacteria first lived lacked atmospheric oxygen. Bacteria utilized chemoautotrophy to secure energy metabolizing sulfur and nitrogen compounds and fixing free nitrogen, all of which bacteria do today.

Bacterial photosynthesis: As oxygen became available, bacteria evolved aerobic respiration and photosynthesis, utilizing a variety of photosynthetic pigments such as carotenoids and chlorophylls.

CHAPTER OUTLINE

PROKARYOTES VERSUS EUKARYOTES (pp. 591-592)
>   multicellularity
>   cell size
>   chromosomes
>   cell division and genetic recombination
>   internal compartmentalization
>   flagella
>   autotrophic diversity

BACTERIAL STRUCTURE (pp. 592-594)

BACTERIAL VARIATION (pp. 594-595)
>   Mutation
>   Genetic Recombination

BACTERIAL ECOLOGY AND METABOLIC DIVERSITY (pp. 595-597)
>   Autotrophic Bacteria
>   Photosynthetic bacteria
>   Chemoautotrophic bacteria
>   Heterotrophic Bacteria
>   Nitrogen-Fixing Bacteria

BACTERIA AS PLANT PATHOGENS (pp. 597-598)

BACTERIA AS HUMAN PATHOGENS (pp. 598-600)
>   Legionnaires' Disease
>   Sexually Transmitted Diseases
>   Dental Caries

BACTERIAL DIVERSITY (pp. 600-607)
>   Archaebacteria
>   Omnibacteria
>   Cyanobacteria
>   carotenoids
>   Chloroxybacteria
>   Mycoplasmas and Spiroplasmas
>   aphragmabacteria
>   Spirochetes
>   Pseudomonads
>   Actinomycetes
>   Myxobacteria
>   Nitrogen-Fixing Bacteria
>   Chemoautotrophic Bacteria

SIMPLE BUT VERSATILE ORGANISMS (pp. 607-608)

KEY TERMS

p. 592: lipopolysaccharide, capsule, bacilli, cocci, spirilla, spores
p. 593: pili, pilus, endospores
p. 595: obligate anaerobes, facultative anaerobes, aerobes
p. 596: saprobes
p. 598: magainins
p. 600: dental plaque
p. 601: Archaebacteria, methanogens, Eubacteria
p. 602: vibrios, obligate parasites, phycobilins

TOPIC EXERCISES

1. Certain groups of bacteria are important in our study of evolution either in helping understand the phylogeny or in the possession of characteristics found in eukaryotes. Some are listed below. Beside each, list the characteristic that makes them of importance to the study of evolution.

   A. Archaebacteria

   B. Cyanobacteria

   C. Chlorozybacteria

   D. Myxobacteria

   E. Chemoautotrophic bacteria

2. Some bacteria are most remembered for their detriment to mankind directly or to crops, etc. Some are listed below. Beside each, list one or more disease of plants or animals possibly including human beings.

   A. Vibrios

   B. Spriochetes

   C. Actinomycetes

   D. Mycoplasmas

3. On the other hand, some bacteria are quite beneficial to mankind. Some are listed below. Beside each list the benefits conferred.

   A. Actinomycetes

   B. Cyanobacteria

   C. Azobacter

   D. Saprobes

LEARNING CHECKLIST

1. List seven distinctions between prokaryotes and eukaryotes.
2. Briefly describe the structure of bacterial cell walls.
3. How does bacterial cell wall structure affect the choice of antibiotic therapy?
4. List the major anatomical characteristics of bacteria.
5. Why is mutation important to genetic diversity of bacteria?
6. How do (a) photosynthetic, (b) chemoautotrophic, and (c) heteroautrophic bacteria obtain food?
7. Illustrate the importance of bacteria as both plant and human pathogens.
8. How are Archaebacteria unique and why are they economically beneficial?

MINI EXAM

A. Circle the letter of the one best answer for each question.

1. An architectural stone consisting of limestone altered by cyanobacteria is
   a. amazonite
   b. travertine
   c. tourmaline
   d. dolomite

2. Thick walled, single-celled structures formed inside bacteria that grow into new bacteria when released are
   a. capsules
   b. pili
   c. heterocysts
   d. saprobes
   e. endospores

3. Gram-negative bacteria can resist antibiotics that kill gram-positive bacteria by interfering with cell wall formation because
   a. the gram-stain, rejected by gram-negative bacteria, makes gram-positive bacteria vulnerable
   b. gram-negative bacteria form endospores which gram-positive bacteria cannot
   c. gram-negative bacteria have peptidoglycan which is lacking in gram-positive bacteria
   d. gram-positive bacteria lack the protective pili found in gram-negative bacteria
   e. the cell walls of gram-negative bacteria are coated on the outside with lipopolysaccharide

4. Red-colored, water soluble pigments in cyanobacteria are called
   a. phycobilins
   b. carotenoids
   c. xanthenoids
   d. bilirubins

5. In addition to the genus <u>Pseudomonas</u>, the pseudomanads include the genus
   a. <u>Xanthomonas</u>
   b. <u>Azobacter</u>
   c. <u>Nitrosomonas</u>
   d. <u>Aphragmonas</u>
   e. <u>Enterobacter</u>

6. Bacteria responsible for the production of the hydrocarbon called march gas are members of a group called
   a. aerobes
   b. methanogens
   c. carboniferous
   d. hydrocarbonagens

7. In the eastern United States, Lyme disease is caused by the spirochete
   a. <u>Ixodes</u>
   b. <u>Treponema</u>
   c. <u>Brucella</u>
   d. <u>Borrelia</u>
   e. <u>Spiroplasma</u>

8. Rod-shaped bacteria are called
   a. cocci
   b. bacilli
   c. spirilla
   d. pili
   e. rhabdi

9. Due to the lack of cell wall, _____ are resistant to penicillin.
   a. staphylococci
   b. spirochetes
   c. mycoplasmas
   d. mycobacteria

10. The sexually transmitted disease, syphilis, is caused by spirochete of the genus
    a. Neisseria
    b. Chlamydia
    c. Rickettsia
    d. Treponema
    e. Spirillum

11. Nitrogen fixation occurs in most cyanobacteria in large specialized cells called
    a. megacysts
    b. heterocysts
    c. monocysts
    d. macrocysts

12. All characteristics listed are those of Archaebacteria by which they differ from all other bacteria except
    a. ability to digest cellulose directly
    b. certain base sequences in rRNA
    c. absence of muramic acid in their cell walls
    d. methane production
    e. accumulation of magnetite crystals

13. Genetic information can be transmitted from one bacteria to another by way of structures called
    a. trichae
    b. cirri
    c. pili
    d. pseudopods
    e. endospores

14. Bacteria in dental plaque cause tooth decay if one's diet is high in
    a. sugars
    b. acids
    c. salt
    d. spices
    e. calcium

15. In gram-negative bacteria, the outermost layer of the cell wall is composed of _____ chained with lipids.
    a. lipopolysaccharide
    b. lipoprotein
    c. glycoprotein
    d. gelatin
    e. polypeptides

16. Spherical bacteria are called
    a. cocci
    b. spirilla
    c. bacilli
    d. spirochetes

17. Bacteria that gain their nutrition from dead organic material are
    a. necrobes
    b. atrobes
    c. saprobes
    d. entropobes

18. Among the nitrogen-fixing bacteria are members of the genus
    a. Salmonella
    b. Xanthomonas
    c. Brucella
    d. Rhizobium

19. The organisms causing tuberculosis and leprosy are
    a. myxobacteria
    b. pseudomonads
    c. mycobacteria
    d. actinomycetes

20. A genus of bacteria noted for the formation of endospores is
    a. Streptococcus
    b. Salmonella
    c. Clostridium
    d. Chlamydia
    e. Proteus

B. Provide the appropriate term to complete each statement.

1. The _____ are unique bacteria believed to have diverged from the main line of bacterial evolution at a very early time.

2. The _____ are a group of comma-shaped bacteria, some of which cause cholera.

3. The chloroxybacteria include but a single genus, _____.

4. The genus _____ is composed of pigmented bacteria that resemble chloroplasts of diatoms.

5. The pseudomonad, _____, lives in salt water and preys on other bacteria.

6. The _____ are sliding bacteria that serve as a useful model for the study of development in multicellular organisms.

7. Nitrosomonas is a member of the _____ bacteria that can manufacture their own amino acids without sunlight.

8. The majority of today's antibiotics are derived from the bacterial group _____.

9. The _____ have flagella under their lipoprotein membrane.

10. The rickettsias are _____ within cells of vertebrates and arthropods.

C. Briefly answer each of the following questions.

1. Explain the importance of nitrogen-fixing bacteria.

2. What is the evolutionary significance of (a) cyanobacteria, and (b) chloroxybacteria?

3. What are the most prominent structural features of omnibacteria, mycoplasmas, spirochetes, pseudomonads, actinomycetes, and myxobacteria?

CHAPTER ANSWERS

TOPIC EXERCISES

1. A. Chemically distinct from other bacteria and believed to have branched from the others very early in evolution.
    B. Photosynthetic pigments resemble those of red algae. It is believed that the red algae pigments were derived from symbiotic cyanobacteria.
    C. Photosynthetic pigments are similar to those of green algae. The green algae are believed to have derived their pigments from chloroxybacteria.
    D. The gliding myxobacteria are considered useful models for studying development of multicellular organisms.
    E. Because their metabolism does not require oxygen, but is better suited to the ancient earth atmosphere; they represent a very early form of life.

2. A. cholera
    B. syphilis, yaws, and Lyme disease
    C. tuberculosis and leprosy
    D. pneumonia

3. A. antibiotics
    B. oxygen production and nitrogen fixation
    C. nitrogen fixation
    D. decay and waste disposal

LEARNING CHECKLIST

1. (a) multicellularity
    (b) cell size
    (c) chromosomes
    (d) cell division and genetic recombination
    (e) internal compartmentalization
    (f) flagella
    (g) autotrophic diversity
    (pp. 591-592)

2. Bacteria have an inner wall of various thicknesses made of peptidoglycan, a network of polysaccharide molecules with polypeptide cross-links. The gram-negative bacteria attack lipopolysaccharide molecules to the outside of the peptidoglycan. (p. 592)

3. The lipopolysaccharide protects gram-negative bacteria from antibiotics that interfere with cell wall formation in gram-positive bacteria. (p. 592)

4. Bacteria are in the shape of rods (bacilli), spheres (cocci), or coiled (spirilla). They may occur singly or attached to each other. (p. 592)

5. Being restricted to binary fission as a means of reproduction, bacteria have no source of genetic recombination except for the few that can conjugate. Mutation is the only source of genetic variation for most bacteria. (pp. 594-595)

6. (a) photosynthesis (sunlight required), (b) oxidation of nitrogen, sulfur, iron, or hydrogen, (c) digestion of dead organic material. (pp. 595-597)

7. Examples of plant diseases include, wilts, rots, blight and cankers. Human bacterial diseases include strep throat, pneumonia, tuberculosis, septicemia, encephalitis, meningitis, gangrene, sexually transmitted diseases and numerous food poisonings. (pp. 597-600)

8. Archaebacteria produce methane, fix nitrogen, reduce sulfur and aid herbivorous animals by digesting cellulose. (pp. 601-602)

MINI EXAM

A.

1. b	2. e	3. b	4. a	5. a	6. b
7. d	8. d	9. c	10. d	11. b	12. e
13. c	14. a	15. a	16. a	17. c	18. d
19. d	20. c				

B.

1. Archaebacteria	2. vibrios	3. Prochloron
4. Heliobacterium	5. Bdellovibrio	6. myxobacteria
7. chemoautotrophic	8. Actinomycetes	9. spirochetes
10. obligate parasites		

C. 1. Nitrogen occurs primarily as a free gas in the atmosphere. Plants and animals are unable to use nitrogen in this form. The nitrogen used by plants to produce proteins, later utilized by animals, must be "fixed," combined to some other substance in molecular form. Lightening is one of the few ways of fixing nitrogen other than that done by microbes such as bacteria. (p. 597)

2. (a) Cyanobacteria are important oxygenators, nitrogen fixers, limestone depositors, and petroleum producers as well as probably providing a source of chloroplast for red algae as an endosymbiont.
(b) Chloroxybacteria, as well as being oxygenators for aerobes and nitrogen fixers, are believed to be the endosymbiotic source of chloroplasts in eukaryotes. (pp. 602-603)

3. See Table 30-1 p. 600 of the text.

31: PROTISTS

IN THE GRAND SCHEME

In any filing system there is the inevitable "miscellaneous" file. The miscellaneous array of organisms grouped into the kingdom, Protista, do not represent a group of closely related organisms. Though this kingdom contains the ancestors of virtually all multicellular eukaryote kingdoms, the protists do not represent a transition from simpler forms. There is no such transition. There are no extant transitional members between the bacteria and the protists.

If the lack of transitional organism is a disappointment, the diversity is not. It is incredible that there are so many ways to construct a single-celled organism and so many ways for them to make a living. Sexuality ranges from none in the Amoeba to complex interactions and multiple generations in Plasmodium. In all of this diversity of diversity, there are similarities which may or may not indicate phylogenetic relationships. There are similarities of photosynthetic pigments, cell wall composition, spore formation and locomotion. In this kingdom of misfits they are more like each other than organisms of any other kingdom. Despite these differences, somewhere in this kingdom lie the ancestors of all other eukaryotes.

FOR REVIEW

Symbiotic origin of mitochondria and chloroplasts: It is evident that mitochondria were acquired by eukaryotes through symbiosis with aerobic prokaryotes. Chloroplasts are thought to have been acquired through symbiosis with anaerobic prokaryotes.

Flagella and cellular motility: Numerous eukaryotes possess flagella of a "9 + 2" structure, a structure unique to eukaryotes. Such flagella often provide the eukaryote with locomotion.

Evolution of mitosis: Prokaryotes divide by binary fission accompanied by equal distribution of genetic information. Eukaryotes move replicated genetic material in an orderly fashion, manipulated by microtubules.

Sexuality and multicellularity: Prokaryotes exchange genetic material, but not in an orderly, predictable manner as in eukaryotes. Prokaryotes are all haploid, thus lacking syngamy and meiosis, characteristic of eukaryotes. Prokaryotes often adhere to each other following cell division and form three-dimensional structures, but do not have the kind of differentiation and interaction found in multicellular eukaryotes.

Life cycles of eukaryotes: Eukaryotes alternate syngamy and meiosis in their life cycles. The life cycles differ mostly in the placement of meiosis in the life cycle. Those with zygotic meiosis are predominantly haploid. For them, the diploid condition is terminated by meiosis soon after it is established by syngamy. Some eukaryotes are predominantly diploid with meiosis occurring in the formation of gametes (gametic meiosis) that will soon unite to reestablish the diploid condition. Other eukaryotes have sporic meiosis. Meiosis occurs in the formation of spores. The duration of diploid and haploid phases vary from one extreme to another.

Cyanobacteria, Heliobacterium, and Prochloron: Cyanobacteria are believed to be the source of chloroplasts of red algae. Heliobacterium is evidently the source of chloroplasts of brown algae, diatoms, and dinoflagellates. The choroplasts of green algae evidently were derived from a bacterium like Prochloron.

CHAPTER OUTLINE

EVOLUTIONARY RELATIONSHIP OF PROTISTS (pp. 611-614)
   Features of the Eukaryotes

KEY TERMS

p. 612: algae, phycologists, protozologists, protozoa
p. 615: sorocarp, macrocysts
p. 618: gametangia, gametangium
p. 619: pellicle
p. 620: cytoproct, micronuclei, macronuclei
p. 621: conjugation
p. 622: zooxanthellae
p. 624: reservoir, stigma, tests
p. 625: podia, plasmodium
p. 626: hyphae, zoospores, oogonium, antheridium
p. 627: oospore, kelps
p. 628: sporophyte, gametophyte
p. 629: pseudopods
p. 630: oocyst, sporozoite, gametocytes

TOPIC EXERCISES

Utilize the following list of phyla for all three topic exercises:

A. Acrasiomycota
B. Bacillariophyta
C. Chlorophyta
D. Ciliophora
E. Dinoflagellata
F. Euglenophyta
G. Foraminifera

H. Myxomycota
I. Oomycota
J. Phaeophyta
K. Rhizopoda
L. Rhodophyta
M. Sporozoa
N. Zoomastigina

1.   On the line below, list the letters of all phyla whose members are capable of autotrophism.

Bacilleriophta   Chlorophyta   Euglenophyta
BcDEPR   Rhodophyta   Phaeophyta
Dinoflagellata

ABMRZ

2. On the line below, list the letters of all phyla that have an ameboid phase. *Zoomastigina*
Rhizopoda

Acrasiomycota   Bacillariophyta   Myxomycota

3. On the line below, list the letters of all phyla for which parasitic members are described in the text.

Rhizopoda   Zoomastigina Oomycota   Rhodophyte
URSZ   Sporozoa

LEARNING CHECKLIST

1. Why is Protista the most diverse of all eukaryotic kingdoms?
2. What are believed to be the origins of mitochondria and the three types of chloroplasts?
3. How are the Acrasiomycota unique among protists?
4. What is the evolutionary significance of the phylum Chlorophyta?
5. Discuss the unicellular complexity of Ciliophora.
6. Explain the exclusion of Oomycota from the kingdom Fungi.
7. Which phyla of protists contain significant numbers of multicellular members?

MINI EXAM

A. Circle the letter of the best answer for each question.

1. A characteristic of Oomycota that differs from those of fungi is
   a. a chitinous cell wall
   b. sexually produced zoospores
   c. a heterotrophic habit
   d. hyphae
   e. a cellulose cell wall   *e*

2. Euglenoids have photosynthetic pigments most similar to those of
   a. diatoms
   b. red algae
   c. Chlorophyta
   d. brown algae   *b*

3. The zooxanthella of dinoflagellates are
   a. symbiotic
   b. parasitic
   c. commensalistic
   d. saprophytic   *a*

4. Diatoms belong to the
   a. Phaeophyta
   b. Chlorophyta
   c. Bacillariophyta
   d. Foraminifera   *c*

5. All of the following are caused by a trypanosome except
   a. chagas
   b. eastern equine encephalitis
   c. sleeping sickness
   d. east coast fever   *b*

6. The notorious "red tide" is caused by the
   a. Rhodophyta
   b. Bacillariophyta
   c. Dinoflagellata
   d. Euglenophyta   *c*

7. Of the various photosynthetic protists, which contains phycobilins?
   a. dinoflagellates
   b. diatoms
   c. brown algae
   d. red algae   *d*

8. All of the following belong to the same phylum except
   a. Chlamydomonas
   b. Chlorella
   c. Ulva
   d. Actinosphaerium

9. Filamentous hyphae characterize the
   a. Chlorophyta
   b. Oomycota
   c. Rhodophyta
   d. Myxomycota

10. All of the following have a life cycle alternating sexual and asexual phases except
    a. Sporozoa
    b. Phaeophyta
    c. Rhodophyta
    d. Euglenophyta
    e. Chlorophyta

11. The white cliffs of Dover are primarily made up of
    a. diatoms
    b. coralline algae
    c. foraminifera
    d. encrusting Rhizopoda

12. Scientists who study heterotrophic protists are known as
    a. zoologists
    b. mycologists
    c. phycologists
    d. protozologists

13. The stage of Plasmodium that infects human hosts is
    a. sporozoite
    b. oocyst
    c. merozoite
    d. trophozoite

14. Some ciliates, such as Paramecium, have more than one nucleus. In such a case, which one divides by mitosis?
    a. micronuclei
    b. meganuclei
    c. macronuclei
    d. protonuclei

15. The choanoflagellates belong to the
    a. Dinoflagellate
    b. Euglenophyta
    c. Zoomastigina
    d. Ciliophora

16. Amoebas of the Acrasiomycota fuse sexually to form
    a. sorocarps
    b. macrocyst
    c. oocysts
    d. zygospores

17. Mitosis in dinoflagellates is unique in that it occurs within the
    a. spore
    b. nucleus
    c. zygote
    d. nucleolus

18. The sexual reproductive process in Paramecium is called
    a. pleomixus
    b. conjugation
    c. fusiformation
    d. oogenesis

19. Large structures known as kelps are found in the phylum
    a. Rhodophyta
    b. Chlorophyta
    c. Rhizopoda
    d. Phaeophyta

20. The foraminifera swim and gather food with their
    a. podia
    b. pseudopodia
    c. plamodia
    d. mastiga

B. Provide the appropriate term to complete each statement.

1. In the alteration of generations of the Phaeophyta, the diploid phase is called the _____ generation.

2. Members of the sexual phase of the genus, <u>Plasmodium,</u> are called _____.

3. Members of the genus, _____, sometimes called "nori" are eaten by the Japanese.

4. Motile spores of the oomycetes are called _____.

5. The slime colds of the Myxomycota move in a multinucleate mass known as _____.

6. Dinoflagellates lacking their cellulose plates are known as _____.

7. Ciliates void solid wastes through an opening known as the _____.

8. Complex reproductive structures of stone warts in which gametes are found are called _____.

9. The _____ is a spore containing mass of the cellular slime molds.

10. Scientists who study algae are called _____.

C. Briefly answer each of the following questions.

1. Compare diatoms and dinoflagellates in terms of anatomy, cell wall composition and chloroplasts.

2. Use Euglenophyta and Zoomastigina to illustrate the plant-animal dilemma resulting in the classification of protists.

3. Characterize the (a) Foraminifera, (b) Rhizopoda, (c) Sporozoa, and (d) Myxomycota.

CHAPTER ANSWERS

TOPIC EXERCISES

1. B, C, E, F, J, L

2. A, B, H, K, N

3. I, K, M, N

LEARNING CHECKLIST

1. All eukaryotic groups comprised primarily of unicellular members are placed in the kingdom Protista. The differences among them are considerable. However, there are even greater gaps between the protists and other eukaryotes. In a sense it is a default group for non-bacteria, non-plants, non-animals and non-fungi. (p. 611)

2. (a) Mitochondria from nonsulfur purple bacteria, (b) red algal chloroplasts from cyanobacteria, (c) chloroplasts from brown algae, diatoms and dinoflagellates from bacteria similar to <u>Heliobacterium</u>, (d) chloroplasts of plants, green algae and euglenoids from a bacterium like <u>Prochloron</u>. (p. 613)

3. The Acrasiomycota organisms aggregate in response to starvation and form a structure called a sorocarp. (pp. 615-616)

4. The Chlorophyta are believed to have given rise to the plants. Within the Chlorophyta, have evolved several multicellular forms such as round flagellate colonies, sheet-like growth forms and branching bushy forms such as <u>Chara</u> (pp. 617-618)

5. Within the Ciliophora can be found organisms with numerous nuclei, a mouth (cytosome) and waste exit (cytoprost), contractile vacuoles, and of course, cilia. (pp. 619-621)

6. Oomycota have cell walls of chitin. Oomycota are also distinguished from fungi by gametic meiosis. (pp. 626-627)

7. The red algae, brown algae, and green algae contain significant numbers of multicellular members. (pp. 627-628, 629, 617, 621)

MINI EXAM

A.
1. e	2. d	3. a	4. c	5. b	6. c
7. d	8. d	9. b	10. d	11. c	12. a
13. a	14. a	15. c	16. b	17. b	18. b
19. d	20. a				

B.
1. sporophyte	2. gametocyte	3. <u>Porphyra</u>
4. zoospores	5. plasmodium	6. zooxanthellae
7. cytoproct	8. gametangia	9. sorocarp
10. phycologists		

C. 1. Diatoms and dinoflagellates have similar chloroplast contents. Though dinoflagellates have cellulose in their cell walls, the cell walls may include silica such as that comprising the diatom cell walls. Diatoms lack flagella. Dinoflagellates have two flagella. See Table 31-1 on page 614 of your text. (pp. 616, 622-623)

2. Euglenas have flagella, a mouth and gullet, an eye-spot, and chloroplasts. Members of Zoomastigina have all but the chloroplast. If an euglena loses its chlorophyll, it can continue to survive as an obligate heterotroph as do the Zoomastigina. (pp. 624, 632-633)

3. (a) Ameboid organism in a shell. Extends cytoplasmic podia through pores of the shell (pp. 624-625) (b) Unicellular, heterotrophic, asexual, organism that uses pseudopodia to move and feed. (pp. 628-629) (c) Complex unicellular, spore forming parasites (p. 620) (d) Multinucleate protoplasmic mass. Heterotrophic spore-formers with syngamy and meiosis. (pp. 625-626)

32: FUNGI

IN THE GRAND SCHEME

The study of fungi must be regarded as a side trip in the study of evolution on earth, because the ancestors of fungi are uncertain, and the evolutionary future is no clearer. Yet they cannot be ignored. They are both a boon and a bane to our species. While coevolving with the rest of life on earth, some fungi became symbionts of considerable benefit. Others became parasites, causing disease to plants and animals. Still other fungi joined the prokaryotes in the niche of decomposer, a role as important to us as any other. The fungi are primarily made up of filaments that lie fairly loosely as in molds, but may weave intricate structures like mushrooms, morels and cups. Their filaments, called hyphae, vary in the degree of septation or may lack septation. Two of the phyla, Ascomycetes and Basidiomycetes, have unique modes of sexual reproduction involving a coexistence of nuclei from different organisms within a single cell without fusion. In Ascomycetes, the fruiting structure may be woven from filaments of different nuclear content. Some fungi form symbiotic associations with photosynthetic protists, cyanobacteria or plants. Two of the groups of fungi are aggregations of fungi of diverse kinds and dubious affinity. The Fungi Imperfecti are so designated because their common trait is the absence of a sexual phase. The yeasts, too, have various affinities. Their common characteristic is unicellular habit. The uniqueness of fungi leaves little doubt as to why they are a separate kingdom.

FOR REVIEW

Cyanobacteria: The cyanobacteria represent the most primitive autotrophic organisms. The photosynthetic forms are believed to have been the source of chloroplasts for eukaryotes through symbiosis. The aerobic members are believed to have been the source of mitochondria by symbiosis.

Diversity of protists: The kingdom, Protista, is the most diverse of all. It consists of many phyla, mostly unicellular, with little relationship between them, and no clear ancestry.

Mitosis: Mitosis is an orderly process by which eukaryotic cells are duplicated. The five phases, Interphase, Prophase, Metaphase, Anaphase and Telophase, result in cells genetically like the parent cell.

Mutualism: An obligate symbiotic relationship between two organisms wherein each member of the relationship benefits from that relationship.

Relationships among the eukaryotes: Although all eukaryotes arose from protists, they did not all arise from the same protists. Multicellular green algae are considered to be the ancestors of the plants. Animals and fungi arose from different unicellular ancestors, not including fungus like protists.

CHAPTER OUTLINE

NUTRITION AND ECOLOGY (pp. 638-639)
STRUCTURE (p. 639)
      mycelium
      chitin
REPRODUCTION (pp. 639-640)
FUNGAL DIVISIONS (pp. 640-646)
   Division Zygomycetes
   Division Ascomycetes
     Yeasts

KEY TERMS

p. 637: mycologists
p. 638: lichens, mycorrhizae
p. 639: hyphae, septa, spindle plaques
p. 640: heterokaryotic, homokaryotic, dikaryotic, monokaryotic, sporangia, gametangia, conidia, zygomycetes, ascomycetes, basidiomycetes
p. 641: zygospores
p. 642: ascus, asci, ascocarp, ascogonia, trichogyne, antheridium
p. 643: ascospores
p. 644: basidium, basidiospores, sterigma
p. 645: primary mycelium, secondary mycelium, basidiocarps
p. 647: parasexuality
p. 650: mycorrhizae
p. 651: endomycorrhizae, ectomycorrhizae

TOPIC EXERCISES

1. It has been suggested that the Zygomycota may be ancestral to the other two phyla. In the table below, Zygomycota characteristics are listed. In the other two columns, list the changes required to become a member of the other phyla.

Zygomycota	Ascomycota changes	Basidomycota changes
1. Septation only to cut off gametes		
2. Asexual reproduction spores in sporangium		
3. Nuclear content of vegetative hyphae		
4. Product of syngamy zygospore that germinates into monokaryotic hyphae		
5. Gametangia simple terminal cell cut off		
6. Sexual spore forming no sexual spore formed		
7. Location of sexual spores		

2. Few, if any, fungi are neutral in terms of human economy. This is equally true of the Fungi Imperfecti. In the spaces provided below, list: (A) some benefits to the human existence from Fungi Imperfecti, and (B) some undesirable effects on human existence from Fungi Imperfecti.

A.

B.

LEARNING CHECKLIST

1. Why are fungi placed in a kingdom of their own?
2. What relationships exist between fungi and photosynthetic plants?
3. Briefly describe the life cycle of a zygomycete.
4. How are yeasts unique among fungi?
5. Compare endomycorrhizae and ectomycorrhizae.

MINI EXAM

A. Circle the letter of the best answer for each question.

1. Collectively, the hyphae of a fungus are called
   a. basidium
   b. millennium
   c. conidium
   d. mycelium

2. All of the following are involved in sexual reproduction except
   a. ascogonia
   b. conidia
   c. antheridia
   d. trichogyne

3. Fungi Imperfecti are so named because
   a. they are primarily parasitic
   b. they require more than one host to complete their life cycle
   c. the do not have chitin cell walls
   d. they can reproduce only by binary fission
   e. no sexual reproduction has been observed

4. Mushrooms are formed from
   a. monokaryotic hyphae
   b. heterokaryotic dikaryotic hyphae
   c. monokaryotic and dikaryotic hyphae
   d. homokaryotic and heterokaryotic hyphae
   e. homokaryotic dikaryotic hyphae

5. Yeasts reproduce mostly with
   a. asci
   b. hyphae
   c. buds
   d. basidia
   e. binary fission

6. The basidiospores of basidiomycetes are
   a. asexual spores found in the basidiosporangium
   b. haploid mitotic products
   c. borne on the outside of basidium following meiosis
   d. each heterokaryotic, having been produced by daryogamy
   e. protected within the basidium until dispersal

7. Fungal cell walls are made of
   a. chitin
   b. cellulose
   c. lignin
   d. pectin
   e. peptidoglycan

8. The fungal symbiont of lichens is usually a(n)
   a. zygomycete
   b. basidiomycete
   c. ascomycete
   d. deuteromycete

9. Athlete's foot is caused by members of
   a. Zygomycota
   b. Fungi Imperfecti
   c. Ascomycota
   d. Basidiomycota

10. The visible portion of a morel or cup fungus is called the
    a. ascocarp
    b. antheridium
    c. ascogonium
    d. ascus
    e. basidiocarp

11. Basidiospores are borne on the ends of
    a. sterigmata
    b. pili
    c. trichogynes
    d. sporophores

12. In exchange for nutrients, mycorrhizae provide plants with
    a. fixed carbon dioxide
    b. moisture conserving capacity
    c. antibiotic resistance to parasitic fungi
    d. micronutrients as a byproduct of mycorrhizae metabolism
    e. the ability to absorb certain minerals

13. Aspergillus is an economically important genus of
    a. Zygomycota
    b. Basidiomycota
    c. Ascomycota
    d. Fungi Imperfecti

14. Most yeasts were derived from _____ ancestors.
    a. zygomycete
    b. basidiomycete
    c. ascomycete
    d. deuteromycete

15. Zygomycete hyphae are
    a. divided by partial septa into diploid segments
    b. aseptate and multinucleate
    c. septate and dikaryotic
    d. septate and multinucleate until syngamy
    e. aseptate and haploid until after plasmogamy

16. Fungal hyphae formed from two genetically distinct individuals are called
    a. monokaryotic
    b. homokaryotic
    c. bikaryotic
    d. heterokaryotic

17. Cells from the male gametangium of ascomycetes pass through the _____ on the way to the female gametangium.
    a. antheridium
    b. trichogyne
    c. ascocarp
    d. ascophore

18. Lichens can be described as _____ to environmental pollution.
    a. highly resistant
    b. fairly tolerant
    c. somewhat sensitive
    d. highly sensitive

19. Basidiomycetes reproduce mainly by
    a. haploid conidia
    b. diploid basidiospores
    c. diploid conidia
    d. haploid basidiospore
    e. plasmogamy

20. In nature, _____ seeds germinate only in the presence of mycorrhizae of a particular kind of basidiomycete.
    a. tomato
    b. orchid
    c. pineapple
    d. banana

B. Provide the appropriate term to complete each statement.

1. _____ are present in ascomycete hyphae, but zygomycete hyphae lack them.

2. The union of gametangia of two different strains of zygomycetes results in _____.

3. The _____ is the filament extending from an ascogonium.

4. In fungal mitosis, the role of centrioles is performed by the _____.

5. _____ are symbiotic fungi within the roots of plants.

6. Genetic recombination in Fungi Imperfecti is called _____.

7. _____ are scientists who study fungi.

8. The life form called the _____ is a mutualistic relationship between fungi and algae or

cyanobacteria.

9. An example of the fungal division _____ is bread mold.

10. The oomycetes differ from fungi in that their spores are _____.

C. Briefly answer each of the following questions.

1. Compare the major characteristics of the three fungal divisions.

2. Compare Ascomycetes and Basidiomycetes with respect to (a) structure and (b) sexual cycle.

3. Characterize the Fungi Imperfecti.

CHAPTER ANSWERS

TOPIC EXERCISES

1. A1: perforated hyphae between vegetative cells
   A2: conidia produced without sporangium
   A3: heterokaryotic hyphae
   A4: forms heterokaryotic hyphae
   A5: specialization into ascogonium with trichogyne and antheridium
   A6: produce asci in ascocarp
   A7: within asci
   B1: perforated hyphae between vegetative cells
   B2: rarely, if so, conidia
   B3: heterokaryotic hyphae
   B5: no gametangia; normal hyphae fuse
   B6: produce basidia in basidiocarp
   B7: on surface of basidia

2. A. Flavors, aromas, citric acid, antibiotics
   B. Plant pathogens, skin disease

LEARNING CHECKLIST

1. Fungi are primarily filamentous and secrete enzymes that digest food which the fungus then absorbs. (p. 637)

2. Fungi house symbiotic algae in a life form called a lichen. Fungi may live upon or within the roots of photosynthetic plants where they aid their host in absorbing nutrients and receive nutrition for their services. (pp. 648-650)

3. See Figure 32-5 on page 641 of your text.

4. They are unicellular. They may actually have been derived from several fungal lines. (pp. 643-644)

5. The hyphae of endomycorrhizae penetrate the outer region of the host root, whereas the ectomycorrhizae remain on the exterior of the roots. In both cases, the hyphae extend far out into the soil. (pp. 650-652)

MINI EXAM

A.
1. d	2. b	3. e	4. b	5. c	6. c
7. a	8. c	9. b	10. a	11. a	12. e
13. c	14. c	15. b	16. d	17. b	18. d
19. d	20. b				

B.
1. septa	2. zygospore	3. trichogyne
4. spindle plaque	5. mycorrhizae	6. parasexuality
7. mycologists	8. lichen	9. Zygomycota
10. motile		

C. 1. See Table 32-1 on page 646 of your text

2. (a) Ascomycetes range from single-celled yeast cells and fuzzy filamentous molds to complex structures such as cup fungi and morels. All complex structures are woven from hyphal threads. Basidiomycetes are best typified by mushrooms, puffballs and bracket fungi. These structures, woven from hyphae, disperse spores from gills, pores, or bags.
(b) The reproductive structure of an ascomycete is that for which it is named, ascus. The hyphae of two different haploid parents join to produce a hyphae to two kinds of nuclei (dikaryotic.) Walling off two of these different cells results in a terminal cell called ascus. The two nuclei fuse (karyogamy.) The ascus in this form is the only 2N cell in the life cycle. Meiosis occurs in the ascus and ascospores result. The meiosis results in nuclei of different kinds, thus two strains of spores. The spores germinate and restart the cycle. See fig. 32-8 on page 642 of your text. The basidium is the reproductive structure of basidiomycetes. These structures are borne on surfaces of gills, pores, etc. Two haploid monokaryotic hyphae join to form a dikaryotic mycelium that develops the fruiting structure (mushroom, etc.) As in Ascomycetes, two different nuclei are walled off together into a basidium. Meiosis occurs in the basidium and basidiospores are extruded to the surface of the basidium to be shed. See Figure 32-12 on page 645 of your text. (pp. 646-647)

3. Fungi Imperfecti are fungi for which no sexual phase has been observed. It is presumed that the ability to reproduce sexually has been lost. There is occasionally a fusion of hyphae of different organisms. Some genetic material is exchanged in a process called parasexuality. (pp. 647-648)

33: DIVERSITY OF PLANTS

IN THE GRAND SCHEME

Although they stand mute and unable to travel, vascular plants have used their heritage to dominate the landscape and to control and modify the environment. Habitats are classified according to geology and the plant life present. Plants control humidity and sunlight beneath them and provide food and nesting sites to the animals of the world. One can well marvel at the locomotion adaptation of animals. It is no less marvelous that the vascular plants, rooted in place have adapted themselves for coping with hazards of life as they come, unable to seek better conditions elsewhere. Vascular plants had to evolve more than vascular tissue to dominate the terrestrial environment. Adaptation required waterproofing of structures to prevent evaporative loss through their tissues. Gas exchange was essential to photosynthesis, but again, it had to be accomplished without prohibitive evaporative loss. The need to reach the sunlight above competitors that required vascular tissue also jeopardized the free-swimming sperm. Another method of fertilization had to evolve. Species survival entailed competition for space. In the competition for space, dispersal became key. Much of the competition among plants even today is that of reproduction and dispersal. The vascular plants won the race for the sun. Seed plants won the dispersal race and in suitable habitats it is evident that the flowering, fruit producing seed plants hold the edge over conifers. The competition continues today. Diversity and competition feed evolution.

FOR REVIEW

Alternation of generations: Some organisms have two distinctly different generations, one haploid and one diploid, that occur alternately. One generation reproduces sexually, the other asexually.

Evolutionary history of plants: Plants were the first organisms to colonize land, which they did about 410 million years ago. The first plants were multicellular with the capability of making their own food and conserving water. Within the next 100 million years, the plants were very diverse and forming large forests. Such forests were primarily horsetails, ferns, and primitive seed plants. By about 250 million years ago, conifers predominated in the cooler drier climate. The earliest flowering plants appeared about 127 million years ago.

Classification: Scientists have evolved a classification system that attempts to classify organisms according to phylogeny. Organisms are classified into groups listed here in descending order: Kingdom, phylum or division, class, order, family, genus and species.

Green algae: Green algae, believed to be the ancestors of plants, range in complexity from unicellular to multicellular. Their cell walls and photosynthetic pigments are very similar to those of plants.

Mycorrhizae: Mycorrhizae are fungal symbionts that enter or attach to roots of plants and aid them in the up-take of phosphorous and other ions.

CHAPTER OUTLINE

THE EVOLUTIONARY ORIGINS OF PLANTS (pp. 657-658)
THE GREEN INVASION OF THE LAND (pp. 658-659)
THE PLANT LIFE CYCLE (pp. 659-662)
    Alternation of Generations
    The Specialization of Gametophytes
MOSSES, LIVERWORTS AND HORNWORTS (pp. 662-666)
    The Divisions of Non-vascular Plants

KEY TERMS

p. 658: desiccation, cuticle, cutin, stomata, stoma, vascular tissue

p. 660: spore mother cells, spores

p. 661: gametangium, gametangia, archegonia, archegonium, antheridia, antheridium, microgametophytes, megagametophytes, microspores, megaspores, heterosporous, homosporous, sporangium, sporangia, microsporangia, megasporangia

p. 663: rhizoids

p. 649: seta, sporangium

p. 665: protonemata, protonema

p. 666: heterospory

p. 667: secondary growth

p. 668: sieve elements, tracheary elements, phloem, xylem

p. 671: apical notch

p. 672: rhizomes, fronds

p. 673: dichotomous branching, angiosperms, flowering plants, gymnosperms, pollination, germinates

p. 674: gymnosperms

p. 676: pollen tube

p. 677: carpels, stigma, angiosperms, whorls, stigma, pistils, gynoecium

p. 678: perianth, petals, calyx, sepals, androecium, stamens, filament, anther

p. 679: nucellus, integuments, embryo sac, primary endosperm nucleus, endosperm, double fertilization

TOPIC EXERCISES

The three exercises below relate to an expedition to determine the extant flora of an island so small that it escaped previous exploration. Several collections were made but only four kinds of plants were found. Neither plants 000 001 nor 000 002 had a chromosome number the same as or multiples of those of numbers 000 003 and 000 004. Your task is to classify each as precisely as you can.

1. Plant number 000 001 is characterized by a horizontal underground stem with vascular tissue and true roots. Leaves on the underground stem emerged through the ground. The leaves shed small, hard-walled cells of half the chromosome number as the leaves from which they came.

A. To what plant group do you assign this specimen?

B. What characteristics determine this classification?

2. Plant number 000 002 was robust with upright vascularized stem that branched and bore leaves. Whorls were found that shed small, hard-walled cells of half the chromosome number of the stem and leaves. Similar whorls appeared to be older and withering. These older whorls contained a large hard-walled, globular structure in the center of the whorl. This structure contained cells of the same chromosome number as the stem and leaves. In somewhat younger globular structures, a few cells were found that contained one and a half times the chromosome number as that of the stem and leaves.

A. In what plant group do you place this plant?

B. What characteristics determine this classification?

3. Plants 000 003 and 000 004 strongly resembled each other. Number 000 004 differed from 000 003 only in the structure extending upward from it. Number 000 003 had an erect growth but lacked vascular tissue. It had neither true roots nor leaves. It anchored itself by, and drew moisture with, hair-like structures. Structures resembling leaves radiated around the upright stalk. All of the parts of 000 003 that were above ground were photosynthetic. Swimming sperm were found in a gametangium at the top of one specimen. The chromosome number of the sperm was the same as that of the plant upon which they formed.
Plant 000 004 was like 000 003 but had a long stalked structure extending from its top. At the tip of the long stalk was a swollen region containing hard-walled spores containing half the chromosome number as the long stalk, but the same as that of the plant from which the long stalk grew. The basal part of 000 004 had the same chromosome number as that of 000 003.

A. Into what plant group will you classify 000 003?

B. What characteristics determine this classification?

C. Into what plant group will you place 000 004?

D. What characteristics determine this classification?

LEARNING CHECKLIST

1. What evidence is there that plants evolved from green algae?
2. List adaptations required of plants to become dominant terrestrial organisms.
3. What is meant by vascular versus nonvascular?
4. Compare liverworts and mosses.
5. Compare conifer and flowering plant seed production.
6. Explain the significance of the flower and trace its evolutionary history.

MINI EXAM

A. Circle the letter of the best answer for each question.

1. Horse tails belong to the division
   a. Sphenophyta
   b. Psilophyta
   c. Lycophyta
   d. Pterophyta

2. In ferns, the female gametangium is the
   a. archegonium
   b. androecium
   c. gynoecium
   d. antheridium

3. In vascular plants, carbohydrates are transported through
   a. phloem
   b. xylem
   c. sclerenchyma
   d. rhizoids

4. Which of the following statements about bryophytes is most correct?
   a. The spores when shed are diploid, as is the sporophyte, and undergo meiosis before germinating
   b. The only vascularization in bryophytes is seen in the stalk of the sporophyte of mosses, both generations of the rest being nonvascular.
   c. Sperm are formed meiotically in the diploid antheridium.
   d. The egg cell of the liverwort, <u>Marchantia</u>, is fertilized in the archegonium of the gametophyte, then undergoes meiosis and gives rise to haploid spores and sporophyte.
   e. The haploid gametophyte is free living and usually supports the diploid usually parasitic sporophyte.

5. Which of the following is part of the calyx?
   a. sepal
   b. carpel
   c. ovary
   d. anther

6. All of the following are homosporous except
   a. Pterophyta
   b. Psilophyta
   c. Bryophyta
   d. Ginkophyta
   e. Sphenophyta

7. All of the following structures or processes are characteristic of angiosperms, but not gymnosperms except
   a. double fertilization
   b. nucellus
   c. endosperm
   d. embryo sac
   e. integument

8. Earliest plants transported water through
   a. sieve elements
   b. spicule elements
   c. phloem elements
   d. tracheary elements

9. Mosses absorb water and minerals through
   a. roots
   b. rhizomes
   c. rhizoids
   d. peristomes
   e. scales

10. Double fertilization is unique to
    a. gymnosperms
    b. cycads
    c. ginkgoes
    d. angiosperms
    e. modern ferns

11. In the life cycle of the pine, which of the following is haploid?
    a. megasporangium
    b. ovule
    c. food reserve in seed
    d. microsporangium
    e. seed coat

12. The name for the horizontal, underground stem characteristic of ferns is
    a. root
    b. rhizome
    c. stolon
    d. rhizoid
    e. runner

13. All of the following are characteristics found in vascular plants, but not bryophytes except
    a. large independent sporophyte
    b. heterospory
    c. protenema
    d. free swimming sperm
    e. rhizome

14. All of the following are a part of the gynoecium except
    a. carpel
    b. stigma
    c. style
    d. seta

15. Ferns belong to the division
    a. Lycophyta
    b. Sphenophyta
    c. Pterophyta
    d. Cycadophyta

16. Welwitschia belongs to the division
    a. Coniferophyta
    b. Gnetophyta
    c. Anthophyta
    d. Cycadophyta

17. Which of the following is a part of the perianth?
    a. stamen
    b. corolla
    c. pistil
    d. megasporangium

18. All of the following are a part of the androecium except
    a. stamen
    b. anther
    c. stigma
    d. filament

19. The haploid generation of ferns is the
    a. megasporophyte
    b. microgametophyte
    c. megagametophyte
    d. microsporophyte

20. The endosperm in angiosperms is
    a. triploid
    b. diploid
    c. haploid
    d. nonexistent

B. Provide the appropriate term to complete each statement.

1. _____ is the characteristic of producing two distinctly different spores; one that produces egg-forming structures and one that produces sperm-forming structures.

2. The arrival of pine microspores in the vicinity of the ovules is called _____.

3. In ferns archegonia form on the lower surface near the _____.

4. Because of the location of ovules and seeds, flowering plants are called _____.

5. In flowering plants, meiosis occurs within the kind of megasporagium called _____

6. A mature flowering plant megagametophyte is called a(n) _____.

7. Plants may be protected from drying by a waxy substance called _____.

8. In the sporophyte generation of plants meiosis takes place in the _____.

9. The gametes of the first plants differentiated in specialized organs called _____.

10. A germinating moss spore produces a filamentous structure called _____.

C. Briefly answer each of the following questions.

1. Describe the alternation of generations in a generalized fashion.

2. Compare the gametophytes and sporophytes of (a) non-vascular plants, (b) ferns, (c) lycopods, (d) conifers, and (e) angiosperms including spore and gamete production.

3. Discuss the evolutionary significance of the seed for terrestrial plants.

CHAPTER ANSWERS

TOPIC EXERCISES

1. A. Fern (Pterophyta)
    B. Vascular, horizontal underground stem, spores from leaves

2. A. Angiosperm
    B. Vascular, erect, spores produced in whorls. Globular structure (seed) from whorl.

3. A. Moss (Bryophyte)
    B. No vascular structures, erect and leafy, 1N, sporophyte (long stalked structure), dependent upon gametophyte, is 2N.
    C. Moss (Bryophyte)
    D. Same as 000 003 but with attached sporophyte.

LEARNING CHECKLIST

1. The biochemistry, such as pigmentation and the mode of cytokinesis, are shared by plants and green algae. (p. 657)

2. Competition for a place in the sun places a premium on height. To achieve great height, plants had to have a good conduction system for water and nutrients and strong tissues to support them. A waterproofing material was required to prevent loss of water in the heat of the sun whose light was essential to photosynthesis. A means of gas exchange with the environment without too great a loss of water vapor was needed. Plants also had to evolve physical and chemical means of extracting water from the soil under variable conditions of moisture. Height also required a good system of anchorage. At some point, height requires a change from the free swimming sperm type of fertilization. (pp. 658-659)

3. As used to describe plants, the term vascular means having specialized tubular structures for the transport of liquids. (p. 658)

4. Thalloid liverworts gametophytes are prostate, leaf-like plants. Others are erect and resemble mosses. Sporangium are thin-walled, and splits open, sometimes elevated. Moss gametophyte is usually erect and leafy. Sporophyte grows from the tip of gametophyte and is characterized by a capsule on the end of a stalk. Unlike the liverworts, moss capsules have complex spore release mechanisms including a lid that falls off when spores are mature. (pp. 663-666)

5. Angiosperm seeds result from a complicated double fertilization process in which both sperm fertilize a cell. One fertilization results in the zygote while the other results in formation of a food material called endosperm. Other than double fertilization, pine and flowering plants have essentially the same seed producing process. See Figures 33-25 and 33-30 in your text for a comparison. (pp. 674-680)

6. As plants evolved, spore bearing leaves called sporophylls become closer together at the apex of a shoot as internodes between them become shorter. Such a tightly clustered whorl of sporophylls is known as a strobilus. In pine trees, nearly all sporophylls bear seeds. In flowers, some sporophylls are fused to form the carpels, some have reduced blades and are called stamens, while others are modified to protect the flower bud and/or to attract insects. Thus, the flower is a highly evolved and evolving whorls of sporophylls. (pp. 677-680)

MINI EXAM

A.
1. a	2. a	3. a	4. e	5. a	6. b
7. e	8. d	9. d	10. d	11. c	12. b
13. c	14. d	15. c	16. b	17. b	18. c
19. b	20. a				

B.
1. Heterospory	2. pollination	3. apical notch
4. angiosperm	5. nucellus	6. embryo sac
7. cuticle	8. spore mother cell	9. gametangia
10. protonema		

C. 1. See figure 33-5 on page 660 of your text for illustrations. Plant generations alternate between haploid and diploid forms. Spores are produced by meiosis and gametes by mitosis. All haploid forms belong to the gametophyte (gamete making plant) generation. All diploid forms belong to the sporophyte (spore making plant) generation. Plants vary greatly as to the duration and complexity of each generation. Cycles by their nature have an infinite number of beginning points. We will arbitrarily begin with meiosis. Spores are formed by meiosis and thus begin the haploid gametophyte generation. Spores germinate to form a gametophyte. If spores differ (heterospory,) there will be male and female gametophytes on separate plants. If the spores are produced by a plant (homosporous,) structures for both sexes will be on the same plant. The gametophyte forms gametes by mitosis. The gametes fuse to form a zygote, the first member of the diploid sporophyte generation. The sporophyte will mature and produce spores by meiosis etc. (pp. 659-661)

2. Gametophyte: (a) green, prostrate or erect. No true root, stem or gametes in gametogia, (b) minute leaf like prostrate gametes in gametangia, (c) similar to fern (d) parasitic on sporophyte contained in pollen gran or ovule (e) as in conifers.
Sporophyte: (a) mostly parasitic on gametophyte spores in capsular sporangium, (b) horizontal stem, true roots and leaves, spores in sporangia usually under leaves, (c) horizontal stem, erect branches with leaflets and sporangia in cone-like structure, (d) large dominant trees, spores produced in once (e) small to large, herbivorous to woody, spores in modified cone called flower. (pp. 663-666, 670-672, 673, 674-676)

3. In seed plants, the megaspore is retained by the sporophyte and equipped by the sporophyte for its role as a dispersal unit. Whereas, a megaspore of a non-seed plants contains the nutrients to develop an independent sporophyte upon germination, the seed plant continues to nourish the developing embryo within the seed. Dispersal mechanisms are often built into the seed. Spores of non-seed plants must germinate soon after being shed. The waterproof seed coat and food supply furnished by the sporophyte enables a seed to remain dormant, awaiting suitable conditions for growth. Having overcome perils faced by many competitors, seeds make their species a formidable opponent for seedless plants. (pp. 669-670)

34: FLOWERING PLANTS

IN THE GRAND SCHEME

The seed gave its producers a great edge in the competition among plants, but the seed was not the finale. As the seed bearing structure coevolved with animals, more reliable means of pollination and array of better seeds emerged along with diverse fruits. The ancestor of flowering plants was surely a gymnosperm. That ancestor is nowhere to be seen today. All of today's gymnosperms are highly specialized. Since at least part of today's gymnosperms probably evolved from the same ancestor as that of the angiosperms, it is reasonable to assume that the common ancestor became extinct long ago, yielding in the competition to the more highly evolved forms. Sterile leaves were pressed into service as a protective cover for the flower bud and then later as colored attractors of pollinators. These were the sepals. Spore bearing leaves were modified in two ways. The outer whorl of spore bearing leaves lost their sporangia, developed color, and became petals. The next inner whorl reduced the blade of the leaf, leaving the sporangium supported by the midrib. These modified leaves are the stamens. The carpels of the more primitive extant flowers are clearly derived from spore bearing leaves. There is no such clear evidence for the carpels of more modern flowers and their origin is open to speculation. Perhaps, since flowers are structures of determinate growth, the carpel of the more modern flowers represent the final growth of the apical meristem into a more novel carpel. As some flowers coevolved with animals into symbiotic relationships of feeding and pollination, others spurred the practice and evolved more efficient wind pollination techniques. Special techniques evolved to promote outcrossing, increasing variation. Some flowers hedge against the risk of not being cross-pollinated and have provided for self-pollination. All of the efforts to insure the formation of a new generation would be largely lost if all of the progeny become competitors at the feet of the parents. In some cases seeds and in other cases fruits, become modified to enhance dispersal. Some relied upon animals for dispersal, others on physical forces of nature. The process goes on.

FOR REVIEW

Hybridization and the origin of species: When an organism outcrosses, hybridization results. If the resulting offspring is sufficiently different from the rest of the population and is genetically stable, it is considered a new species.

Origin of land plants: Land plants evolved from green algae ancestors that were probably already semiterrestrial.

Evolution of the seed: The potential for a seed was provided by heterospory. The retention of the megaspore on the sporophyte provided for continued nutrition during the embryonic growth before and after germination. The ovule, in which the magaspore is retained and fertilized and in which the embryo grows, forms a seed coat that confers benefits, including dormancy, on the embryo.

Gymnosperms: Gymnosperms produce seeds on a structure in which the seed is exposed, rather than enclosed. However, the category of gymnosperms should not be regarded as a taxonomic unit.

Flowering plant life cycle: Microgametophytes, called pollen, are shed from the anther of a flower and are transported by wind or animal to the stigma of another flower. The microspore germinates, and a pollen tube extends down through the style of the carpel and delivers two sperm. The megaspore within the ovule divides to produce eight haploid cells. One of the eight cells is an egg cell, and two are called polar cells. One sperm fertilizes the egg cell to produce the zygote. One sperm fuses with the two polar nuclei to form the primary endosperm. The zygote grows and differentiates into an embryo. The primary endosperm divides rapidly into a food reserve. The ovule hardens into a seed coat. The carpel matures into a fruit. The embryo grows into a mature sporophyte.

CHAPTER OUTLINE

KEY TERMS:

TOPIC EXERCISES

1.   Imagine that your are designing a flower for animal pollination. Put an "X" under the chosen animal.

	A	B	C	D
	Bee	Moth	Butterfly	Hummingbird
a. Large amounts of pollen				
b. Moderate nectar				
c. Strong scent				
d. Tubular corolla				

	A	B	C	D
	Bee	Moth	Butterfly	Hummingbird

e. Flat landing platform

f. Bright red color

g. Bright yellow color

h. White color

i. Day opening

j. Night opening

2. In terms of floral specialization, indicate which characteristics are primitive or modern by placing a "P" or "M" in the blank following each description.

    A. Spirally arranged petals and sepals

    B. Petals and sepals in whorls

    C. Petals or sepals few

    D. Petals or sepals fused

    E. Long floral axis

    F. Corolla fused to calyx

    G. Corolla or calyx absent

    H. Stamens or pistils absent

    I. Floral parts separate

    J. Radial symmetry

3. Complete the chronology below by filling the blanks with numbers of millions of years when the characteristic occurred.

    A. Probable origin of angiosperms

    B. First definite angiosperm

    C. Angiosperms dominate

    D. Current families, such as beeches, appear

LEARNING CHECKLIST

1. Why is it believed that all angiosperms have evolved from a common gymnosperm ancestor?

2. Differentiate between monocots and dicots?

3. What is meant by determinate and indeterminate growth? Apply the terms to angiosperm parts.

4. Explain ways in which flowering plants promote outcrossing.

5. Characterize wind pollinated plants.

6. Relate various bee types to flower pollination.

7. What flower characteristics attract (a) butterflies, (b) moths, and (c) birds?

8. How are seeds and fruits adapted to seed dispersal?

MINI EXAM

A. Circle the letter of the best answer for each question.

1. With regard to its flower, the oak tree is
   a. monoecious
   b. dichogamous
   c. dioecious
   d. exoganious

2. Which of the following is a modern dicot characteristic?
   a. five flower parts
   b. parallel veins
   c. single-pored pollen
   d. single seedling leaf
   e. fused whorl of three petals

3. Which of the following is a part of the calyx?
   a. stamen
   b. carpel
   c. sepal
   d. petal

4. All of the following are a part of the gynoecium except
   a. carpel
   b. stigma
   c. ovary
   d. embryo

5. Which of the following flowers would be considered the most modern?
   a. rose
   b. petunia
   c. violet
   d. snapdragon
   e. cactus

6. Which of the following is a monocot?
   a. maple
   b. oak
   c. lily
   d. violet
   e. pea

7. Birds are attracted to flowers that are colored
   a. yellow
   b. blue
   c. red
   d. white
   e. red

8. Bees are attracted to flowers that are
   a. yellow
   b. red
   c. white
   d. pink
   e. blue

9. All of the following flower characteristics are useful in attracting moths except
   a. strong scents
   b. bright colors
   c. tubular structure
   d. flat landing surface

10. Which of the Gondwanaland conditions favored angiosperm evolution?
    a. dryness
    b. cold
    c. reduced sunlight
    d. wetness
    e. fog

11. Flowers producing only megaspores are called
    a. monoecious
    b. staminate
    c. dioecious
    d. pistillate
    e. macandrous

12. Angiosperms dominated terrestrial habitats about _____ million years ago.
    a. 100
    b. 80
    c. 160
    d. 200

13. All of the following are a monocot except
    a. tulip
    b. iris
    c. grass
    d. lily
    e. rose

14. The term monoecious refers to the number of
    a. flower types on a plant
    b. plants required to produce both kinds of spores
    c. spore types produced in one flower
    d. seedling leaves in the seed

15. Which of the flower characteristics listed is disadvantageous to insect pollination?
    a. strong scent
    b. bright colors
    c. large amounts of nectar
    d. large petals

16. Flowers producing only microspores are called
    a. monoecious
    b. pistillate
    c. staminate
    d. dioecious
    e. dichogamous

17. The term monocot is derived from
    a. the number of seedling leaves
    b. haploid condition
    c. number of spore types in one flower
    d. number of spore types produced on one plant
    e. number of ovules per ovary

18. In floral evolution, which of the following is considered primitive?
    a. short central axis
    b. tubular development
    c. fused parts
    d. many parts
    e. distinct whorls

19. Families of flowers that exist today, such as the magnolia appeared as long ago as
    _____ million years.
    a. 165
    b. 95 e.
    c. 65
    d. 25
    120

20. Self-fertilization is best characterized as
    a. sometimes advantageous
    b. ideal
    c. never advantageous
    d. unimportant
    e. almost always advantageous

B. Provide the appropriate term to complete each statement.

    1. The failure of the shoot to grow after the formation of the flower is called
        _____.

    2. _____ are characterized by reticular venation of leaves and flower parts in
        fours or fives.

    3. A flower with a gynoecium but no androecium is called _____.

    4. Being dioecious helps ensure _____.

    5. Reduction and fusion of flower parts indicates advances in _____.

    6. A flower whose androecium and gynoecium are active at different times is _____.

    7. _____ is a means of increasing outcrossing by flowers with both
        stamens and pistils.

    8. Glands providing food to pollinators are called _____.

    9. Odorless plants that produce lots of nectar tend to attract _____.

    10. _____ plants have staminate flowers on one plant and pistillate flowers on
        another.

C. Briefly answer each of the following questions.

    1. Briefly discuss floral evolution.

    2. Explain the origin of each whorl of a flower from other plant parts.

    3. Discuss circumstances and advantages of self-pollination.

CHAPTER ANSWERS

TOPIC EXERCISES

1. A. a, c, d, h, j

    B. c, d, e, f, i, k

    C. c, d, e, f, h, j

    D. b, e, g, j

2. | A. P | B. M | C. M | D. M | E. P | F. M |
    |------|------|------|------|------|------|
    | G. M | H. M | I. P | J. P | | |

3. A. 150   B. 123   C. 90   D. 65

LEARNING CHECKLIST

1. Such features as double fertilization and the structure of fruit make it unlikely that such traits would have evolved more than once. Similarities to gymnosperms tend to indicate that the ancestor of the angiosperms would be a gymnosperm. None of today's gymnosperms qualify as angiosperm ancestors since they are each to specialized. (pp. 684-685)

2. Monocots are plants which have only one seedling leaf whereas dicots have two seedling leaves. Other monocot characteristics are parallel veins and flower parts in whorls of three. Dicots have netlike veins and flower parts of four or five per whorl. (pp. 685-687)

3. If meristem does not continually grow and differentiate specialized plant parts, the growth is called determinate. If the meristem continues to grow and differentiate parts, one after another for an indefinite period, the growth is indeterminate. Flowers tend to be formed by determinate growth. Leaves and twigs tend to be formed by indeterminate growth. (p. 689)

4. Outcrossing is promoted by separation of carpels and stamens into separate flowers on one tree or onto separate trees. Similar effects result from staggered maturation times for stamens and carpels. Yet another technique is genetic self-incompatibility, wherein the pollen of one plant will not function on the stigmas of flowers of the same plant. (pp. 690-693)

5. Wind pollinated plants tend to be small, greenish, and odorless with corollas reduced or absent. They tend to be grouped together in fairly large numbers and hang down in tassels. (p. 696)

6. Generally, bees are attracted to blue or yellow flowers. Flowers pollinated by bees tend to have markings that lead to the nectaries. Social bees tend to visit many kinds of flowers, whereas solitary bees tend to visit only one kind of flower. (pp. 693-694)

7. (a) Landing platform, daytime opening, long slender nectaries, white to yellow in color; (b) as for butterflies, except heavy scent and night opening, pastel colors; (c) red color, much nectar, deep tubes to nectaries, day opening. (p. 694)

8. Fleshy fruits lead to animal dispersal of seeds eaten in the fruit. Some seeds and some fruits are adapted for airborne dispersal. Both seeds and fruits may be adapted to travel in animal furs by barbs or hooks. (pp. 697-698)

MINI EXAM

A.

1. a	2. a	3. c	4. d	5. d	6. c
7. e	8. a	9. b	10. a	11. d	12. b
13. c	14. b	15. c	16. c	17. a	18. d
19. c	20. a				

B.

1. determinate growth	2. Dicots	3. pistillate
4. outcrossing	5. floral evolution	6. dichogamous
7. Genetic self-incompatibility	8. nectaries	9. hummingbirds
10. Dioecious		

C. 1. Primitive flowers are characterized by numerous, spirally arranged flower parts. Evolutionary trends are reduction of flower part numbers, separation of flower parts into definite whorls and fusion of previously separate flower parts. (pp. 688-690)

2. Sepals of the calyx were derived from leaves. Petals of the corolla appear to have been derived from spore bearing leaves or fruits (sporophylls) as were stamens. Essentially, petals are sporophylls without the sporangium whereas stamens are sporophylls without the leaf blade. Primitive flowering plants have leaf-like carpels which were probably derived from leaves. Most modern plants have much more specialized carpels. (pp. 689-690)

3. Self-pollination is better than the lack of pollination that could result from sparse, widely scattered population. Genetically, self-pollination is a disadvantage unless the flower is well adapted to its environment. Uniformity tends to increase if flowers self-pollinate. (p. 696)

35: VASCULAR PLANT STRUCTURE

IN THE GRAND SCHEME

In studying the plant kingdom it is appropriate to view the diversity as you have. The evolution and function of the flower is impressive. But to really appreciate the word "plant," this chapter is essential. In this chapter you will learn of the diversity of the plant cell types and their arrangement in different parts of different plants. The structure of a plant body is something akin to the structure of a building. The details that must go into the planning of a house are not apparent until one examines a detailed set of house plans. The depth of such planning becomes even more apparent when one tries to create their own set of detailed house plans. Such a view of the plant body is given in this chapter. First, the structural members are defined. Then, the specific arrangement of those components in each part of the plant that is necessary to provide support, to convey water and nutrients and to protect the plant from the elements, is laid out. Once that complexity is understood, you will be confronted by the characteristic that makes plants so different from animals. The growth of an animal zygote to an adult is awesome. Once done, however, the job is pretty well finished except to repair damage. The growth of a plant from a zygote is also impressive but, unlike an animal, the job is never done. The plant is so organized that perpetually embryonic tissue is positioned to elongate and thicken the plant and to provide for continual branching, leafing and flowering. In the light of this chapter, a tree, or for that matter, a weed takes on new majesty.

FOR REVIEW

Cell structure: Plant cells are surrounded on the outside by a cell wall. Just inside the wall is the cell membrane. Most of the inside of the cell membrane is filled with cytoplasm and one or more vacuoles. Included in the cytoplasm is usually a nucleus, one or many plastids and mitochondria.

How cells divide: Vegetative structures of plants divide by mitosis. Chromosomes are duplicated, and a copy of each chromosome is carried to opposite poles. The cell is then divided into two cells by the formation of a cell wall midway between the clusters of chromosomes.

Major groups of plants: All plants are multicellular eukaryotes. They are divided into vascular and non-vascular plants. Vascular plants are divided into seed producers and nonseed producers. Seed producers are divided into flowering plants and nonflowering plants. Flowering plants are divided into monocots and dicots.

Reproduction of flowering plants: Flowers produce pollen in an anther and an egg in an ovule. The pollen is shed, is carried by wind or animal, and pollinates a flower on the stigma. The pollen extends its pollen tube down through the style into the ovary of the carpel, carrying the two sperm with it. The embryo sac, developed within the ovule, contains eight nuclei, including one egg and two polar nuclei. The egg is fertilized by one sperm while the other sperm fuses with the two polar bodies. The zygote develops into an embryo. The triploid nucleus formed by the sperm and polar nuclei grows rapidly to produce the endosperm.

Monocots and dicots: Monocots are flowering plants characterized by flower parts in threes, parallel veins in leaves, and scattered vascular bundles in the stems. Dicots have flower parts in fours or fives, reticular venation, and vascular tissue in cylinders in the stem.

CHAPTER OUTLINE

KEY TERMS

TOPIC EXERCISES

1. Below are listed cell types. On the line immediately following each cell type, briefly state the general function of the cell type. On the line below, list the subsets (variations as to type or as to cell types included.)

A. Meristems   a.

     b.

B. Parenchyma   a.

     b.

C. Collenchyma   a.

     b.

D. Sclerenchyma   a.

     b.

E. Xylem   a.

     b.

F. Phloem   a.

     b.

G. Epidermis   a.

     b.

2. Meristems are easily confused. Listed below are meristem types. Opposite each, list the derivatives of the meristem type.

    A. apical

    B. lateral

    C. marginal

    D. ground

3. Like meristems (from which they form,) cambia are also confusing. To straighten them out, complete the table below.

	(a) Source	(b) Function
A. Procambium		
B. Vascular Cambium		
C. Cork Cambium		

LEARNING CHECKLIST

1. How do plant and animal growth patterns differ?
2. List the names and functions of the three basic types in plants.
3. Differentiate between primary and secondary growth.
4. Explain primary growth in leaves and stems.
5. Relate vascular cambium and cork cambium to secondary growth.
6. What is wood? How is wood formed? What is the significance of annual growth rings?
7. Give examples of modifications of (a) stem, (b) root, and (c) leaf.
8. Explain the growth differences between root branches and shoot branches.

MINI EXAM

A. Circle the letter of the best answer for each question.

1. The role assumed by collenchyma in a plant is
    a. making up the innermost layer of cortex as the vascular cambium differentiates
    b. providing strength in the heartwood of softwoods
    c. as a major constituent of the phelloderm as the periderm differentiates
    d. as the primary component of the casparian strip in taproots
    e. strengthening plant structures in which secondary growth has not taken place

2. Tree branches grow from the
    a. radicle
    b. plumule
    c. hypocotyl
    d. epicotyl
    e. endosperm

3. Leaf blades develop from
   a. marginal meristem
   b. apical meristem
   c. lateral meristem
   d. radial meristem

4. All of the following are primary meristems except
   a. phelloderm
   b. protoderm
   c. ground meristem
   d. procambium

5. The small, leaf-like structure where the petiole joins the stem is the
   a. lentical
   b. leaflet
   c. tendril
   d. stipule

6. All of the following are part of the periderm except
   a. cork cambium
   b. phelloderm
   c. pericyle
   d. cork

7. The mesophyll consists of
   a. xylem and phloem
   b. parenchyma and spongy parenchyma
   c. collenchyma and palisade parenchyma
   d. spongy parenchyma and palisade parenchyma
   e. all of the above

8. Gases are exchanged through the periderm by way of
   a. stomata
   b. guard cells
   c. spiricles
   d. lenticels

9. Xylem elements include
   a. sieve tubes
   b. sieve cells
   c. trichomes
   d. tracheids
   e. companion cells

10. Leaves spirally arranged on a plant are said to be
    a. alternate
    b. spirate
    c. opposite
    d. whorled

11. The potato is an example of an underground modified stem called
    a. corm
    b. tuber
    c. stolon
    d. bulb
    e. rhizome

12. The meristem from which cork grows is _____ meristem.
    a. lateral
    b. apical
    c. marginal
    d. ground
    e. primary

13. When only primary growth has occurred, the inner portion of the ground tissue is called
    a. cortex
    b. pith
    c. sapwood
    d. cambium
    e. stele

14. Cambial cells that produce conduction elements are called
    a. protoderm initials
    b. ray initials
    c. fusiform initials
    d. phelloderm initials
    e. primary initials

15. The choicest hardwood is taken mostly from
    a. sapwood of slow growing northern deciduous dicots
    b. the center of the trunk of giant Sequoias
    c. the heartwood of deciduous monocots
    d. the petrified forest
    e. secondary xylem of dicots

16. The shoot apical meristem in plant embryo is located at the tip of the
    a. plumule
    b. hypocotyl
    c. epicotyl
    d. cotyledon

17. The innermost layer of the cortex in dicot roots is the
    a. endodermis
    b. casparian strip
    c. pericycle
    d. peridermis
    e. vascular cambium

18. Cork cells contain a large amount of a fatty substance called
    a. sudum
    b. lignin
    c. suberin
    d. phellogen
    e. pectin

19. Wood is accumulated
    a. secondary xylem
    b. primary xylem
    c. primary phloem
    d. secondary phloem
    e. none of the above

20. When a monocot taproot dies, it is replaced by
    a. rosettes
    b. adventitious roots
    c. adventitious shoots
    d. another taproot
    e. a rhizome

B. Provide the appropriate term to complete each statement.

1. Replacement roots from stem tissue are called _____.

2. The nucleated member of phloem is the _____.

3. _____ is responsible for primary growth.

4. _____ is a leaf modified for attachment.

5. A(n) _____ is an epidermal hair on a leaf.

6. Plants that bloom several times before death are called _____.

7. A major type of tissue in which vascular tissue is imbedded is _____.

8. Sclerenchyma cells that are not long fibers are _____.

9. Primary xylem is derived from _____.

10. Parenchyma masses that occur in leaves are called _____.

C. Briefly answer each of the following questions.

1. Describe each plant cell type, give its function and further growth potential.

2. Describe the structure of the typical leaf and tell how that structure relates to photosynthesis.

3. Differentiate among (a) stems of monocots and herbaceous dicots and (b) monocot and dicot roots.

CHAPTER ANSWERS

TOPIC EXERCISES

1. A. a. produce specialized tissues
      b. apical, lateral, marginal, ground
   B. a. photosynthesis
      b. spongy, palisade
   C. a. support
      b. fibers
   D. a. rigidity
      b. fibers, sclereids
   E. a. water conduction
      b. tracheids, vessel elements
   F. a. food conduction
      b. sieve cells, sieve-tube members, companion cells
   G. a. covering, moisture barrier
      b. guard cells, trichomes, root hairs

2. A. epidermis, primary vascular strands, ground meristem
   B. periderm
   C. leaves
   D. ground tissue

3. A. (a) apical meristem
      (b) forms primary vascular strands
   B. (a) lateral meristem
      (b) forms secondary xylem
   C. (a) lateral meristem
      (b) develops periderm

LEARNING CHECKLIST

1. Plants never become adults as animals do. Plants just keep growing and adding new parts or cells. (p. 702)

2. Vascular tissue, ground tissue and dermal tissue. Vascular tissue conducts water and nutrients. Ground tissue embeds vascular tissue. Dermal tissue provides a protective cover. (p. 703)

3. Primary growth forms the initial plant body and elongates it. Secondary growth thickens the plant body. (p. 703)

4. At the tip of a stem, the apical meristem differentiates leaf primordia at positions called nodes and, at the internodes between the nodes, differentiates stem. Ground tissue within the stem, first differentiates into inner pith and outer cortex. The pith differentiates primary xylem and phloem. (pp. 711-713)

5. In dicots, vascular cambium differentiates from the cortex and the primary vascular tissues, a cylinder of dividing cells whose products will specialize into xylem to the interior and phloem to the exterior as secondary growth progresses. Lateral meristem in the outer region of the stem forms the cork cambium which consists of cork to the outside and phelloderm to the inside. The cork forms bark on the outside while the phelloderm forms parenchyma on the inside. (pp. 713-715)

6. Wood is accumulated secondary xylem. As lateral growth occurs, only the xylem and its ground tissue survive. The expansion that results from the division of meristem and the growth of the new cells that occurs to the outside of the xylem but to the inside of the phloem and cork crushes the phloem and tissues beyond it. Changing rates of growth with seasonal variations cause density differences in the xylem which manifests themselves as growth rings. (pp. 715-717)

7. (a) Stem modifications include rhizomes, stolons, tubers, corms and bulbs
   (b) Root modifications include taproots and adventitious roots
   (c) Leaf modifications include tendrils, succulence and bulbs. (pp. 717-718)

8. Stem branching is superficial and occurs by means of buds in the axils of leaves. Root branching is initiated deep within the root tissues by division of pericycle cells. (p. 720)

MINI EXAM

A.

1. e	2. d	3. a	4. a	5. d	6. c
7. d	8. d	9. d	10. a	11. b	12. a
13. b	14. c	15. e	16. c	17. a	18. c
19. a	20. b				

B.

1. adventitious	2. companion cell	3. Apical meristem
4. Tendril	5. trichome	6. polycarpic
7. ground tissue	8. sclereids	9. procambium
10. mesophyll		

C. 1. Meristems and unspecialized cells that divide to form new growth, some cells of which will specialize. Parenchyma cells are thin walled cells that may contain chloroplasts or aid in water absorption of gas exchange. Collenchyma cells are thicker walled, usually elongated cells that give structural support and rigidity to the plant. Sclerenchyma cells may be elongated or irregular in shape. They are strengthening cells. Xylem cells are found in two basic forms, vessel elements and tracheids. In either case, they are elongated hollow, and perforated, lacking any protoplast when mature. Through the perforations they connect to each other and distribute water to other cell types. Phloem is made of sieve cells and sieve-tube members. Both have pores and protoplasts but neither have nuclei. The sieve elements are accompanied by specialized parenchyma cells called companion cells that have a nucleus and apparently carry on metabolic activities for the sieve elements. Phloem transports food materials. Epidermal cells are of varied form, providing both a waterproof covering and water absorbing area. Some of the hair-like cells are used for water absorption on roots while others form a wind break on leaves to reduce transpiration. Included are specialized epidermal cells called guard cells that regulate the passage of gas into and out of the leaf. (pp. 703-708)

2. Leaves are comprised of a flattened blade and slender stalk, the petiole. Between the upper and lower epidermis is the mesophyll which consists of parenchyma cells, the conductive tissue and supporting elements. The parenchyma contains chloroplasts and may be irregularly shaped spongy parenchyma or in a vertical columnar form called palisade parenchyma. The epidermises are transparent and allow sunlight to reach the chloroplasts while also conserving moisture with their waterproof covering. Stomata, openings regulated by guard cells, in the epidermis allow carbon dioxide and oxygen to pass through the epidermis while conserving water vapor. Vascular tissue brings water for photosynthesis and carries away the photosynthetic products. Served by all of these structures, the parenchyma cells carry out photosynthesis. The loose arrangement of the parenchyma facilitates air circulation within the mesophyll. (pp. 708-711)

3. Monocot stems have scattered vascular bundles. Herbaceous dicot stems have vascular bundles in a ring surrounding the pith. Monocot roots have scattered vascular bundles much like the arrangement in monocot stems. Dicot roots have central columns of xylem with radiating arms and strands of primary phloem between the arms. These tissues are surrounded by a layer or two of thick celled pericyle. These tissues are surrounded by the cortex whose inner layers are called endodermis. The cortex is surrounded by the epidermis. (pp. 712-715, 718-720)

36: NUTRITION AND TRANSPORT IN PLANTS

IN THE GRAND SCHEME

Plants are committed to a location. They place their roots in the soil and their branches in the air and live or die, thrive or subsist according to what they can do with what they get. The soil is the source of all of their supplies except sunshine and air. The available water is a function of soil type as well as the weather. The soil, friendly provider, can also be an antagonist, clinging grudgingly to moisture needed by the plant. Soil types differ in their ability to retain water against gravity and to release it to plants. Mineral content of soils also varies. Plants require some minerals in fairly large amounts and some in small amounts. The presence of those needed in only trace amounts is just as critical as that which is needed in large amounts.

Once the water and minerals are acquired, the logistical problems are far from over. The mechanism for movement of materials from roots to the uppermost shoots baffled scientists for ages. What forces would transport materials higher than a pump will pump water from a well? It was no less difficult to explain the movement of sugar from the site of photosynthesis to the site of need or storage. These mysteries are explained in this chapter. Also worthy of contemplation, is the issue of the future of soil. When a bag of wheat is empty it is obvious. A soil emptied of nutrients does not disappear. The level of soil in a garden or lawn is no indicator of nutrient levels. Crops, removed from soils, take nutrients with them. Nutrients removed must be replaced or they will be depleted. Wood and wood products are spoken of as a renewable resource. It is true that more trees may be grown. Someday, however, the meager mountain soil will be depleted and must be replaced. There is an ecological axiom, "there is no free lunch."

FOR REVIEW

Adhesion, cohesion, and capillary movement: When one substance clings (adheres) to another substance, this is called adhesion. When a substance clings to more of the same substance, this is called cohesion. Water adheres to surfaces and coheres to itself. In small diameter spaces, the adhesion to the surface pulls on the water. Because of the strong cohesive forces in water, the water responds to the pull as a unit instead of breaking away and sinking. This process by which water rises up small-diameter columns is called capillary action.

Osmosis: The diffusion of water down its own concentration gradient (from low-solute concentration to high-solute concentration gradient) through a differentially permeable membrane is called osmosis.

Transport of ions across membranes: Passages through the cell membrane are bound by proteins that recognize various substances and bind with them to allow passage to the inside. If a substance is to be transported up its concentration gradient instead of down, energy must be supplied at the expense of ATP.

Biogeochemical cycles: All substances utilized by organisms are drawn from its environment. Eventually, the substances are returned to the environment through an organism's metabolic processes, including metabolism and decay. This cycling of substances between organisms and environment makes up biogeochemical cycles.

Xylem and phloem: Xylem conducts water throughout vascular plants. Xylem elements include tracheids and vessel elements. Phloem conducts food throughout the vascular plant. Phloem is composed of sieve cells or sieve-tube elements and carry out the metabolic activity for the sieve tube elements.

Endodermis: The endodermis is the innermost layer of the cortex. It regulates the passage of minerals and nutrients to and from vascular tissue.

Stomata: Stomata are openings in the epidermis through which gases pass. The opening is regulated by a pair of cells called guard cells.

CHAPTER OUTLINE

THE SOIL (pp. 727-729)
        permanent wilting point
WATER MOVEMENT THROUGH PLANTS (pp. 729-735)
   Transpiration
   The Absorption of Water by Roots
   Water Movement in Plants
   The Regulation of Transpiration Rate
   Other Factors Regulation Transpiration
NUTRIENT MOVEMENTS (pp. 735-736)
CARBOHYDRATE MOVEMENT (pp. 736-737)
        loading and unloading
PLANT NUTRIENTS (pp. 737-740)
   The Roles of Plant Nutrients
   Fertilizer
HOW DO PLANTS GROW? (p. 741)

KEY TERMS

p. 728: topsoil, humus
p. 729: capillary water, field capacity, cavitate
p. 730: pressure potential, solute potential, water potential
p. 731: aerenchyma
p. 732: transpiration
p. 733: root pressure, guttation
p. 736: mass flow, source, sink
p. 737: macronutrients, micronutrients

TOPIC EXERCISES

1. In the table below, indicate whether the water moving force will increase (I), decrease (D), be unaffected (U), be virtually absent (A), or strong (S) as a result of the indicate condition.

	a. dawn	b. noon	c. dusk	d. night
A. Transpiration				
B. Root pressure				

2. List five strategies by which plants prevent water loss.

   A.

   B.

   C.

   D.

   E.

LEARNING CHECKLIST

1. What three forces work together to produce upward movement of water?
2. How do vascular plants combat effects of cavitation?
3. How is transpiration important in upward transportation of water?
4. How and where do vascular plants absorb minerals from the soil?
5. Relate atmospheric humidity to transpiration and water conduction in vascular plants.
6. What is guttation and how does it happen?
7. Evaluate the merits of commercial versus natural fertilizer.

MINI EXAM

A. Circle the letter of the best answer to each question.

1. Macronutrients approach or exceed _____ percent of the plant's dry weight.
   a. 10   d. 5
   b. 3   e. 1
   c. 0.1

2. Nitrogen is required for plants for all of the following except
   a. amino acids   d. coenzmes
   b. nucleotides   e. ATP reproduction
   c. chlorophyll

3. Potential resulting from evaporation is called
   a. pressure potential   d. atmospheric potential
   b. water potential   e. vapor pressure
   c. solute potential

4. The transport of which ion is mainly responsible for guard cell turgor?
   a. Cl   d. P
   b. Na   e. K
   c. Ca

5. The most common form of carbohydrate transported in plants is
   a. sucrose   d. maltose
   b. glucose   e. dextrose
   c. fructose

6. Which of the following is a macronutrient?
   a. calcium   d. zinc
   b. chlorine   e. iron
   c. boron

7. Which of the following is a micronutrient?
   a. phosphorous   c. magnesium
   b. manganese   d. potassium

8. All of the following are a component of water potential except
   a. pressure potential   c. electrical potential
   b. solute potential   d. none of these

9. Magnesium is important in forming
   a. nucleic acids   c. ATP
   b. chlorophyll   d. amino acids

10. Mass flow of material transported in phloem results from
    a. cytoplasmic streaming in the protoplast of adjacent sieve elements
    b. capillary action aided by pressure reduction through transpiration
    c. osmosis resulting from solute pressure changes at the sink and source
    d. volume changes causes by loading and unloading
    e. energy driven and enzyme regulated active transport

11. All of the following effect stomatal opening except
    a. transpiration   c. temperature
    b. CO_2 d. light

12. Water is most tightly held by
    a. silt   d. clay
    b. humus   e. loam
    c. sand

13. _____ plays a primary role in allowing K^+ ions to pass rapidly out of guard cells.
    a. tungstic acid   d. abscisic acid
    b. carbonic acid   e. lactic acid
    c. tannic acid

14. Water rises above 10.4 meters (at sea level) as a result of
    a. capillary action   c. osmosis in roots
    b. evaporation from leaves   d. atmospheric pressure

15. Transpiration is most active at
    a. night   c. noon
    b. dawn   d. dusk

16. The water loss through stomata is about _____ percent of the water entering the plant.
    a. 50   d. 90
    b. 10   e. 75
    c. 25

17. Plants require cobalt for
    a. growth of nitrogen fixing bacteria   d. chlorophyll
    b. cell wall synthesis   e. ionic balance of osmosis
    c. enzyme activation

18. Root pressure is caused by
    a. osmosis
    b. weight of soil
    c. height of stem and leaves
    d. hydrostatic pressure
    e. deposits in the xylem vessels

19. About _____ of the total soil volume is empty space.
    a. 50%   d. 75%
    b. 10%   e. 5%
    c. 20%

20. Root pressure is active primarily at
    a. dusk   c. noon
    b. night   d. dawn

B. Provide the appropriate term to complete each statement.

1. The dripping of water from cuts in stems is called _____.

2. The rock components that are broken into soils are _____.

3. The attractive force of solute concentration within a cell is the _____.

4. The point of unloading sucrose is called a(n) _____.

5. Evaporation of water through stomata is called _____.

6. Movement of water or nutrients from place to place in a plant is _____.

7. Decayed or decaying leaves in soil are called _____.

8. Deformation or freezing may cause _____ locally in individual conducting cells of xylem.

9. Movement of water into and up xylem columns as a result of osmosis is called _____.

10. _____ photosynthesis conserves water in dry environments where succulent plants grow.

C. Briefly answer each of the following questions.

1. How do soils differ in particle size and ability to hold water?

2. How are photosynthetic products moved through vascular plants? Relate terms loading, unloading, source and sink to movement of nutrients.

3. Identify (a) macronutrients, and (b) micronutrients, and relate their amount to physiological need.

CHAPTER ANSWERS

TOPIC EXERCISES

1. A. a. I   b. S   c. D   d. A
   B. a. U   b. U   c. U   d. U

2. A. loss of leaves
    B. annual cycles
    C. reduction of stomata number
    D. abundant trichomes
    E. stomata in pits

LEARNING CHECKLIST

1. Pressure potential, solute potential and transpiration. (pp. 730-732)

2. Interconnected vessel elements provide a path around blockages caused by cavitation. (p. 729)

3. Transpiration is the prime mover of water in vascular plants because it maintains a negative pressure at the top of the water columns. (p. 732)

4. Minerals are absorbed by an energy driven transport system in the roots. (p. 737)

5. High humidity has adverse effect on transpiration and may halt it entirely if humidity reaches 100%. (p. 732)

6. Guttation is the oozing of water through special cells at the edge or end of leaves on small herbaceous plants as a result of strong root pressure. (p. 733)

7. There is no reason to believe that organic fertilizers offer any mineral nutrients that commercial fertilizers do not. However, organic fertilizers add humus to soil that may help meter the release of nutrients over a longer period (p. 741)

MINI EXAM

A.
1. e	2. b	3. a	4. e	5. a	6. a
7. b	8. c	9. b	10. c	11. a	12. d
13. d	14. b	15. c	16. d	17. a	18. a
19. a	20. b				

B.
1. guttation	2. minerals	3. solute potential
4. sink	5. transpiration	6. translocation
7. humus	8. cavitation	9. root pressure
10. CAM		

C. 1. Soil particle sizes range from 200 to 2000 micrometers in sand to less than 2 micrometers in clay. Clay holds the most water because of its smaller particle size and its tendency to form hydrogen bonds with water. (p. 728)

2. Nutrients move through vascular plants by mass movement. The site of manufacture of sucrose is called the source at which the sucrose is loaded. The sucrose is then transported through sieve elements to the utilization point called a sink. The movement is because of reduced solute potential in the area of unloading. (pp. 735-736)

3. (a) carbon, oxygen, hydrogen, nitrogen, potassium, calcium, magnesium, phosphorous, sulfur; (b) chlorine, iron, manganese, zinc, boron, copper, and molybdenum. Macronutrients must approach or exceed 1% of the plant's dry weight. Micronutrients are required in only trace amounts. (pp. 737-738)

37: PLANT DEVELOPMENT

IN THE GRAND SCHEME

Dormancy is one of the seed's greatest advantages, but if the seed is to produce a plant, the dormancy must end. Into each seed is built a wake up signal to be triggered by the environment. The environmental stimulus for seed germination is also an environmental condition desirable for growth of the plant. As seeds are dispersed, they may pass through many environments that do not favor growth. Even upon arriving at a suitable environment, the time may be wrong. A mistake in time or place of germination can be fatal. Built into each seed is also a protocol for germination, differentiation and growth. The task of dispersing a seed to grow is much like launching a totally automated space probe to function on a distant planet, without communication with home base. In this view, the seed is a marvel of microtechnology.

Though not unappreciative of the merits of seeds, scientists have sought ways of growing plants without seeds. Rooted cuttings have been used for a long time to produce new plants that would be difficult to duplicate for genetic reasons. Now new plants can be grown from tiny specks of tissue or single cells. Expression of recessive genes can be achieved by pollen culture.

FOR REVIEW

Eukaryotic cell structure: In basic structure, the eukaryotic cell membrane is quite similar to that of prokaryotes. Whereas prokaryotes performed respiratory functions by the use of enzymes incorporated in their membranes, eukaryotes acquired their respiratory structures, the mitochondria, through symbiosis with prokaryotes as they did their photosynthetic structures, the chloroplasts. Eukaryotes have a unique system of membranes by which the cytoplasm is organized. The eukaryotic cell wall, if any, is cellulose.

Mechanisms of gene action: Genes contain nucleotide sequences that code for amino acid sequences in proteins. The information encoded in genes is expressed in two stages: transcription, in which a polymerase enzyme assembles an mRNA molecule whose nucleotide sequence is complementary to that of the gene; and translation, in which a ribosome assembles a protein, using the mRNA to specify the amino acids.

Reproduction in plants: Non-vascular plants reproduce asexually and sexually. When reproducing sexually they use swimming sperm, produced in an antheridium, which fertilize an egg in an archegonium. Seed plants produce microgametophytes in a microsporangium in a cone or flower. The microsporophyte is carried by wind or animals to a sporophyte bearing an ovule in which the egg is contained. The sperm are carried from the microgametophyte to the vicinity of the egg by the growth of a pollen tube from the microgametophyte. The zygote develops into an embryo as the ovule becomes transformed into a seed.

Plant structure: Other than flowers, flowering plants are made up of roots, stems, and leaves. Roots have central vascular tissue of water-conducting xylem and nutrient-conduction phloem. The central vascular tissue is surrounded by a cortex, made primarily of a thin-walled cell called parenchyma. An epidermis surrounds the root. Stems have a central region of parenchyma with vascular tissue scattered through the parenchyma region or surrounding it in a cylinder. The plant stem is surrounded by epidermis and, in some plants, by bark. Leaves are supported by a petiole that continues into the blade of the leaf as a vein. The blade of the leaf is covered by an epidermis that is generally waterproofed by cuticle but ventilated by holes called stomata, which are regulated by pairs of modified epidermal cells called guard cells. The blade of the leaf is filled with mesophyll, which contains chloroplasts. A columnar form of parenchyma called palisade parenchyma, and loosely arranged, irregularly shaped parenchyma called spongy parenchyma make up the mesophyll. Growth of all tissues is controlled by apical, lateral, or marginal meristem, which divides constantly to provide for growth of structure.

CHAPTER OUTLINE

CONTINUOUS DEVELOPMENT: A CHARACTERISTIC OF PLANTS (pp. 745-746)
DIFFERENTIATION IN PLANTS: EXPERIMENTAL EVIDENCE (pp. 746-750)
    Cell Culture
    Tissue Culture
        embryoid
    Embryo Culture
    Pollen Culture
FACTORS IN THE GROWTH MEDIUM (pp. 750-751)
    Experimental Studies
    Regeneration in Nature
PLANT EMBRYONIC DEVELOPMENT (pp. 751-753)
GERMINATION IN PLANTS (pp. 753-755)
    The Role of Seed Dormancy
    Germination
    Mobilization of Reserves
THE ROLE OF THE APICAL MERISTEMS (pp. 755-757)
    The Autonomy of Apical Meristem
    Leaf Primordia: Irreversibly Determined?
THE VASCULAR CAMBIUM: A DIFFERENTIATED MERISTEM (pp. 757-758)

KEY TERMS

p. 745: homeostasis, adult
p. 746: totipotent
p. 747: callus
p. 749: micropropigation
p. 752: basal cell, micropyle, suspensor
p. 754: stratified, seed pool, amyloplasts
p. 755: scutellum, aleurone layer, gibberellins, auxin
p. 756: cytokinins, indoleacetic acid (IAA), aspical dominance, ethylene

TOPIC EXERCISES

1. In the space below, briefly state the advantages of seed production.

    A.

    B.

    C.

2. Briefly state the roles in plant development of the plant substances listed below.

    A. Auxin

    B. Gibberellin

    C. Ethylene

LEARNING CHECKLIST

1. How do plant and animal development differ?
2. What experimental evidence indicates that plant cells are totipotent?
3. To what degrees do various plant tissues regenerate parts?
4. How is energy provided for seed germination in the absence of photosynthesis?
5. What effect does indoleacetic acid have on meristematic growth?
6. Compare leaf primordia and vascular cambium to apical meristem.

MINI EXAM

A. Circle the letter of the best answer to each question.

1. The first nutrients used in cereal grain germination come from
    a. the aleurone layer
    b. cytokinins
    c. indoleacetic acid
    d. amyloplasts
    e. the scutellum

2. The major cause of embryo dormancy in seeds is lack of
    a. hormones
    b. water
    c. food
    d. enzymes

3. Lateral bud development is inhibited by all of the following except
    a. ethylene
    b. indoleacetic acid
    c. cytokinins
    d. gibberellin

4. All plant cells can produce the entire plant because they are
    a. omminpotent
    b. haploid
    c. totalitarian
    d. totipotent
    e. diploid

5   From which plant cells can a plant be cultured in which all genes are expressed?
    a. pollen
    b. petal cells
    c. root cap cells
    d. suspensor
    e. phloem

6. Aleurone hydrolase production is mediated by
    a. auxin
    b. cytokinins
    c. amyloblasts
    d. gibberellins
    e. ethylene

7. Pollen culture was developed in the
    a. 1930s
    b. 1980s
    c. mid 1940s
    d. 1960s

8. Plants may be developed from flowers of
    a. Pseudotsuga
    b. Populus
    c. Agave
    d. Pelargonium

9. A plant cultured from a pollen grain is
   a. a haploid sporophyte
   b. a diploid sporophyte
   c. a haploid gametophyte
   d. useless
   e. diploid gametophyte

10. Seed germination begins with the uptake of
   a. oxygen   c. carbon dioxide
   b. water   d. heat

11. Many plant cells proved impossible to culture until _____ was added to the culture medium.
   a. gibberellin   c. indoleacetic acid
   b. liquid endosperm   d. amyloplasts

12. The mass of dividing, undifferentiated cells formed in cell culture of plants is called
   a. callus   c. embryo
   b. kernel   d. embryoid

13. In angiosperm development, the basal cell divides several times and becomes the
   a. micropyle   c. antipodals
   b. endosperm   d. suspensor

14. In terms of development, a plant can never really be considered a(n)
   a. embryo   c. adult
   b. organism   d. zygote

15. Which is usually the most easily formed from plant cuttings?
   a. adventitious leaves   c. adventitious stems
   b. adventitious roots   d. none of the above

16. _____ is the process by which seeds are induced to germinate by subjecting them to a period of cold.
   a. stratification   c. solstization
   b. vernalization   d. scarification

17. When differentiated, vascular cambium becomes _____ permanently
   a. xylem   c. phloem
   b. parenchyma   d. meristem

18. In cereal grains, the cotyledon is modified into the
   a. scutellum   d. micropyle
   b. suspensor   e. synergid
   c. primordium

19. All of the following are produced from apical meristem except
   a. leaves   c. roots
   b. stems   d. shoots

20. In addition to auxins, normal development of roots requires
   a. indoleacetic acid   c. gibberellin
   b. cytokinins   d. ethylene

B. Provide the appropriate term to complete each statement.

1. _____ stimulate the release of aleurone hydrolases.

2. _____ is a naturally occurring auxin.

3. _____ are regulators of plant growth.

4. The first cell produced in the formation of angiosperm embryos is the _____.

5. _____ are starch-storing modified chloroplasts.

6. Seeds that have been exposed to a period of cold simulating winter are said to be _____.

7. The essence of animal development is internal _____, or stability.

8. The term, _____, means that each cell contains the full genetic potential of the organism.

9. Production of large numbers of genetically similar individuals in a short time is accomplished commercially by _____.

10. Plant development differs from animal development in that plant cells don't _____ but animal cells do.

C. Briefly answer each of the following questions.

1. Briefly explain the three procedures for plant cell culture and the significance of each.

2. Compare early embryo development in gymnosperms and angiosperms.

3. Discuss the role and mechanisms of seed dormancy. List several factors that initiate germination of dormant seeds.

CHAPTER ANSWERS

TOPIC EXERCISES

1. A. Dormancy postpones germination for favorable conditions.
    B. Conditions good for seed germination are good for plant growth.
    C. Many seeds aid in plant's dispersal.

2. A. Suppresses lateral growth of branches and promotes cell elongation.
    B. Controls the synthesis and secretion of aleurone hydrolysase.
    C. An example of an auxin (see above.)
    D. Prevents lateral bud development.

LEARNING CHECKLIST

1. Animals grow to adulthood and attempt to maintain homeostasis. Plants grow continually. (pp. 745-746)

2. In the 1950's and 1960's, techniques were developed by which entire plants could be cultured from single cells. (pp. 746-747)

3. Plants develop adventitious roots readily but develop adventitious shoots reluctantly. (p. 751)

4. Energy for seed germination comes from stored reserves of starch filled amyloplasts or of fats and oils. (pp. 754-755)

5. Indoleacetic acid produced by apical meristem inhibits growth of other meristems. (pp. 755-756)

6. Apical meristem continues to proliferate indefinitely. Leaf primordia and vascular cambiums are permanently differentiated. (pp. 756-758)

MINI EXAM

A.
1. e	2. b	3. d	4. d	5. a	6. d
7. d	8. c	9. a	10. b	11. b	12. a
13. d	14. c	15. b	16. a	17. d	18. a
19. c	20. b				

B.
1. Gibberellins	2. Indoleacetic acid	3. Hormones
4. basal cell	5. Amyloplasts	6. stratified
7. homeostasis	8. totipotent	9. micropropagation
10. move		

C. 1. (a) Cell culture. Single cells are placed on filter paper floating either on a defined medium or on one enriched with natural material such as coconut milk. The cell multiplies into a "callus" and then on into an embryo and finally into a new plant.
(b) Tissue culture. Phloem tissue is extracted and grown in a liquid medium. "Embryoids" formed were transferred to a nutrient agar where they developed roots and shoots. (c) Pollen culture, in a manner similar to those just discussed, pollen grains are cultured and grown into haploid plants. The first two methods provide means of growing monoclonial crops. Pollen culture holds a promise for breeding experiments. (pp. 746-750)

2. Although different in timing of cell wall formation and differentiation, both angiosperms and gymnosperms develop in essentially the same way. Cell migration that is typical of animal embryology is absent. The position in which a cell is formed with respect to other cells determines its future role. (pp. 752-753)

3. Seed dormancy is the result of an air and water tight seed coat and will continue as long as those conditions are maintained. The conditions that cause germination are those good for growth. Even then some seeds require special environmental changes to occur. Some require "stratification" which is a period of sufficient cold. Some require exposure to certain light wavelengths. Seed germination begins with water absorption. Some seeds will grow only if released from a burned plant. (pp. 753-755)

38: REGULATION OF PLANT GROWTH

IN THE GRAND SCHEME

Just as human growth and reproduction is hormone regulated, plant growth, flowering, fruiting, and leaving are hormone regulated. Also, as human hormones interact, so do plant hormones. As growers gain knowledge of plant hormone actions, they are able to regulate many plant processes to their own benefit. Fruit ripening may be retarded for shipment and accelerated for marketing. Fruit, flowers and leaves may be held on the plant or dropped prematurely. As we learn more of the language of plant behavior, we become more able to direct it.

FOR REVIEW

Turgor Pressure: Most plants are hypertonic with respect to their environment. The resulting osmotic pressure that presses the cell membrane against the rigid cell wall is referred to as turgor pressure.

Flowering plant life cycle: Flowers produce pollen in an anther and an egg in an ovule. The pollen is shed, is carried by wind or animal, and pollinates a flower on the stigma. The pollen extends its pollen tube down through the style into the ovary of the carpel, carrying the two sperm with it. The embryo sac, developed within the ovule, contains eight nuclei, including one egg and two polar nuclei. The egg is fertilized by one sperm while the other sperm fuses with the two polar bodies. The zygote develops into an embryo. The triploid nucleus formed by the sperm and polar nuclei grows rapidly to produce the endosperm. There is no firm rule for judging trees versus shrubs. Trees and shrubs are either deciduous or evergreen. Deciduous plants shed their leaves each fall. Evergreens do not become bare as a result of shedding thier needles. It is evident, though, to anyone who has walked through the needle-strewn floor of a pine forest that evergreens do shed leaves. Plants that flower once and die are called noncarpic. Those that bloom repeatedly are polycarpic.

Apical meristems: Apical meristem forms three kinds of primary meristem. The three primary meristems and their maturation products are protoderm, which produces epidermis; procambium, which produces primary vascular tissue; and ground meristem, which produces ground tissue.

Seed germination: The first prerequisite of seed germination is water penetration of the seed coat. Other environmental conditions must also be met, such as temperature, light type, light period, and history, i.e. such as having experienced cold.

Auxin and plant growth: Auxin stimulates shoot and root elongation, both uniform and differential, while inhibiting lateral bud growth.

Cytokinins and differentiation: Although auxin is sufficient to promote differentiation of stems and leaves, a plant must also have cytokinins to fully differentiate into a complete plant.

CHAPTER OUTLINE

KEY TERMS

p. 762: phototropism
p. 736: auxin
p. 764: indolacetic acid (IAA), indolacetic acid oxidase
p. 765: abscission, separation layer, senescent, dioxin, cytokinins
p. 766: gibberellins, ethylene
p. 767: climacteric, abscisic acid
p. 768: tropisms
p. 769: phototropism, gravitropism, thigmotropism
p. 770: pulvinus, motor cells
p. 771: photoperiodism, short-day plants, long-day plants
p. 772: day neutral
p. 773: phytochrome
p. 774: etiolated

TOPIC EXERCISES

1. For each hormone listed below, provide a commercial use.

    A. Auxin

    B. Gibberellin

    C. Ethylene

2. For the following plant movements state the mechanism.

   A. Prayer plant leaf movement

   B. Venus flytrap closing

   C. Sensitive plant (<u>Mimosa</u>) leaf folding

3. Classify the following plants as to length of day required for flowering. Indicate by placing the words; long, short, or neutral in the blank

   A. Rose

   B. Iris

   C. Tomato

   D. Chrysanthemum

   E. Clover

   F. Ragweed

   G. Snapdragon

LEARNING CHECKLIST

1. What is the only naturally occurring auxin?
2. What are the physiological effects on monocots of auxin, 2, 4 D, and 2,4,5-T?
3. Explain hormonal interactions associated with abscission.
4. Why is it difficult to isolate the action of a single plant hormone?
5. How does phototropism affect the growth of different plant parts?
6. What are short-day plants and long-day plants?
7. How do various wavelengths of light affect photoperiodism?

MINI EXAM

A. Circle the letter of the best answer to each question.

1. The plant hormone that promotes early setting of growth of fruits is
   a. auxin
   b. abscisic acid
   c. ethylene
   d. cytochrome
   e. gibberellin

2. The hormone that retards flowering is
   a. P_r
   b. 2,4-D
   c. P_{fr}
   d. 2,4,5-T
   e. indoleacetic acid

3. Lateral bud growth is inhibited by
   a. phytochrome
   b. gibberellin
   c. cytokinin
   d. ethylene

4. Gravitropism results from the action of gravity upon:
   a. auxin
   b. ameleron layer
   c. cytochrome
   d. phytochrome
   e. abscisic acid

5. Seeds adapted to a temperate climate may not germinate under ideal circumstances until they have been
   a. stratified
   b. etiolated
   c. senescented
   d. chronified
   e. climacterized

6. Far-red light inhibits flowering in
   a. long-day flowers
   b. short-day plants
   c. dark-day flowers
   d. day-neutral flowers
   e. none of the above

7. Which of the following is a short-day plant in flowering habit?
   a. hollyhock
   b. rose
   c. clover
   d. iris
   e. golden rod

8. Flowering is inhibited by which of the following lightings?
   a. prolonged 730 nm
   b. a flash of 730 nm
   c. prolonged 770 nm
   d. a flash of 660 nm
   e. a flash of 770 nm

9. "Foolish seedlings" of rice were caused by a form of
   a. auxins
   b. cytochromes
   c. gibberellins
   d. phytochromes

10. Bananas were prematurely ripened when shipped with oranges as a result of
    a. ethylene
    b. carbon dioxide
    c. abscisic acid
    d. cytochrome
    e. citric acid

11. All are plant actions to survive periods of cold except
    a. leaf loss
    b. estivation
    c. seed formation
    d. dormancy

12. Auxins tend to
    a. stimulate cell elongation
    b. stimulate lateral bud growth
    c. inhibit cell elongation
    d. inhibit mRNA transcription
    e. inhibits fruit development

13. Which of the following is a day-neutral plant in flowering habit?
    a. rose
    b. hollyhock
    c. clover
    d. goldenrod

14. In earlier times, _____ leaking from street lamps caused leaves of nearby trees to fall.
    a. carbon dioxide
    b. methane
    c. xylene
    d. ethylene
    e. kerosine

15. Which of the following phytochromes suppresses flowering?
    a. P_{rr}
    b. P_{fr}
    c. P_r
    d. P_{rf}
    e. P_{ff}

16. Phytochromes are thought to have been evolved by:
    a. green algae
    b. cyanobacteria
    c. red algae
    d. diatoms
    e. brown algae

17. If the operator of a fruit market wished to hasten the ripening of poorly ripened tomatoes, he should
    a. place them near bananas
    b. keep them away from bananas
    c. keep them away from oranges
    d. store them overnight on a compost pile where carbon dioxide will be liberated
    e. place them near oranges

18. In lighted plants, auxins migrate from
    a. dark side to light side
    b. light side to dark side
    c. top to bottom only
    d. bottom to top only

19. Which wavelength of red light converts P_r to P_{fr}?
    a. 730 nm
    b. 560 nm
    c. 660 nm
    d. 840 nm
    e. 770 nm

20. Which of the following is a long-day plant in flowering habit?
    a. soybean
    b. rose
    c. clover
    d. goldenrod
    e. chrysanthemum

B. Provide the appropriate term to complete each statement.

1. A plant unaffected by day length is called _____.

2. _____ was first studied as the cause of "silly seedling disease."

3. The first plant hormone to be identified was _____.

4. _____ grow to close the Venus flytrap.

5. _____ are essential to differentiation of plant cells.

6. The formation of the _____ causes the dropping of fruits.

7. _____ appears to be the only naturally occurring auxin.

309

8. The phase in a plant's life in which it produces large amounts of ethylene is called the
   _____.

9. The hormone _____ promotes leaf senescence.

10. _____ is the current, more correct term for geotropism.

CHAPTER ANSWERS

TOPIC EXERCISES

1. A. Prevents fruit drop, promotes pineapple flowering, rooting of shoots
   B. Increases fruit size, set and ripening
   C. Speeds ripening of citrus fruits

2. A. Pulvini and motor cells
   B. irreversible cell enlargement
   C. Pulvini and rapid loss of K^+ by motor cells

LEARNING CHECKLIST

1. Indoleacetic acid (p. 764)

2. Accelerates growth to a lethal level. (p. 765)

3. Auxin inhibits abscission. Ethylene counteracts auxin and promotes abscission. (pp. 766-768)

4. Plant hormones are produced in small quantities and are so integrated in their action that it is difficult to separate their effects. (p. 768)

5. Phototropism causes stems to bend toward the light and roots to bend away from the light. (p. 769)

6. Short-day plants flower as day length becomes less and long-day plants flower as day length becomes greater. (pp. 771-772)

7. See Figure 38-13 on page 773 of your text (pp.772-774)

MINI EXAM

A.
1. e	2. c	3. d	4. a	5. a	6. b
7. e	8. d	9. c	10. a	11. b	12. a
13. a	14. d	15. b	16. a	17. e	18. b
19. c	20. c				

B. 1. day-neutral   2. Gibberellin   3. auxin
    4. Motor cells   5. Cytokinins   6. abscission layer
    7. Indoleacetic acid   8. climacteric   9. abscisic acid
    10. Gravitropism

C. 1. See table 38-1 on page 761 of your text for names and effects. Commercial applications are as follows. Auxin: Prevention of fall of leaves, flowers or fruits. Synthetic auxins are used in weed control. Cytokinins: Promote lateral branches, reduce yellowing of detached leaves. B=Gibberellins: Increase fruit size and set and cluster size in grapes. Delay citrus ripening and speed strawberry flowering. Speeds partial digestion of starch in germinating barley for brewing. Ethylene: Speeds ripening of citrus fruits an tomatoes. Hastens fruit and leaf drop. Induce flowering in pineapples and ornamental bromeliads. Abscisic acid: Little commercial use yet. (pp. 761-768)

   2. Gravitropism causes stems to grow away from gravitational pull and roots to grow toward it. The consequences are stems receiving more sunlight and roots finding more water. (p. 769)

   3. Many plant movements involve a pulvinus. A pulvinus is a multicellular structure in which differential inhibition of water causes bending of joints as a result of changes in turgor pressure. Especially rapid pulvinus action results from rapid transfer of K^+ resulting in rapid water movements. The Venus flytrap movement results from rapid H^+ transfer. Sun tracking movements and some flower openings and closings are a result of pulvinus-like activity. (pp. 770-771)

39: THE PRIMITIVE INVERTEBRATES

IN THE GRAND SCHEME

The most primitive animals, the sponges, have a distinct organization and body form, but lack tissues. So loosely is the body organized, that it can be filtered through a fine cloth and reassemble on the other side. From such a loosely organized ancestor, evolved an animal that had true tissues, a feature to be retained by all animals evolved thereafter. The cnidarians became predatory two-layered bags with two specialized tissues. The asymmetry of the sponges gave way to radial symmetry in the cnidarians. The cnidarians were also able to digest larger prey with their extracellular digestion. The digestive cavity had a double duty opening. Of the food taken in, that which could not be digested and absorbed, was ejected through the same opening it entered. This feature was retained by the next higher organism, the flatworms. Flatworms have their digestive cavity in a bilaterally symmetrical body. The flatworms added features such as cephalization, the possession of a head end that is the sensory center. Another innovation was a body cavity. The body cavity allowed for expansion of the digestive tube and provides hydrostatic skeletons. Both flatworms and round worms have parasitic members. The parasites have a reduced array of anatomical features, but are as highly evolved as the free-living relatives. The parasites are as well suited to their life style as are their free-living kin. This chapter introduces the principle of the coelomate body style, but it is in the next chapter that such organisms will be studied in detail.

FOR REVIEW

Evolutionary theory: The tendency of animals to overproduce results in a struggle for survival in the face of limited resources. Organisms with traits better suiting them to compete will have greater success in the struggle and will survive to reproduce, passing on their unique traits. Differential survival among the diverse organisms eventually results in the formation of new species.

Evolutionary history: The earth is about 4.6 billion years old. The oldest fossils of living things are about 3.5 billion years old. All life evolved in the sea until about 410 million years ago, when invasion of the land began. Throughout the history of living things, continental drift has had a profound influence. Continental movements have caused extinction through loss of habitat and have accelerated evolution by increasing competition through formation of land bridges and isolation through loss of land bridges. Throughout all continental migrations, adaptation to climatic change by the living "passengers" was often the key to survival.

Symbiosis: The living together of two dissimilar organisms. Once, the term was used for a mutually beneficial relationship. This connotation is no longer used. "Living together" and interacting is symbiosis.

Classification: Five kingdoms are recognized: Monera, Protista, Fungi, Plantae, and Animalia. Kingdoms are divided into phyla (divisions in plants,) which are subdivided into classes. Classes are divided into orders, and in turn, families, genera, and species.

Choanoflagellates: The choanoflagellates are believed to be ancestral to sponges and possibly, to the rest of the animal kingdom. Choanoflagellates have a single flagellum surrounded by a "picket fence" collar of filaments used to strain food particles from the sea.

CHAPTER OUTLINE

KEY TERMS

TOPIC EXERCISES

1. Numerous "firsts" are encountered in this chapter. For each "first" listed below, name the organism or group of organisms first to display the trait. ("First" may equal "most primitive" or, if that is not specified, then let it equal first mentioned in the text.)

   A. Animal *sponge*

   B. Tissue *cnidarians*

   C. Extracellular digestion *cnidarians*

   D. Anal opening *comb jelly*

   E. Bilateral symmetry *acolemates*

   F. Excretory system *flatworms*

   G. Circulatory system *ribbon worm*

2. Several of the organisms studied in this chapter have important effects on the well being of human beings. For each organism listed, state its effect on man.

   A. Sponges *cleaning*

   B. Jellyfish *painful stings & fatal*

   C. Corals *reefs*

   D. Trematodes *human parasites*

   E. Cestodes *" "*

3. As you study further in biology, the relationships and derivatives of the embryonic layers will have increasing importance. State the derivatives for each embryonic tissue.

   A. Ectoderm *nervous system outer covering*

   B. Endoderm *intestines & digestive organ*

   C. Mesoderm *mus & skeletal elements*

LEARNING CHECKLIST

1. Compare the organization of animals to plants, protists and fungi.
2. Compare Parazoa and Eumetazoa in terms of (a) evolution, (b) complexity, (c) symmetry and embryonic organization.
3. What are "lower" versus "higher" invertebrates?
4. Compare the cnidarian digestive system to that of sponges.

5. Characterize the platyhelminth body plan and compare their various organ systems to those of "lower" invertebrates.
6. Using the flatworm as a model, discuss changes in structure and physiology associated with adaptation to a parasitic life habit.
7. Describe the general organization of nematode bodies and compare their systems to those of acoelomate invertebrates.

MINI EXAM

A. Circle the letter of the best answer to each question.

1. The larval form that develops within the eggs of flukes is the
   a. cercaria
   b. miracidium
   c. filaria
   d. metacercaria
   e. rediae

   b

2. An example of a triploblastic, bilaterally symmetrical, acoelomate eumatazoan is the
   a. sponge
   b. planarian
   c. nematode
   d. ctenophore
   e. rotifer

   e

3. Nematocysts are contained in
   a. cnidocytes
   b. choanocytes
   c. nematocytes
   d. pyrocytes

   a

4. In triploblastic organisms, the muscles develop from
   a. myoderm
   b. ectoderm
   c. endoderm
   d. mesoderm

   d

5. The development of a pseudocoelom provides its owner with a(n)
   a. exoskeleton
   b. endoskeleton
   c. cytoskeleton
   d. hydrostatic skeleton

   d

6. All of the following are bilaterally symmetrical throughout their life except
   a. nematodes
   b. cestodes
   c. sponges
   d. rotifers
   e. planaria

   c

7. The simplest animals with blood in a circulatory system are
   a. nematodes
   b. flatworms
   c. cestodes
   d. rotifers
   e. ribbon worms

   e

8. The most primitive bilaterally symmetrical animals are the
   a. ctenophora
   b. coelomates
   c. pseudocoelomates
   d. acoelomates

   d

9. Serious infections result from ingesting pork containing cysts of the nematode
   a. Dugesia
   b. Trichinella
   c. Filaria
   d. Enterobius

   b

10. The _____ are the only animals with a body cavity bound by mesoderm.
    a. acoelomates
    b. speudocoelomates
    c. coelomates
    d. mesocoelomates

    c

11. The only eumetazoans whose tissues are not organized into organs are the
    a. Ctenophora
    b. Cnidaria
    c. Cestoda
    d. Rotifera

    b

12. The most primitive animals to exhibit extracellular digestion are the
    a. cnidarians
    b. mesozoans
    c. poriferans
    d. nematodes

    a

13. Many species of _____ reproduce by parthenogenesis.
    a. planari
    b. nematodes
    c. rotifers
    d. tapeworms

    c

14. Of the nearly 4 million species of animals living today, those without backbones make up about
    a. 1%
    b. 15%
    c. 43%
    d. 75%
    e. 99%

    d

15. All of the following produce nematocysts except
    a. hydroids
    b. nudibranchs
    c. corals
    d. jellyfish
    e. sea anemone

    b

16. _____ occurs only in human beings without intermediate hosts.
    a. Ascaris
    b. Taenia
    c. Schistosoma
    d. Clonorchis
    e. Rhynchocoela

    a

17. Which of the following have a gut with two openings?
    a. comb jellies
    b. hydroids
    c. medusae
    d. flatworms
    e. polyps

    a

18. Most _____ are hermaphroditic.
    a. comb jellies
    b. flatworms
    c. medusa
    d. hydroids

    b

19. The larvae of most flukes occur in
    a. fish
    b. slugs
    c. snails
    d. aquatic arthropods

    c

20. Most of the phyla of the animal kingdom live
    a. in the sea
    b. in fresh water
    c. on land
    d. as internal parasites

    a

B. Provide the appropriate term to complete each statement.

1. _____Choanocytes_____ circulate water through sponges with their flagella.

2. A tape worm attaches itself to the host by the segment called _____scolex_____.

317

3. Nematocysts are ejected from cells called ___cnidocyte___.

4. Animals having an ectoderm and endoderm but no mesoderm are said to be ___diploblastic___.

5. Calcium carbonate structures providing skeletal support for sponges are called ___spicules___.

6. The lower surface of a bilaterally symmetrical organism such as a flatworm is called the ___ventral___ surface.

7. ___Ctenophores___ are the largest animals to use cilia for locomotion.

8. Jellyfish are so named because of their possession of ___mesoglea___.

9. A major evolutionary development of cnidarians is the ___internal extracellular___ digestion of food.

10. Nematodes suck food by the action of a muscular chamber, the ___pharynx___.

C. Briefly answer the following questions.

1. Discuss the (a) organization, (b) reproduction, and (c) metabolism of sponges.

2. Contrast the cnidarian body plan with that of most other animals.

3. Characterize and relate (a) acoelomate, (b) pseudocoelomate, and (c) eucoelomate organisms.

CHAPTER ANSWERS

TOPIC EXERCISES

1. A. sponge   B. cnidarians   C. cnidarians   D. comb jellies
  E. acoleomates F. flatworms   G. ribbon worms

2. A. used for cleaning   B. painful to fatal stings
  C. reef formation   D. human parasites
  E. human parasites

3. A. nervous system and outer covering   B. intestine and digestive organs
  C. muscles and skeletal elements

LEARNING CHECKLIST

1. Animal cells lack cell walls that are typical of the other kingdoms. Except for sponges, animal cells are organized into tissues that are organized into organs. Plants have tissues but lack organs. Protists are unicellular or colonial. Fungi are filamentous. (pp. 781-782)

2. (a) It is believed that all animals, including Parazoa, are evolved from a choanoflagellate ancestor in the phylum Zoomastigina. See figure 39-2, p. 783
(b) Parazoa lack symmetry, tissues and organs. Eumatazoa are symmetrical and have tissues and organs. (pp. 782-783)

3. The "lower" invertebrates are the sponges, cnidarians, platyhelminths and nematodes. The "higher" invertebrates are the remaining invertebrate phyla. "Higher" and "lower" refer to the degree of complexity of tissue organization. (p.783)

4. Digestion in sponges is entirely intracellular. Cnidarians digest food extracellularly. Small particles resulting from the extracellular digestion are taken into cells of the gastrovascular cavity by endocytosis. The cnidarians can digest larger organisms than sponges can. (p. 786)

5. The platyhelminths are bilaterally symmetrical. They have a distinct head and tail end. They have tissues derived from three germ layers, endoderm, mesoderm, and ectoderm. They have a branched digestive system with only an oral opening. There is no body cavity. Because the digestive tube branches throughout the body, a circulatory system is not needed. The digestive tube is a gastrovascular cavity much like that found in cnidarians. The platyhelminthes do, however, have an excretory system for liquid wastes. The nervous system is simple but does terminate in cerebral ganglia that coordinate nervous actions more than possible with the nerve net of the cnidarians. (pp. 792-794)

6. Parasitic flatworms lack the cilia, eyespot and other sensory structures of the free-living flatworms. The parasitic forms are modified to cling to the digestive tract of the host and to resist its digestive enzymes. The emphasis in the parasitic body plan is on absorbing predigested food and reproduction. (pp. 794-797)

7. Unlike the acoelomate flatworms, the nematodes have one-way digestive system and a body cavity. The body cavity acts as a hydrostatic skeleton that aids in movement. (pp. 797-800)

MINI EXAM

A.
1. b	2. b	3. a	4. d	5. d	6. c
7. e	8. d	9. b	10. c	11. b	12. a
13. c	14. d	15. b	16. a	17. a	18. b
19. c	20. a				

B.
1. Choanocytes	2. scolex	3. cnidocyte
4. diploblastic	5. spicules	6. ventral
7. Ctenophores	8. mesoglea	9. interval extracellular
10. pharynx		

C. 1. For illustration, see Figure 39-4 on p. 784 of your text. (a) Sponges have an outer epithelial wall whose cells extend inward forming pores. The overall structure is supported by a skeleton of spicules among which amoebocyte cells move. The inner lining surrounds a central cavity and is composed of collared, flagellated choanocytes.
(b) Sponges reproduce asexually by fragmentation. Sponges reproduce sexually with heterogametes. The zygote develops into a larva with choanocytes facing outward. The larva settles down and turns inside out so that the choanocytes face inward.
(c) Food is trapped by the choanocytes as it passes through the collar. The food is either digested by the choanocyte or a neighboring amoebocyte and shared with the rest of the colony. (pp. 783-785)

2. The basic cnidarian body plan consists of a blind-ended gastrovascular cavity with an oral opening surrounded by two tissue layers. The two tissue layers are separated by a jelly-like layer called mesoglea. Some Cnidarians have migrating cells in the mesoglea. There are two basic body types. One is sedentary and has the mouth facing upward. This form is called a polyp. The other form, the familiar jellyfish, is called a medusa. All cnidarians are radially symmetrical as adults. Both forms have flagellated cells and gland cells lining the gastrovascular cavity. The gland cells provide extracellular digestion and the flagellate cells provide circulation, thus the term "gastrovascular" cavity. The inner and outer tissue layers contain muscular cells that allow body movements. Both forms have tentacles lined with harpoon-like nematocysts used for food gathering. Some cnidarians also have nematocysts on their outer body wall. Cnidarians may have only a polyp form or only a medusa form while some alternate between the two. (pp. 785-790)

3. (a) Acoelomate animals have no body cavity surrounding their digestive tube.
(b) Pseudocoelomates, have a body cavity between the endoderm of their digestive tube and the mesoderm of their body wall.
(c) Coelomates have a body cavity bounded by the mesoderm around the digestive tube and mesoderm of the body wall. See Figure 39-5 on p. 784 of your text for illustration. All three body forms are believed to have evolved from a common ancestor. See Figure 39-2 on p. 783 of your text for illustration. (pp. 791-792)

40: MOLLUSKS AND ANNELIDS

IN THE GRAND SCHEME

A protostome coelomate was the common ancestor of mollusks and annelids. The mollusks evolved from an ancestor resembling the chiton in body plan. The mollusks then evolved three main body plans; one clam-like, one like the octopus and squid, and one like snails and slugs. All three kinds of mollusks became, and still are, wide spread in the sea. The gastropods (snails, etc.) and bivalves (clams, etc.) occupy both marine and fresh water bodies. The gastropods also occupy the land. The more highly evolved annelids exhibit segmentation, a trait that characterizes all advanced animals. The terrestrial annelid, the earthworm, is familiar to all. The tube within a tube construction is also characteristic of advanced animals. Less familiar is the bristled annelid, the polychaete that is abundant in marine waters. The leech can be found in fresh and salt water and in terrestrial habitats.

FOR REVIEW

Classification: Five kingdoms are recognized: Monera, Protista, Fungi, Plantae, and Animalia. Kingdoms are divided into phyla (divisions in plants,) which are subdivided into classes. Classes are divided into orders and, in turn, families, genera, and species.

Major features of evolution: The earth is about 4.6 billion years old. The oldest fossils of living things are about 3.5 billion years old. All life evolved in the sea until about 410 million years ago, when invasion of the land began. Throughout the history of living things, continental drift has had a profound influence. Continental movements have caused extinction through loss of habitat, and have caused accelerated evolution by increasing competition through formation of land bridges and isolation through loss of land bridges. Throughout all continental migrations, adaptation to climatic change by the living "passengers" was often the key to survival.

Body plans of bilaterally symmetrical animals: Bilaterally symmetrical animals have one of three body plans.
1. Acoelomate, having no body cavity surrounding the viscera.
2. Pseudocoelomate, having a body cavity with one layer of mesoderm between the endoderm of the viscera and the ectoderm.
3. Coelomate, having, in addition to the structure of the pseudocoelomate, a second layer of mesoderm by the body cavity.

CHAPTER OUTLINE

THE ADVENT OF THE COELOM (pp. 805-806)
     parietal peritoneum
     visceral peritoneum
AN EMBRYONIC REVOLUTION: PROTOSTOMES AND DEUTEROSTOMES (pp. 806-808)
LOPHOPHORATES (pp. 808-810)
     lopophore
   Phylum Phoronida: The Phoronids
   Phylum Ectoprocta: The Ectroprocts
   Phylum Brachiopoda: The Brachiopods
PHYLUM MOLLUSCA: THE MOLLUSKS (pp. 810-817)
   Body Plan of the Mollusks
   Reproduction in Mollusks
   The Classes of Mollusks

KEY TERMS

p. 806: protostomes
P. 807: deuterostomes, spiral cleavage, radial cleavage
p. 811: visceral mass, mantle, gills, bivalve, mollusks, radula
p. 812: nephridia, nephrostome, trochophores
p. 813: veliger, operculum
p. 814: torsion
p. 815: adductor muscle, palps
p. 817: spermatophore, oviduct
p. 818: septa, setae
p. 819: clitellum
p. 820: commensal, parapodia

TOPIC EXERCISES

1. A major development discussed in this chapter is that of a body cavity. In the space below, briefly state the three main advantages of a coelom.

    A.

    B.

    C.

2. A second characteristic featured in this chapter is segmentation. Briefly stated, what are the advantages of segmentation.

    A.

    B.

LEARNING CHECKLIST

  1. What evolutionary advantages are associated with the development of the coelom?
  2. How do lopophorates relate to protostomes and deuterostomes?
  3. Describe the basic features of mollusks and the relation of the mantle to that plan.

4. Explain the advantage of segmentation in coelomic organisms.
5. Compare the organ systems of mollusks and annelids.
6. Why are annelids considered more advanced than mollusks?

MINI EXAM

A. Circle the letter of the best answer to each question.

1. The mantle is modified into lungs in some
   a. bivalves
   b. gastropods
   c. cephalopods
   d. brachiopods

2. The bodies of nautilus are
   a. externally segmented only
   b. internally segmented only
   c. externally and internally segmented
   d. unsegmented

3. The keenest vision is found in
   a. snails
   b. slugs
   c. squids
   d. scallops
   e. earthworms

4. Plumed worms are
   a. polychaetes
   b. spirochetes
   c. oligochaetes
   d. deuterochaetes

5. Nephridia are used for
   a. getting food
   b. defense
   c. locomotion
   d. respiration
   e. excretion

6. Polychaetes are usually
   a. separate-sexed
   b. hermaphroditic and self-fertilizing
   c. hermaphroditic and cross-fertilizing
   d. sexless

7. The _____ is the only kind of mollusks not having a radula.
   a. bivalve
   b. squid
   c. snail
   d. octopus

8. Among annelids, parapodia are unique to
   a. hirudinea
   b. polychaetes
   c. oligochaetes
   d. cephalopods

9. The _____ are the only lopophorates with nonmarine species.
   a. brachiopods
   b. phoronida
   c. ostracods
   d. bryozoans

10. The ancestral mollusk is believed to most resemble today's
    a. snails
    b. oysters
    c. nautilus
    d. chitons

11. Of all known coelomate animals, _____ phyla are deuterostomes.
    a. 2
    b. 3
    c. 4
    d. 7

12. Ectoprocts are connected to other members of the colony by a tiny chitinous chamber called
    a. lopophore
    b. veliger
    c. zoecium
    d. trochophore
    e. statoblast

13. The mollusk heart is _____ chambered.
    a. 4
    b. 3
    c. 2
    d. 1

14. The trochophore larval stage is absent in
    a. polychaetes
    b. oligochaetes
    c. oysters
    d. giant clams

15. Mollusks remove wastes from their coelom with their
    a. gills
    b. veliger
    c. nephridia
    d. mantle

16. _____ cleavage refers to those animals whose cleavage occurs parallel or perpendicular to the polar axis.
    a. Axial
    b. Radial
    c. Spiral
    d. Perpendicular

17. The _____ are annelids that have well-developed heads with sense organs.
    a. polychaetes
    b. cephalodia
    c. hirudinea
    d. oligochaetes

18. The largest of all mollusks is the
    a. giant squid
    b. giant clam
    c. nautilus
    d. octopus

19. Embryos whose cleavage occurs at an angle to the polar axis are said to have _____ cleavage.
    a. spiral
    b. axial
    c. oblique
    d. radial

20. Which of the following lacks any form of a shell?
    a. scallop
    b. limpet
    c. slug
    d. octopus

B. Provide the appropriate term to complete each statement.

1. The _____ secretes the shells of bivalves.

2. The excretory organ of mollusks and annelids is the _____.

3. The _____ of some mollusks may be used as a harpoon.

4. The _____ is the body portion of gastropods that is housed in the shell.

5. The structure found in coelomates but lacking in pseudocoelomates is the _____.

6. The anterior end of the annelid nervous system is enlarged into the _____ .

7. The _____ are so named for the development of the mouth from or near to the blastopore.

8. Those animals whose mouths developed later than, and elsewhere from, the blastopore are _____.

9. The _____ have characteristics intermediate between protostomes and deuterostomes.

10. _____ are hard reproductive cells formed by bryozoans in unfavorable seasons.

C. Briefly answer the following questions.

1. How do protostomes develop differently than deuterostomes?

2. Compare gastropods, bivalves and cephalopods in regard to body plan, feeding, and respiration.

3. Compare earthworms, polychaetes and leeches.

CHAPTER ANSWERS

TOPIC EXERCISES

1. A. closed circulatory system
   B. space for expansion of organs
   C. facilitates muscle driven body movement

2. A. reduced effect of damage
   B. better locomotion

LEARNING CHECKLIST

1. The coelom permitted the development of a closed circulatory system, provided a fluid environment within which to suspend viscera, provided space for elongation of the digestive tract. (pp. 805-806)

2. Lopophorates have several characteristics in common with protostomes and deuterostomes, but their relationship is uncertain. (pp. 808-809)

3. Mollusks have three body sections: head, visceral mass, and foot. They possess a body fold called a mantle that is used variously to enclose their visceral mass and gills, and for jet propulsion. Most mollusks have a rasping tongue called a radula. (pp. 811-812)

4. Segmentation allows redundancy of repeated complete units, minimizing the effects of damage. Independently movable segments aid locomotion. (p. 807)

5. Annelids and most mollusks have closed circulatory systems. Annelids respire through their skin while mollusks respire with gills or lungs. Both mollusks and annelids have a one-way digestive system. Annelids and mollusks both have similar nephridia. (pp. 811-812, 818-819)

6. Segmentation, lacking in mollusks and present in annelids, underlies the organization of all advanced animals. (pp. 818-819)

MINI EXAM

A.
1. b	2. d	3. c	4. a	5. e	6. a
7. a	8. b	9. d	10. d	11. c	12. c
13. b	14. b	15. e	16. b	17. a	18. a
19. a	20. d				

B.
1. mantle	2. nephridium	3. radula
4. visceral mass	5. visceral peritoneum	6. cerebral ganglion
7. protostomes	8. deuterostomes	9. lopophorates
10. Statoblasts		

C. 1. Protostomes (a) blastopore develops into mouth, (b) spiral cleavage of embryo, (c) immediate fate determination of embryo cells upon cleavage, (d) coelom develops by mesoderm cells moving apart.

Deuterostomes (a) blastopore development into anus, (b) radial cleavage of embryo, (c) delayed fate determination of embryo cells, (d) more movement of cells to form coelom. (pp. 806-808)

2. Gastropods, the snails and slugs, have their head and foot in contact with the substrate. Some gastropods have a shell into which they can retreat and in which their visceral mass is housed. In some, the shell is greatly diminished. The visceral mass is twisted. Gastropods may be predatory, scavengers, or grazers. The mantle cavity may serve as a lung or may contain gills. Bivalves have a hinged shell for which they are named. Their visceral mass lies within the shell and is enclosed by the mantle. The mantle cavity houses gills over which a constant stream of water flows. The foot extends from the mantle cavity and shells. It is used to move about on the floor of the body of water in which it lives. Bivalves feed on plankton collected by its gills. Cephalopods are represented by squid, octopus, and nautilus. Their shells may be internal as in squid, external as in the nautilus or absent as in the octopus. They all have an excellent nervous system including eyes. In all of them, the foot is modified into tentacles. Their mantles are used for propulsion by forcing water through siphons. Sexes are separate. The male transfers a sperm mass called spermatophore into the females mantle cavity. She fertilizes eggs as she lays them. They feed by catching prey with their tentacles then eating them with their beak. (pp. 813-815, 816-817)

3. Polychaetes have a well developed head including specialized sensory organs such as eyes. Polychaetes have paired appendages called parapodia. Sexes are separate and fertilization is external. Polychaetes are marine. Earthworms have light sensing capacity, but lack eyes. Bristles are present but shorter and fewer than those of polychaetes. Parapodia are absent. Earthworms are hermaphroditic but not self fertilizing. Leeches are aquatic, marine or terrestrial. They are usually dorsoventrally flattened. Coelome is reduced and extends through the body. Suckers are present at one or both ends. Setae are usually absent. Leeches are predators, scavengers or parasites. They are hermaphroditic, but cross-fertilization is mandatory. (pp. 820-822)

41: ARTHROPODS

IN THE GRAND SCHEME

The ancestry of arthropods is uncertain. From one common ancestor or from several ancestors, arose the arthropod subphyla, the chelicerates, the crustaceans, and the uniramians. They have in common the exoskeleton and jointed appendages. They also share the phenomenon called tagmatization, fusion of segments. Though no cause and effect relationship is suggested, it is interesting to note a parallel. As flowers evolve, there is a trend toward fusion of parts. As arthropods evolved from a segmented ancestor, they to, fused parts. The chelicerates, represented by spiders, scorpions, etc. are distinct from other arthropods in the possession of pinchers for mouthparts instead of jaws. The crustaceans are represented by lobsters, crabs, shrimp and barnacles. They are predominantly marine or aquatic. The crustaceans share with the chelicerates the feature of legs on the abdomen as well as the thorax. Their two paired antennae are unique as is the biramous nature of most appendages. The Uniramia are represented by centipedes, millipedes and insects. The millipedes and centipedes are largely inhabitants of soil and detritus. The centipedes are mostly predatory, and millipedes are mostly herbivores. The insects are probably the most evolved. They occupy an astounding number of niches and habitats. The insects include the only flying arthropods. The insects, some admired for their beauty, and others viewed with disgust, probably impact mankind directly more than any other group of animals. They are highly evolved internally and externally. They are limited in size by the weight to size ratio of their exoskeleton and in intelligence by their solid brain. Yet with their diversity, their adaptability, and their reproductive capacity, they are well suited to dominate the terrestrial earth should the mammals yield that dominance as the dinosaurs did to the mammals.

FOR REVIEW

Chitin: Chitin is a modified form of cellulose in which a nitrogen group has been added to the glucose units. Chitin is tough, resistent surface material.

Origin of species: Genetically based adaptation to the environment is the basis for selection for survival. Increased survival of better adapted members of a population is the source of new species.

Evolutionary history: The earth is about 4.6 billion years old. The oldest fossils of living things are about 3.5 billion years old. All life evolved in the sea until about 410 million years ago, when invasion of the land began. Throughout the history of living things, continental drift has had a profound influence. Continental movements have caused extinction through loss of habitat and accelerated evolution by increasing competition through formation of land bridges and isolation through loss of land bridges. Throughout all continental migrations, adaptation to climatic change by the living "passengers" was often the key to survival.

Protostomes and Deuterostomes: Protostomes form their mouth from the blastopore, and the anus develops elsewhere. Protostome embryos cleave by spiral cleavage. Deuterostomes form their anus from the blastopore, and the mouth develops elsewhere. Deuterostomes have radial cleavage of the embryo.

CHAPTER OUTLINE

GENERAL CHARACTERISTICS OF ARTHROPODS (pp. 826-828)
MAJOR GROUPS OF ARTHROPODS (pp. 828-829)
      biramous
EXTERNAL FEATURES (pp. 829-831)
   Exoskeleton
   Compound Eye
INTERNAL FEATURES (pp. 831-833)
   Circulatory System
   Respiratory System
   Excretory System
   Nervous System
EVOLUTIONARY HISTORY OF ARTHROPODS (pp. 833-834)
SUBPHYLUM CHELICERATA: THE CHELICERATES (pp. 834-839)
   Class Arachnida: The Arachnids
      Order Scorpiones: the scorpions
      Order Aranae: the spiders
      Order Acaro: the mites
      Order Opiliones: the daddy longlegs
   Class Meristomata: The Horseshoe Crabs
   Class Pycnogonida: The Sea Spiders
SUBPHYLUM CRUSTACEA: THE CRUSTACEANS (pp. 840-841)
SUBPHYLUM UNIRAMIA: (pp. 842-850)
   Classes Diplopoda and Chilopoda: The Millipedes and Centipedes
   Class Insecta: The Insects
      External features
      Internal organization
      Sense receptors
      Life histories
THE LARGEST PHYLUM (p. 850)

KEY TERMS

p. 826: tagmata, tagma, tagmatization
p. 827: cephalothorax, exoskeleton, metamorphosis
p. 828: mandibulates, mandibles, chelicerates
p. 829: nauplius, ecdysis
p. 830: compound eye, ommatidia, rhabdon, apposition eyes, superposition eyes, pigment cells
p. 831: simple eyes, ocelli
p. 832: tracheae, tracheoles, spiracles, book lungs
p. 833: Malpighian tubules
p. 834: chelicerae, pedipalps
p. 840: labyrinth, carapace, swimmerets
p. 844: maxillae, labium, labrum
p. 847: fat body, sensory hair, tympanum, pheromones, simple, complete
p. 848: nymphs
p. 850: molting hormone, ecdysone

TOPIC EXERCISES

1. In the table below, indicate if an adult member of the group has the feature shown on the left by placing Y (yes), or N (no) in the column of that group. It should help you sort out the group characteristics.

	chelicerates	crustaceans	uniramian
Ecdysis			
Biramous appendages			
Lungs			
Gills			
Trachea			
Legs on abdomen			
Mandibles			
Two pairs of antennae			

2. Many Arthropods, though of ecological importance to human beings, do not impact our species directly. On the other hand, some members of some orders have a direct impact. In the spaces below, list the orders containing members that fit the categories listed.

    A. Cause disease

    B. Used for food or produce substances of economical value

LEARNING CHECKLIST

1. Why are segmentation and jointed appendages necessary for arthropods?
2. Compare mandibulates and chelicerates with regard to appendages and mouthpart structure.
3. Relate the three subphyla of arthropods with respect to evolution.
4. Describe the process of ecdysis and explain its necessity in arthropods.
5. What are the major external features that distinguish arthropods from animals previously presented?
6. Explain the size limitations of arthropods.
7. What are the members of the subphyla Chelicerata and Crustacea?
8. Compare millipedes and centipedes.

MINI EXAM

A. Circle the letter of the best answer to each question.

1. The upper lip of insects with chewing mouthparts is the
   a. labium
   b. mandible
   c. maxilla
   d. chelicera
   e. labrum

2. The most anterior appendages of crustaceans are
   a. chelicerae
   b. pedipalps
   c. antennae
   d. ocelli
   e. uropods

3. In compound eyes, the lenses are found on
   a. retinuale
   b. ommatidia
   c. ocelli
   d. rhabdoms

4. A structure unique to daddy longlegs of all arachnids is the
   a. ovipositor
   b. labyrinth
   c. chelicera
   d. swimmeret
   e. telson

5. The appendages giving crustaceans such as lobsters the fastest mobility are the
   a. uropods
   b. swimmerets
   c. pedipalps
   d. deverticula
   e. scaphognathites

6. Of the chelicerates, the living form that is most likely to have been derived from the trilobite is the
   a. lobster
   b. scorpion
   c. sea spider
   d. horseshoe crab
   e. hermit crab

7. Which of the following have mandibles?
   a. scorpions
   b. ticks
   c. spiders
   d. crabs
   e. mites

8. _____ are probably the most ancient group of terrestrial arthropods.
   a. Insects
   b. Spiders
   c. Trilobites
   d. Centipede
   e. Scorpions

9. _____ depend upon the respiratory system, rather than blood to transport oxygen.
   a. Crustacea
   b. Chelicerata
   c. Uniramia
   d. All arthropods

10. Simple metamorphosis is characteristic of
    a. fleas
    b. mayflies
    c. ants
    d. butterflies

11. Which of the following are crustaceans?
    a. scorpions
    b. isopods
    c. horseshoe crab
    d. mites

12. In most crustaceans, the exoskeleton is impregnated with
    a. calcium carbonate   c. calcium phosphate
    b. sodium silicate   d. nothing

13. All of the following are found in arthropods except
    a. trachea   c. book lungs
    b. book gills   d. branchioles

14. All of the following except _____ are included in the eleven orders of Arachnida.
    a. ticks   d. harvestman
    b. scorpions   e. mites
    c. sea spiders

15. Unlike annelids, arthropods completely lack
    a. a coelom   d. blood
    b. cilia   e. branchiostegites
    c. chitin

16. Of all those listed, onychophora are most nearly related to the
    a. chilopoda   c. arachnida
    b. cirripedia   d. cladocera

17. Which of the following is a chelicerate?
    a. horseshoe crab   c. shrimps
    b. barnacles   d. ostracods

18. All but _____ are barriers to development of a large body size by arthropods.
    a. tracheal respiratory system
    b. open circulatory system
    c. mass-to support ratio
    d. brain size

19. All of the following are uniramians except
    a. millipede   c. copepod
    b. insect   d. centipede

20. An arthropod can perform all of the following functions with its brain removed except
    a. see   c. copulate
    b. move   d. eat

B. Provide the appropriate term to complete each statement.

   1. In incomplete metamorphosis, the larva is called a(n) _____.

   2. The process of skin shedding in molting is called _____.

   3. The compound eyes of moths are called _____.

   4. In terms of mouthparts, scorpions are _____.

   5. _____ is the subphylum of centipedes.

   6. _____ are appendages on the abdomen of crustaceans.

331

7. When the anterior portions of an arthropod fuse to form a tagma, the structure is called a(n) _____.

8. _____ is the orderly process of changing characteristics from stage to stage.

9. Arthropods lacking mandibles are called _____.

10. All crustacean appendages, being of two branches, are called _____.

C. Briefly answer the following questions.

1. Describe arthropod systems for (a) circulation, (b) respiration, (c) excretion, and (d) nervous control.

2. Characterize insects external features.

3. Compare simple and complete metamorphosis.

CHAPTER ANSWERS

TOPIC EXERCISES

1.

	chelicerates	crustaceans	uniramian
Ecdysis	yes	yes	yes
Biramous appendages	no	yes	no
Lungs	yes	no	no
Gills	yes	yes	no
Trachea	yes	no	yes
Legs on abdomen	no	yes	yes
Mandibles	no	yes	yes
Two pairs of antennae	no	yes	no

2. A. acari, insecta
    B. decapods, insecta

LEARNING CHECKLIST

1. Without segmentation and jointed appendages, the hard exoskeleton would render them immobile. (pp. 828-829)

2. In mandibulates, the most anterior appendages are antennae. The next appendages are mandibles. Appendages are biramous. In chelicerates, the most anterior appendages are pincher-like or feeler-like chelicerae. The remainder of the appendages are legs.

3. The relationship of the arthropods is uncertain. There is evidence both for a common ancestry and for separate evolutionary paths for the three subphyla. (pp. 828-829)

4. A new exoskeleton forms under the old one. A fluid separates the new exoskeleton from the old one. With the new exoskeleton completed, the old one is split, usually down the back, by fluid pressure. The new exoskeleton is expanded by fluid pressure and eventually hardens. It is the only way the animal can grow larger. (pp. 829-830)

5. Major external features occurring in arthropods are external skeleton, jointed appendages, compound eyes, and wings. (pp. 829-830)

6. The weight to support the exoskeleton limits the size of arthropods. This is reminiscent of the days in our history when knights were so armored that they had to be placed on their horse by a block and tackle and were helpless if dismounted. The solid brain requires more space to provide the same intelligence as hollow brains such as ours. (pp. 833-834)

7. See page 828, Table 41-1 in your text.

8. Centipedes are dorsoventrally flattened. Millipedes are more cylindrical in cross section. Centipedes have one pair of legs per segment. Millipedes have two legged segments called tagmata which represent fusion of ancestral segments of only one pair of legs. Centipedes are carnivores, mostly predatory upon insects. Most millipedes are herbivores. (p. 842)

MINI EXAM

A.
1. e	2. c	3. b	4. a	5. a	6. d
7. d	8. e	9. c	10. b	11. b	12. a
13. d	14. c	15. c	16. a	17. a	18. b
19. c	20. a				

B.
1. nymph	2. ecdysis	3. superposition
4. chelicerates	5. Uniramia	6. Swimmerets
7. cephalothorax	8. Metamorphosis	9. chelicerates
10. biramous		

C. 1. (a) The circulatory system is open, flowing through body cavities. Blood is pumped by a valved dorsal blood vessel that acts as the heart. Respiratory pigments include hemocyanin and hemoglobin.
(b) Respiration is accomplished by passage of air through a system of tubes. Air enters through usually valved holes called spiracles. The air then is distributed by a system of tubes called trachea and tracheoles. Muscle movements propel the air.

(c) Excretory processes differ in arthropods but a unique system involves a collection of tubules called the Malpighian tubules associated with the digestive system. Located between the midgut and hindgut, the Malpighian tubules collect wastes from the midgut and precipitates them and transfers them to the hindgut for excretion. Salts and fluids are returned to the body fluids.

(d) Two parallel chains of ganglia run along the ventral body wall. The chains terminate in anterior ganglia that constitute the brain. Sharp vision is supplied by simple and/or compound eyes. (pp. 831-833)

2.   Insects have three body segments; head, thorax, and abdomen. They have no more than six legs in the adult. Mouth parts consist of jaws called maxillae and mandibles flanked by a labrum above and labrum below that serve as lips. Compound eyes may be accompanied by simple eyes. All have antennae. Some have two or four wings. Internal features were described in number 1 above. (pp. 843-846)

3.   In simple metamorphosis, the egg hatches into a somewhat incomplete replica of the adult called a nymph. As the nymph grows, it passes through several stages called instars, each of which brings it closer to the adult form. In complete metamorphosis, the egg hatches into a worm-like larva that grows to a relatively large size and enters into a dormant stage called the pupa. In the pupa stage, the body undergoes a complete change into the adult form which then emerges from the confines of its pupa case. (pp. 847-850)

42: ECHINODERMS AND CHORDATES

IN THE GRAND SCHEME

At some point the deuterostomes diverged from the protostomate ancestry. The deuterostomes were still coelomate but the mode of coelom formation was different. The most striking difference between deuterostomates and protostomates is the reversal of the fate of the blastopore. The protostomate blastopore became the mouth but the deuterostomate blastopore became the anus, and the mouth developed elsewhere. As the deuterostomates were different from the protostomes, so are the two phyla of the deuterostomes different from each other. The echinoderms differ greatly from the chordates. Echinoderms, though bilaterally symmetrical as larvae, are all radially symmetrical as adults. The echinoderms are entirely marine, filling their ceolom with seawater. The chordates are either asymmetrical or bilaterally symmetrical. Chordates all share, at some time in their life, the characteristic of a notochord. The notochord is a cartilage-like rod that provides longitudinal support. The chordates range from the simple jug-like tunicates to a broad range of vertebrates. The vertebrates evolved an internal skeleton and a hollow dorsal nerve chord. Vertebrates also have pharyngeal gill clefts at least in the embryo. Various structures are derived from those gill clefts and the tissue between them. There is also a broad range of diversity in the class Vertebrata. The vertebrates include the jawless fishes, Agnatha that retain the notochord in the adult. Chondrichthyes are vertabrates that have cartilage instead of bones. The osteichthyes are vertebrates that have bones. Leaving the fishes behind and invading the land are the amphibians. Better adapted to a life on land are the reptiles. The birds live on land, in the air, and on but not in the water. The mastery of all three environments is left to the mammals. The vertebrates will not be elaborated on in this chapter because they are the subject of the remaining chapters on animals, perhaps reflecting the illiteracy of the invertebrates.

FOR REVIEW

Evolutionary theory: Variations occur within populations. The higher the degree of polyploidy, the greater potential for variation. Some variations will give members of a population greater capacity to adapt and to be selected by nature for survival and reproduction. The accumulated variations and the selection by nature for survival and reproduction of those organisms with the most advantageous variations is the essence of the evolutionary process.

Vertebrate evolution: The first vertebrates to evolve were jawless marine fishes. From them evolved the cartilaginous fishes and then the bony fishes. Bony fishes are the most abundant vertebrate species on the earth today. Amphibians evolved from the lobe-finned bony fishes, but reptiles were the first truly terrestrial vertebrates. The reptiles gave rise to both birds and mammals, the only two homeothermic classes of vertebrates.

Classification: Five kingdoms are recognized: Monera, Protista, Fungi, Plantae, and Animalia. Kingdoms are divided into classes. Classes are divided into orders and, in turn, families, genera, and species.

Protosomes and deuterostomes: Protostomes form their mouth from the blastopore, and the anus develops elsewhere. Protostome embryos cleave by spiral cleavage. Deuterostomes from their anus from the blastopore, and the mouth develops elsewhere. Deuterostomes have radial cleavage of the embryo.

CHAPTER OUTLINE

KEY TERMS

p. 854: archenteron, ossicles, tube feet
p. 855: nerve ring, ring canal, radial canals, madreporite, ampulla
p. 856: skin gills
p. 860: cloaca

p. 861: nerve cord, notochord, pharyngeal slits
p. 862: tunic
p. 864: vertebrae, tetrapods
p. 867: denticles, pectoral fins
p. 868: swim bladder
p. 869: lateral line system
p. 873: amniotic egg, yolk, albumin, allantois, amnion, chorion
p. 874: ectothermic, endothermic, homeotherms, poikilotherms
p. 875: beaks, gizzards
p. 876: double circulation
p. 878: placenta

TOPIC EXERCISES

1. Tube feet are characteristic of all echinoderms, but their use differs from one kind of echinoderm to another. For each echinoderm listed below, list the functions of their tube feet.

    A. Sea lilies

    B. Sea stars

    C. Sea urchins and sand dollars

    D. Sea cucumber

2. Fishes demonstrate several important characteristics adapting them for success in their environment. For each characteristic listed below, state the most primitive group of fish to demonstrate the characteristic and the advantage of the characteristic.

	Group	Advantage
Skeleton		
Jaw		
Swim bladder		

3. In adaptation to a terrestrial existence, amphibians and reptiles solved problems differently. For each terrestrial problem listed below, briefly state the solution by the class of vertebrates.

	Amphibians	Reptiles
Reproduction		
Breathing		
Moisture conservation		

LEARNING CHECKLIST

1. Compare the symmetry of the larval and adult echinoderms.

2. Discuss regeneration in echinoderms and relate it to reproduction.

3. What are the principle chordate characteristics?

4. Compare and give examples of the three chordate subphyla.

5. (a) What are the major vertebrate characteristics? (b) What characteristics separate vertebrates into classes?

6. How are agnatha unique among vertebrates?

7. (a) Evaluate the Chondrichthyes skeleton. (b) What structure did they evolve to compensate for the disadvantage?

8. How are reptiles more advanced than amphibians and better adapted to a terrestrial existence?

9. Compare monotremes, marsupials, and placental mammals.

MINI EXAM

A. Circle the letter of the best answer to each question.

1. The only completely sessile echinoderm is the
   a. sea lily
   b. sea star
   c. sea cucumber
   d. brittle star
   e. sea urchin

2. An example of a craniate chordate is
   a. agnathia
   b. acorn worm
   c. lancelet
   d. chondrichthyes
   e. tetrapods

3. All of the following are a part of a water vascular system except
   a. madreporite
   b. scaphognathite
   c. ampulla
   d. stone canal
   e. tube feet

4. Which of the following never have pharyngeal slits?
   a. mammals
   b. arrow worms
   c. agnathia
   d. acorn worms

5. The number of arms in echinoderms is not the same in every animal, but the echinoderm body plan calls for rays or segments in the number of
   a. 3
   b. 5
   c. 10
   d. 12

6. Which of the following is a swimming echinoderm
   a. sea urchin
   b. sand dollar
   c. sea star
   d. sea lily
   e. brittle star

7. A unique respiratory device, called a respiratory tree, is characteristic of
   a. sea stars
   b. sea urchins
   c. sea lilies
   d. sea cucumbers

8. The mammal characteristic, being poikilothermic, is shared with
   a. some reptiles
   b. birds
   c. some fishes
   d. some amphibians
   e. all of the above

9. Pseudomorphosis is characteristic of
   a. arrow worms
   b. sea cucumbers
   c. tunicates
   d. acorn worms
   e. lancelets

10. Some _____ are capable of inserting their stomach into shells of bivalves and digesting the inhabitant.
    a. sea cucumbers
    b. brittle stars
    c. sea stars
    d. sea lilies
    e. sea urchins

11. All of the following are classes of vertebrates except
    a. fishes
    b. reptiles
    c. birds
    d. amphibians
    e. humans

12. Reptiles differ from amphibians in the
    a. amniotic egg
    b. absence of legs
    c. possession of scales
    d. possession of lungs

13. In which function listed below do vertebrates differ from all other animals?
    a. nervous
    b. digestive
    c. respiratory
    d. excretory

14. Other than a better breathing technique, the major advantage of bony fish over shark is
    a. teeth
    b. structure of the eye
    c. scales
    d. buoyancy

15. A "rowing" type of locomotion is characteristic of
    a. sea urchins
    b. brittle stars
    c. crinoids
    d. sea cucumbers

16. Notochords persist throughout the life of
    a. agnathans
    b. sharks
    c. skates
    d. rays

17. All characteristics listed below are common to all chordates except
    a. pharyngeal slits
    b. cranium
    c. notochord
    d. nerve chord

18. A soft bodied echinoderm is the
    a. sea lily
    b. sea cucumber
    c. sand dollar
    d. brittle star

19. In order to breath, shark must constantly
    a. swallow
    b. flex gills
    c. swim
    d. move ribs

20. The chordate characteristic of pharyngeal slits is shared only with the non-chordate
    a. acorn worms
    b. tunicates
    c. worms
    d. sea cucumbers

B. Provide the appropriate term to complete each statement.

    1. With regard to a skull, Agnatha are classified as _____.

    2. The blastopore is the opening of the embryonic gut called _____.

    3. In sea cucumbers, the process of excretion and respiration are accomplished by the _____.

    4. The _____ pumps water through the respiratory structure of sea cucumbers.

    5. The tube connecting the sieve plate of sea stars to the ring canal is called the _____.

    6. Another name for the sieve plate in echinoderms is _____.

    7. Locomotion is accomplished by echinoderms by means of tubular extension of the water vascular system called _____.

    8. In vertebrates, the vertebrae replaces the _____.

    9. Lampreys differ from hagfish in the structure of their _____.

    10. Of all of the vertebrates, only birds and mammals are capable of regulating their _____ internally.

C. Briefly answer each of the following questions.

    1. Compare the symmetry of the larval and adult echinoderms.

    2. Compare the five classes of echinoderms with respect to (a) body plan, (b) locomotion, (c) tube feet modification, and (d) feeding strategy.

    3. (a) Define and evaluate endothermy and ectothermy. (b) Classify the vertebrates with regard to those two characteristics.

CHAPTER ANSWERS

TOPIC EXERCISES

1. A. plankton collection
    B. locomotion and opening bivalve shells
    C. locomotion
    D. locomotion and sediment collection.

2.

	Group	Advantage
Skeleton	agnathia	movement
Jaw	sharks	predation
Swim bladder	bony fishes	energy conservation

3.

	Amphibians	**Reptiles**
Reproduction	return to water	amniotic egg with shell
Breathing	lungs and moist skin	lungs
Moisture conservation	mucous coat	scales

LEARNING CHECKLIST

1. Adults are radially symmetrical. Larvae are bilaterally symmetrical. See Figure 42-3 on p. 858 of your text.

2. Echinoderms lose parts by accident or drop them or eject them in self defense. These usually regenerate. It is possible to reproduce asexually in this manner, but such cases are more accidental than not. Most echinoderm reproduction is sexual. (p. 856)

3. Nerve chord, notochord, pharyngeal slits. (p. 861)

4. Urachordata: tunicates, sack-like, sessile, marine adults, notochord only as larva. No segmentation. Cephalocordata: Lancelets, small minnow-like, swimming adult, scales absent, permanent notochord, filter feeder. Vertebrata: fish, amphibians, reptiles, birds, mammals; notochord only when immature, except in Agnatha. Vertebrae of either bone or cartilage present hollow dorsal nerve chord. (pp. 861-864)

5. (a) Vertebrae, heart and closed circulatory system, liver, kidney, endocrine glands, cranium
    (b) Agnatha are fish that lack jaws. Chondrichthyes are fish that have jaws but have cartilage instead of bone. Osteichthyes are fishes with bones. Amphibians are not fish and can live both in water and on land. Most lack scales and none have egg shells. Reptiles have scales and lay eggs with leathery shells. Birds are feathered and most exercise flight. Mammals are hairy and provide food for infants from glands on their body. (p. 864)

6. Agnatha are the only jawless vertebrates. (p. 865-866)

7. The osteichthyes skeleton provided strength and improved muscle action. Buoyancy was achieved by the development of swim bladders. (pp. 868-869)

8. The reptilian dry skin that retards water loss, more efficient lungs and amniotic egg make the reptiles distinctly advanced over amphibians and better adapted to terrestrial existence. (pp. 872-873)

9. Monotremes lay eggs. Marsupials bear young in pouches. Placental mammals bear young internally, providing nutrition, respiration and excretion by means of a placenta. (pp. 876-878)

MINI EXAM

A.

1. a	2. c	3. b	4. b	5. b	6. e
7. d	8. b	9. c	10. c	11. b	12. a
13. d	14. d	15. b	16. a	17. b	18. b
19. c	20. a				

B.

1. craniate	2. archenteron	3. respiratory
4. cloaca	5. stone canal	6. madreporite
7. tube feet	8. notochord	9. mouth
10. temperature		

C. 1. Like protostomes, deuterostomes are coelomate. Unlike protostomes, the deuterostome coelom develops from an evagination of the archenteron. The protostome blastopore becomes the mouth whereas the deuterostome blastopore becomes an anus. Deuterostomes have radial rather than spiral cleavage and daughter cells are totipotent for a period. Many deuterostome cells migrate in embryo formation but those of the protostomes do not. The radial body plan is unique; not occurring in other deuterostomes. It is found only in lower protostomes. (p. 854)

2. Crinoidea: (a) sessile and detached (b) no locomotion for sessile forms, detached form moves by flexing rays; (c) tube feet mucous coated to trap food, (d) filter feeders.
Asteroidea: (a) five or more arms sharply set off from central disk; mouth in center of lower surface of disk, (b) arm flexing and tube feet, (c) no modification, (d) preys upon bivalve shell, inserts stomach into shell opening and digest prey.
Ophiuroidea: (a) slender branched areas, well set off from central disk, (b)"row" along substrate by flexing arm, some swim, (c) sensory tube feet assist in directing food into mouth, (d) catches suspended microplankton with tube feet.

Echinoidea: (a) arms lacking, body covering rigid, mouth in bottom of disk, sand dollars flattened, urchins "pumpkin shaped," (b) crawl on tube feet extended through disk (c) no modification, (d) feed on algae with rasping beak-like mouth parts.
Holothruoidea: (a) soft leathery coating, oriented as if only on ray, anterior mouth with tentacles, (b) moves on tube feet, (c) tube feet around mouth modified into tentacles, others unmodified, (d) traps plankton in mucous net on tentacles, inserts tentacles into pharynx for food removal. (pp. 857-860)

3. Ectothermic organisms regulate heat by deriving it from the environment and radiating heat into the environment. Endothermic organisms conserve their energy since their energy is not used to generate heat, but they must also regulate their activity according to their temperature. Endothermic organisms require more energy but may remain active when the temperature drops. Reptiles, amphibians and fish are ectothermic. Birds and mammals are endothermic. (p. 874)

43: ORGANIZATION OF THE VERTEBRATE BODY

IN THE GRAND SCHEME

As members of the vertebrate subphylum, humans are generally more interested in the biology of vertebrates than in the biology of any other group of organisms. With this chapter, we begin our detailed examination of vertebrate biology. We start with how vertebrates are put together. In the following chapters we will see how the various parts carry out the myriad of vertebrate life processes. But first, the foundation: each vertebrate body is made up of a variety of organs and organ systems that carry out different life processes such as digestion, respiration, and reproduction. Organs are made up of groups of specialized cells that have similar structures and functions. These groups of cells are called tissues. Although there are between 50 and several hundred types of cells, and there are subdivisions within each tissue type, vertebrates have just four basic kinds of tissue: epithelium, connective tissue, muscle, and nerve.

FOR REVIEW

Eukaryotic cell structure: All organisms are composed of one or more cells, and all cells are either prokaryotic or eukaryotic. Bacteria are composed of prokaryotic cells; all other organisms are eukaryotic. Eukaryotic cells are more complex than prokaryotic cells and have a highly organized interior with many different functional compartments. Organelles found inside eukaryotic cells, but not prokaryotic cells, include a membrane-bound nucleus, endoplasmic reticulum, Golgi bodies, lysosomes, microbodies, mitochondria, chloroplasts, and multiple chromosomes. Like prokaryotic cells, eukaryotic cells have a plasma membrane and sometimes a cell wall.

The evolution of vertebrates: Vertebrates represent a major subphylum of the chordates. Chordates and echinoderms represent the two major phyla of deuterostomes, which evolved about 630 million years ago and have distinct embryological development patterns. The first vertebrates to appear were the jawless fish. They evolved at least 470 million years ago and approximately 410 million years ago gave rise to the jawed fish. Lobe-finned fishes gave rise to the amphibians about 350 million years ago. Approximately 300 million years ago the amphibians gave rise to the reptiles. One branch of reptiles gave rise to birds 225 to 150 million years ago, and another branch of reptiles gave rise to mammals about 200 million years ago. All vertebrates are characterized by a vertebral column surrounding a dorsal nerve cord.

Basic structure of chordates: Chordates are animals characterized by three principal features: (1) a hollow nerve cord running just beneath the dorsal surface, (2) a notochord, a flexible rod running parallel to and between the nerve cord and the gut, and (3) pharyngeal slits. The notochord and pharyngeal slits may be present only during certain embryological stages or may persist throughout the life of the chordate, depending on the species. Chordates also tend to have bilateral symmetry, some degree of body segmentation, distinct blocks of muscles, an internal skeleton, and a tail that extends beyond the anus.

CHAPTER OUTLINE

KEY TERMS

p. 885: thoracic cavity, abdominal cavity, skeleton, skull, vertebrae, spinal cord, tissues, organs, organ system, endoderm, mesoderm, ectoderm

p. 887: epithelium, connective tissue, muscle, nerve, epithelial cells, simple epithelium, stratified epithelium, glands, squamous, cuboidal, columnar, simple squamous

p. 888: simple cuboidal, simple columnar, stratified squamous epithelium, keratin, exocrine glands, endocrine glands, matrix, defensive connective tissue, structural connective tissue, sequestering connective tissue

p. 889: macrophages, lymphocytes, mast cells, antibodies, B cells, antigen, plasma cell

p. 890: inflammation response, histamine, serotonin, heparin, hypersensitivity, fibroblasts, cartilage, bone, collagen, piezoelectric current, reticulin, elastin

p. 891: tendons, ligaments, erythrocytes, leukocytes, hemoglobin, plasma, myofibrils

p. 892: smooth muscle, striated or skeletal muscle, cardiac muscle

p. 893: fiber, muscle fiber, sarcoplasm, depolarization, neurons, supporting cells, sensory cells, motor cells

p. 894: dendrites, axon

p. 895: nerves, glial cells, neuroglia, peripheral nervous system, Schwann cells, homeostasis

p. 896: hypothalamus, feedback loop

p. 897: negative feedback, positive feedback, setpoint, sensors, error signals, perturbations, effectors
p. 899: antidiuretic hormone (ADH), aldosterone
p. 900: vasodilation

TOPIC EXERCISES

1. Place the following terms in the appropriate places of the outline to form the proper listing of connective tissues and their cells.

Terms	Outline of Connective Tissue
bone	I. Defensive Connective Tissues
cartilage	
erythrocytes	A.
fat cells	
fibroblasts	B.
lymphocytes	
macrophages	C.
mast cells	
	II. Structural Connective Tissues
	A.
	B.
	C.
	III. Sequestering Connective Tissues
	A.
	B.

2. Match the following types of cells with their proper function or characteristic.

a. erythrocytes   i.   secrete proteins such as collagen

b. neurons   ii.   produce antibodies

c. fibroblasts   iii.   produce compounds involved in the inflammation response

d. glial cells   iv.   conduct electrical currents

e. mast cells   v.   provide nutrients for neurons

f. lymphocytes   vi.   produce and accumulate hemoglobin

3. Name each of the types of cells or tissues illustrated below.

A.

B.

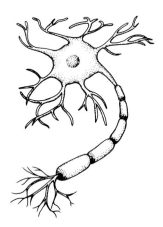

C.

LEARNING CHECKLIST

1. Name the four principal kinds of tissue found in adult vertebrates.
2. Name the four functions of epithelium.
3. List the three general classes of epithelial tissue. In what three shapes do simple epithelium cells occur?
4. What are the two types of gland systems? What is the major anatomical difference between the two types?
5. List the three categories of connective tissue.
6. List the three principal cell types of defensive connective tissue.
7. Name the three principal components of structural connective tissue.
8. Name two types of sequestering connective tissue.
9. What are the three types of vertebrate muscle cells?

10. What two types of cells make up nerve tissue?
11. What term describes the maintenance of constant extracellular conditions in the body? What type of mechanism is commonly used to maintain this constancy?

MINI EXAM

A. Circle the letter of the one best answer for each question.

1. Sarcoplasm is the special name given to the cytoplasm of
   a. skeletal muscle cells
   b. stratified epithelium cells
   c. neurons
   d. fibroblasts
   c. erythrocytes

2. Which of the following is <u>not</u> a type of epithelial cell?
   a. cuboidal cells
   b. squamous cells
   c. mast cells
   d. columnar cells
   e. all of the above are epithelial cells

3. Cells that are specialized for conducting electrical currents are called
   a. leukocytes
   b. smooth muscle
   c. lymphocytes
   d. mast cells
   e. neurons

4. Phagocytic cells of the immune system are called
   a. macrophages
   b. erythrocytes
   c. lymphocytes
   d. mast cells
   e. fibroblasts

5. The most abundant protein in vertebrate bodies is
   a. keratin
   b. cartilage
   c. reticulin
   d. collagen
   e. hemoglobin

6. Fibroblasts are a type of _____ connective tissue.
   a. defensive
   b. structural
   c. sequestering
   d. none of the above - fibroblasts are not a type of connective tissue

7. Hemoglobin is produced and accumulated in
   a. leukocytes
   b. supporting cells
   c. mast cells
   d. exocrine glands
   e. erythrocytes

8. Glial cells and Schwann cells are types of
   a. epithelium
   b. connective tissue
   c. muscle tissue
   d. nerve tissue
   e. none of the above

9. Lymphocytes produce
   a. antigens
   b. antibodies
   c. inflammatory responses
   d. bone tissue
   e. keratin

10. Your skeletal muscles are also called
   a. smooth muscle
   b. striated muscle
   c. cardiac muscle
   d. all of the above

11. Muscle cells are formed from
   a. endoderm
   b. ectoderm
   c. mesoderm
   d. all of the above
   e. none of the above

12. In all vertebrates, the dorsal nerve cord is surrounded by the
   a. lamellae
   b. spinal cord
   e. skull
   d. skeleton
   e. vertebrae

13. Which of the following is a function of epithelium?
   a. protection
   b. secretion
   c. sensory surface
   d. all of the above
   e. none of the above

14. Callouses and hair are composed of
   a. keratin
   b. elastin
   c. antigens
   d. collagen
   e. heparin

15. The liver is an example of
   a. nerve tissue
   b. an exocrine gland
   c. connective tissue
   d. an endocrine gland
   e. stratified epithelium

16. Connective tissue is derived from
   a. endoderm
   b. ectoderm
   c. mesoderm
   d. all of the above
   e. none of the above

17. Histamine, serotonin, and heparin are all produced and released by
   a. lymphocytes
   b. erythrocytes
   c. Schwann cells
   d. mast cells
   e. neuroglia

18. How many principal organ systems does the human body contain?
   a. 11
   b. 4
   c. 27
   d. 62
   e. it varies from individual to individual

19. The fluid matrix of blood is called
   a. hemoglobin
   b. aldosterone
   c. neuroglia
   d. histamine
   e. plasma

20. The earliest type of muscle to evolve was
    a. cardiac muscle
    b. smooth muscle
    c. skeletal muscle
    d. stratified muscle

B. Provide the appropriate term to complete each statement.

1. _____ glands are ductless.

2. Keratin is produced by _____ tissue.

3. The rapid rise in levels of LH in the blood resulting in ovulation is an example of _____ feedback in the human body.

4. Collagen is secreted by _____ cells.

5. Histamine and serotonin are substances that help cause the _____ response.

6. In muscle cells, actin and myosin microfilaments are bunched together into thousands of strands called _____.

7. The heart and lungs of a human are located in the _____ cavity.

8. _____ are composed of groups of cells that are similar in structure and function.

9. Epithelial cells that have an irregular, flattened shape with tapered edges are called _____ cells.

10. A plasma cell is a mature _____ cell and contains a unique version of the gene for antibodies.

C. Briefly answer each of the following questions.

1. Why is bone marrow cancer so lethal?   (Hint: bone marrow produces blood cells).

2. Some broken bones take a very long time to heal. Doctors have discovered that running a small electric current through the affected area will often help the recovery process. Why do you suppose this treatment works?

CHAPTER ANSWERS

TOPIC EXERCISES

1.   I. A,B,C = macrophages, lymphocytes, mast cells (in any order)
        II. A,B,C = fibroblasts, cartilage, bone (in any order)
        III. A,B = erythrocytes, fat cells (in either order).

2.   a. vi   b. iv   c. i   d. v   e. iii   f. ii

3.   A. neuron
        B. cardiac muscle
        C. simple squamous epithelium

LEARNING CHECKLIST

1. epithelium, connective tissue, muscle, nerve (p. 887)

2. provide protection from dehydration and physical injury, provide selectively permeable barrier, provide sensory surfaces, secrete materials (p. 887)

3. simple epithelium, stratified epithelium, glands; squamous, cuboidal, columnar (p. 887)

4. exocrine glands, endocrine glands; exocrine glands have a duct, endocrine glands are ductless (p. 888)

5. defensive, structural, sequestering (p. 888)

6. macrophages, lymphocytes, mast cells (p. 889)

7. fibroblasts, cartilage, bone (p. 890)

8. erythrocytes, fat cells (p. 891)

9. smooth muscle, striated (skeletal) muscle, cardiac muscle (p. 892)

10. neurons, supporting cells (p. 893)

11. homeostasis; negative feedback loops (pp. 895, 897-898)

MINI EXAM

A.

1. a	2. c	3. e	4. a	5. d	6. b
7. e	8. d	9. b	10. b	11. c	12. e
13. d	14. a	15. b	16. c	17. d	18. a
19. e	20. b				

B.

1. Endocrine	2. stratified epithelium	3. positive
4. fibroblast	5. inflammatory	6. myofibrils
7. thoracic	8. Tissues	9. squamous
10. lymphocyte		

C. 1. If the marrow becomes cancerous and stops producing erythrocytes, the circulatory system loses its mechanism for transporting oxygen and carbon dioxide. If leukocytes are not produced, the body will not be defended properly by macrophages and lymphocytes. (pp. 889-891)

2. The current may be analogous to the piezoelectric current, which stimulates the deposition of new connective tissue. (pp. 890-891)

44: NEURONS

IN THE GRAND SCHEME

A characteristic of all living organisms is that they respond to their environments, both internal and external. In animals, the nervous system is intimately involved with those responses. The nervous system is a communications center that sends rapid messages in the form of electrical impulses. It receives information about the state of the external environment and about the internal environment within the animal's body. It processes or integrates this information and sends signals back that will initiate some response to the stimuli. In effect, the nervous system acts as a central switchboard and keeps all parts of the body functioning properly and in harmony with each other. Without the nervous system there would be chaos, and vertebrates as we know them could not exist. We begin our detailed examination of vertebrate organ systems by looking at this vital and complex system. This chapter focuses on the neuron, the functional unit of the system. The next chapter examines the central nervous system, the main processing center. The sensory systems are covered in the third chapter.

FOR REVIEW

Sodium/potassium pump: Cells expend a lot of energy actively pumping Na^+ ions out of the cells and actively pumping K^+ ions into the cells, both against their concentration gradients. This active transport occurs through protein channels in the cell membrane. These special channels are called sodium-potassium pumps. Nerve function depends on the ion imbalance established by the pump.

Ion channels: Many transmembrane protein channels allow the passage of ions into or out of the cell by diffusion, without any expenditure of energy. The ions follow their concentration gradients, moving from areas of high concentration to areas of low concentration. Many of the ion channels are highly selective and allow the passage of only specific ions; this is called facilitated diffusion. In nerve cells, the K^+ ions that are actively pumped into the cell diffuse back out through ion channels and thus help establish the ion concentration difference (i.e., polarization) that is necessary before a nerve can fire.

Neuron: Neurons are cells that are specialized for transmitting nerve impulses (i.e., conducting electric current). Together with their supporting cells they make up nerve tissue, one of the four main tissue types in the vertebrate body. Their ability to function depends on maintaining a charge difference between the interior and exterior of the cell.

Depolarization: Depolarization is the elimination or change of charge differences between the interior and exterior of a cell. It is caused by the rapid movement of ions into the cell through special channels when the cell is stimulated properly. Muscles contract and nerve impulses are transmitted because of depolarization.

CHAPTER OUTLINE

THE NEURON (pp. 903-905)
        structure
THE NERVE IMPULSE (pp. 906-910)
    Membrane Potential
    Ion Channels
    The Resting Potential: Result of a K^+ Concentration Gradient
      Role of the Na^+-K^+ pump
    Initiating a Nerve Impulse

KEY TERMS

p. 903: hormones, neurons, sensory neurons, motor neurons
p. 904: dendrites, axon, neurotransmitters, synaptic cleft, neuromuscular junctions, neuroglia cells, Schwann cells, myelin sheath, nodes of Ranvier
p. 905: nerves
p. 906: gated ion channels, ions, electrolyte solution, cations, anions, concentration gradient, permeability, voltage, membrane potential, current, resting potential, micropipette, polarized, depolarization, hyperpolarizations, ion channels
p. 907: gating, voltage-gated, stimulus-gated, equilibrium, equilibrium potential, Na^+-K^+ pump
p. 908: sensory receptors, synapses
p. 909: action potential, nerve impulse, threshold, Na^+ inactivation, absolute refractory period, relative refractory period
p. 910: diameter, myelinated, conduction velocity, saltatory conduction
p. 911: synaptic cleft, presynaptic membrane, postsynaptic membrane, chemically gated
p. 912: acetylcholine
p. 913: tetrodotoxin (TTX), saxitoxin (STX), ciguatoxin (CTX)
p. 914: acetylcholinesterase, tabun, sarin, parathion, excitatory synapse, inhibitory synapse, gammaaminobutyric acid (GABA)
p. 915: integration

TOPIC EXERCISES

1. Label the following parts on the neuron diagrammed below:

    axon
    cell body
    cell nucleus
    dendrite
    myelin sheath
    node of Ranvier

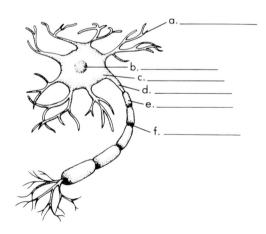

a. _____
b. _____
c. _____
d. _____
e. _____
f. _____

2. Label the following parts on the synapse diagrammed below: axon, postsynaptic membrane, presynaptic membrane, synaptic cleft, vesicle with neurotransmitter.

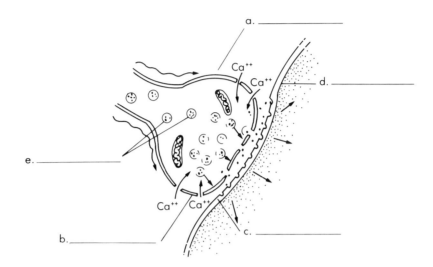

3. Label the following areas on the graph below, which shows the changes in electrical potential associated with the firing of a neuron. A term may be used more than once.

Areas: action potential
        refractory period
        resting potential

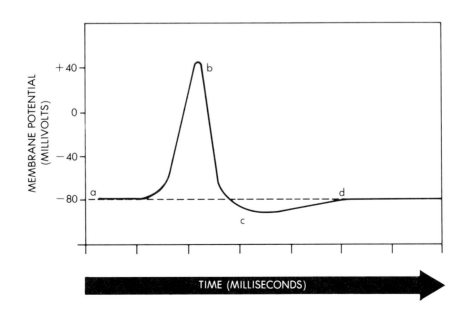

LEARNING CHECKLIST

1. Name two ways of transmitting information within the bodies of vertebrates. Which way is faster?
2. Name the two types of cytoplasmic extensions that protrude from the cell bodies of neurons and state what their functions are with regard to the direction of signal transmission.
3. What two ions are responsible for the polarized, resting potential of a neuron? Where is each of these ions concentrated in a neuron at rest?
4. What mechanism maintains the concentration gradients and polarization of resting neurons?
5. What two events happen during depolarization of a neuron with regard to ion movement?
6. Name three types of cells that neurons synapse with.
7. What is the nature of the signal (chemical or electrical) that carries a nerve impulse from a neuron, across a synaptic cleft to another cell? What is the general name for this type of synaptic signal?
8. Name the two general types of neural synapses.

MINI EXAM

A. Circle the letter of the one best answer for each question.

1. Postsynaptic membranes are most likely to be found on
   a. axons
   b. dendrites
   c. neuron cell bodies
   d. myelin sheaths
   e. hormones

2. What is primarily responsible for establishing the uneven Na^+ ion concentrations inside and outside a neuron during its resting potential?
   a. active transport
   b. simple diffusion
   c. facilitated diffusion
   d. all of the above
   e. none of the above

3. During the resting potential of a neuron, which of the following is least likely to be found in large quantities inside the neuron?
   a. Na^+
   b. K^+
   c. negatively charged anions
   d. none of the above would be found in large quantities inside the neuron

4. During saltatory conduction, a nerve impulse jumps from one _____ to another.
   a. myelin sheath
   b. synapse
   c. node of Ranvier
   d. dendrite
   e. axon

5. GABA (gammaaminobutyric acid) is normally found at
   a. neuromuscular junctions
   b. nodes of Ranvier
   c. sensory receptors
   d. excitatory synapses
   e. inhibitory synapses

6. The firing of a neuron is also called
   a. depolarization
   b. an action potential
   c. both of the above
   d. none of the above

7. Nerve impulses are normally carried toward a neuron cell body by the neuron's
   a. synaptic cleft
   b. axon
   c. myelin sheaths
   d. hormones
   e. dendrites

8. The junction between a neuron and its target cell is called a
   a. neurotransmitter
   b. synapse
   c. node of Ranvier
   d. threshold
   e. stimulus-gated channel

9. Neurotransmitters are released from vesicles at the
   a. cell body
   b. dendrite
   c. cell nucleus
   d. postsynaptic membrane
   e. presynaptic membrane

10. Acetylcholinesterase is
    a. a neurotransmitter
    b. an enzyme that breaks down a neurotransmitter
    c. a stimulant that triggers an action potential
    d. a hormone
    e. none of the above

11. During depolarization
    a. Na^+ moves out of the neuron
    b. K^+ moves into the neuron
    c. organic ions move out of the neuron
    d. all of the above
    e. none of the above

12. Which are faster, hormonal messages or neural messages?
    a. hormonal
    b. neural
    c. neither; they both are the same speed
    d. it depends on the particular hormones and neurons involved

13. The myelin sheath is formed by _____, which wrap around the axons of some neurons.
    a. nodes of Ranvier
    b. dendrites
    c. synapses
    d. Schwann cells
    e. cell bodies

14. In a polarized neuron at rest
    a. the inside of the neuron is more negatively charged than the outside
    b. the outside of the neuron is more negatively charged than the inside
    c. either of the above can be true
    d. the inside and the outside of the neuron have the same electrical charge

15. During an action potential, Na$^+$ moves through
    a. voltage-gated K$^+$ channels
    b. synaptic clefts
    c. voltage-gated Na$^+$ channels
    d. all of the above
    e. none of the above

16. The role of the Na$^+$-K$^+$ pump in the nervous system is to
    a. maintain proper ionic concentration gradients across the neuron membrane
    b. generate the nerve impulse when the neuron is stimulated
    c. transmit the nerve impulse across the synaptic cleft between neurons
    d. provide a source of Na$^+$ and K$^+$ by splitting NaCl and other appropriate molecules
    e. none of the above - it plays no role

17. The neurotransmitter at neuromuscular junctions is
    a. GABA
    b. neuroglia
    c. acetylcholinesterase
    d. acetylcholine
    e. none of the above; neuromuscular junctions don't have neurotransmitters

18. Which of the following statements is true?
    a. all synapses are excitatory
    b. all synapses are inhibitory
    c. all synapses have the same type of neurotransmitters
    d. all of the above are true
    e. none of the above are true

19. Which of the following should have the slowest conduction velocity?
    a. an unmyelinated, small-diameter nerve
    b. an unmyelinated, large-diameter nerve
    c. a myelinated, small-diameter nerve
    d. a myelinated, large-diameter nerve
    e. they would all have the same conduction velocity

B. Provide the appropriate term to complete each statement.

1. The narrow gap between an axon tip and its target cell is called the _____.

2. _____ are made up of bundles of myelinated and nonmyelinated neurons.

3. During depolarization, _____ ions rush into a neuron.

4. A neuron is unable to respond at all to additional stimulation during the _____.

5. The amount of stimulation required to initiate depolarization of a neuron is called the _____ value.

6. The _____ sheath wraps around axons and serves as an electrical insulator.

7. During _____ conduction, the nerve impulse jumps from one node of Ranvier to another.

8. Receptor molecules for neurotransmitters are located in the _____ membrane.

9. The process of subtracting and adding all the inhibitory and excitatory signals that a neuron receives is called _____.

C. Briefly answer each of the following questions.

   1. What would happen to a person who had a severe sodium deficiency?

   2. Is it possible to run a nerve impulse backwards along a neuron?

   3. Why are nerve gases lethal to vertebrates? (hint: nerve gases inhibit acetylcholinesterase)

   4. Do you think there are other compounds analogous to acetylcholinesterase?

CHAPTER ANSWERS

TOPIC EXERCISES

1. a. dendrite   b. cell nucleus
   c. cell body   d. axon
   e. myelin sheath   f. node of Ranvier

2. a. axon   b. presynaptic membrane
   c. synaptic cleft   d. postsynaptic membrane
   e. vesicle with neurotransmitter

3. a. resting potential   b. action potential
   c. refractory period   d. resting potential

LEARNING CHECKLIST

   1. hormones (chemical messages), nerve impulses (electrical messages); nerve impulses are faster (p. 903)

   2. dendrites: generally receive electric signals from other cells and pass them toward the cell body; axon: generally carry signal from the cell body toward the next cell (p. 904)

   3. Na^+ and K^+; Na^+ concentration is greater outside the neuron membrane than inside, K^+ concentration is greater inside (p. 907)

   4. Na^+-K^+ pump (p. 907)

   5. Na^+ ions flood into the neuron through opened voltage-gated Na^+ channels, and then K^+ ions move out of the neuron through voltage-gated K^+ channels (p. 909)

   6. other neurons, muscles, secretory cells (p. 911)

   7. chemical; neurotransmitter (pp. 911-912)

   8. excitatory synapses, inhibitory synapses (p. 914)

MINI EXAM

A.
1. b	2. a	3. a	4. c	5. e	6. c
7. e	8. b	9. e	10. b	11. e	12. b
13. d	14. a	15. c	16. a	17. d	18. e
19. a					

B.
1. synaptic cleft	2. Nerves	3. Na^+
4. absolute refractory period	5. threshold	6. myelin
7. saltatory	8. postsynaptic	9. integration

C. 1. Without sodium ions, neurons could not establish proper resting potentials, and therefore the nervous system could not function since depolarization could not occur. (pp. 907-909)

   2. The depolarization wave can be propagated in either direction along the axon or dendrites, but synaptic vesicles with their neurotransmitters exist only at the end of the axon, so it would not be possible to pass a "backwards" impulse from the dendrites of one neuron to another cell. (pp. 909-911)

   3. Acetylcholinesterase is an enzyme present in synaptic clefts. It removes acetylcholine from the cleft. If acetylcholinesterase is inhibited by nerve gas, acetylcholine remains in the synaptic cleft and there is continuous stimulation of the postsynaptic membrane. This obviously disrupts the normal functioning of the nervous system and can be lethal, because many vital life processes such as breathing and blood circulation require rhythmic muscular contraction (muscles are stimulated to contract by acetylcholine released at neuromuscular junctions). (pp. 911-914)

   4. There should be. It is just as important that excess amounts of the other neurotransmitters be removed, as acetylcholine is. Remember, enzymes are very specific in their functions. You would expect each neurotransmitter to have its own synaptic enzyme. (p. 914)

45: THE NERVOUS SYSTEM

IN THE GRAND SCHEME

In the previous chapter, we looked in detail at how neurons function and laid the foundation for understanding how the entire vertebrate nervous system operates. In this chapter we focus on the nervous system itself - how it is organized or arranged (i.e., its architecture) and how it receives and processes information and then issues commands in response to the information (i.e., its functioning). As mentioned in the last chapter, the nervous system acts as a central switchboard and keeps all parts of the body functioning properly and in harmony with internal and external conditions. The nervous system exerts this fine-tuned control through feedback loops and antagonistic control systems. It has a complex architecture in the higher vertebrates, the result of evolutionary trends leading toward greater complexity, differentiation of parts, and sophistication. Despite the complexity and elaborate functionings, though, remember that the central and peripheral nervous systems are built "merely" of neurons; billions of them, to be sure, but each and every one of them operates on the same basic principles outlined in the previous chapter.

FOR REVIEW

Primitive invertebrates: The primitive invertebrates include the phyla Porifera (sponges), Cnidaria (coelenterates), Ctenophora (comb jellies), Platyhelminthes (flatworms), Rhynchocoela (ribbon worms), Nematoda (nematodes), and Rotifera (rotifers). These are the simplest members of the animal kingdom, but they illustrate the evolutionary history of the major characteristics associated with the more advanced animal phyla. Although these invertebrates are primitive, they are the foundation upon which the more advanced forms were built. In them we can trace the evolutionary history of various organ systems and body architecture. With the nervous system, for example, we can trace the evolutionary trend from the sponge with no nerve cells, to the cnidarian with its nerve net, to the planaria with its complete central versus peripheral nervous system.

Depolarization: When the polarization or charge separation across a cell membrane is reversed or eliminated, we say that depolarization has occurred. It is caused by the rapid movement of ions into and then out of the cell. Depolarization is the basis for the functioning of neurons. A nerve impulse is nothing more than a wave of depolarization.

Neuron: Nerve tissue, one of the four main types of tissues in the vertebrate body, is composed of neurons and their supporting cells. Neurons are cells that are specialized for conducting electric current. This transmission of the nerve impulse depends on the movement of Na^+ and K^+ ions to establish the resting potential, depolarize, and then reestablish the resting potential.

CHAPTER OUTLINE

KEY TERMS

p. 918: nervous system, brain, central nervous system, peripheral nervous system, spinal cord, gray matter, white matter, sensory (afferent) pathways, motor (efferent) pathways, voluntary (somatic) nervous system, autonomic (involuntary) nervous system, neuroendocrine system

p. 919: tracts, nerves, nuclei, ganglia

p. 920: nerve net, reflex, reflex arc, associative activity, interneurons, afferent, efferent

p. 921: hindbrain (rhombencephalon), midbrain (mesencephalon), forebrain (prosencephalon), cerebellum, pons, medulla

p. 924: diencephalon, telencephalon, cerebrum, pyramidal tract, hemispheres, corpus callosum, frontal lobe, parietal lobe, temporal lobe, occipital lobe, cerebral cortex

p. 925: corpus striatum, basal ganglia

p. 926: red nucleus, thalamus, computed tomography (CT scans), magnetic resonance imaging (MRI), position emission tomography (PET scans)

p. 927: hypothalamus, pituitary gland, limbic system, hippocampus, amygdala, reticular formation, reticular activating system, serotonin, electroencephalogram (EEG), alpha waves, slow-wave sleep, REM phase

p. 928: motor cortex, sensory cortex, associative cortex, primary motor cortex, primary somatosensory cortex, auditory cortex, visual cortex, dominant hemisphere, Wernicke's area, Broca's area

p. 929: autonomic, autonomic nervous system, homeostasis

p. 931: monosynaptic reflex arcs

p. 933: flexors, extensors, tendon organs

p. 935: viscera, parasympathetic nervous system, sympathetic nervous system

p. 936: adrenaline, noradrenaline, acetylcholine, monoamines, dopamine, raphe nuclei, glutamate, glycine, gammaaminobutyric acid (GABA), neuromodulators, neuropeptides, corelease, vasopressin, somatostatin, oxytocin, Substance P, enkephalins, endorphins, endogenous opiates, analgesic

TOPIC EXERCISES

1. Provide the appropriate term to complete the following outline of the organization of the vertebrate nervous system.

    I. _____

        A. Brain

        B. _____

    II. Peripheral Nervous System

        A. _____

        B. Motor (efferent) pathways

            1. Somatic (voluntary) nervous system

            2. _____

                a. Parasympathetic nervous system

                b. _____

2. Match the following parts of the brain with its proper location. A location may be used more than once.

    a. cerebellum   i. forebrain
    b. cerebrum   ii. hindbrain
    c. corpus striatum   iii. midbrain
    d. hypothalamus
    e. limbic system
    f. medulla
    g. optic lobes of fish
    h. pons
    i. reticular formation
    j. thalamus

3. Label the following parts on the human brain diagrammed below.

cerebellum
cerebral cortex
hypothalamus
medulla
spinal cord
thalamus

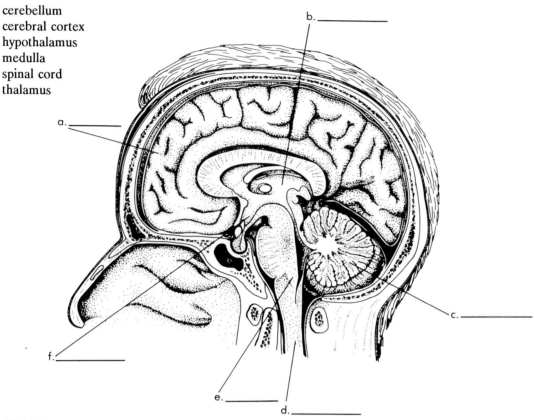

b. _____

a. _____

c. _____

f. _____

e. _____

d. _____

LEARNING CHECKLIST

1. Name the one underlying mechanism of all nervous systems. List the three basic elements of all nervous systems.
2. What two structures compose the central nervous system?
3. List the five principal evolutionary trends that have occurred in animal nervous systems.
4. Name the three principal divisions of the vertebrate brain. Which one is dominant in fish? In mammals?
5. List the four lobes of a cerebral hemisphere.
6. What are the three general kinds of specialized cortexes of the cerebrum? Which takes up the largest area in a human?
7. Name the three separate motor command systems employed by the central nervous system.
8. What are the general names of the two types of antagonistic muscles?
9. By what two general mechanisms does the voluntary (somatic) nervous system function?
10. What are the two antagonistic subdivisions of the autonomic nervous system? How do they differ in the location of their ganglia, their general effect on their target organs, and the neurotransmitter released at the synapse with their target organ?

MINI EXAM

A. Circle the letter of the one best answer for each question.

1. The midbrain of vertebrates is also called the
   a. medulla
   b. mesencephalon
   c. diencephalon
   d. hypothalamus
   e. cerebrum

2. In fish and early vertebrates, the dominant part of the brain was the
   a. cerebrum
   b. forebrain
   c. midbrain
   d. hindbrain
   e. optic lobes

3. In humans and other primates, the hemispheres of the cerebrum are connected by a nerve tract called the
   a. pons
   b. nerve net
   c. thalamus
   d. corpus striatum
   e. corpus callosum

4. Emotions of vertebrates are controlled by the
   a. pyramidal tracts
   b. reticular system
   c. cerebellum
   d. corpus striatum
   e. limbic system

5. Which of the following is not part of the hindbrain?
   a. pons
   b. medulla
   c. cerebrum
   d. cerebellum
   e. all of the above are part of the hindbrain

6. Which of the following is not one of the four lobes of a primate's cerebral hemisphere?
   a. optic lobe
   b. parietal lobe
   c. frontal lobe
   d. temporal lobe
   e. occipital lobe

7. The thalamus is a primary site of
   a. motor reflex coordination
   b. visceral integration
   c. sensory integration
   d. hormone production
   e. none of the above

8. Which of the following is not part of a monosynaptic reflex arc?
   a. a sensory neuron
   b. a motor neuron
   c. a synapse
   d. an interneuron
   e. all are part

9. What type of nervous system does a sponge have?
   a. a nerve net
   b. central nervous system
   c. peripheral nervous system
   d. all of the above
   e. none of the above

10. Bundles of nerve fibers are called tracts if they are located in
    a. the central nervous system
    b. the peripheral nervous system
    c. ganglia
    d. the neuroendocrine system

11. An automatic consequence or response to a nerve stimulation is called a(n)
    a. associative activity   d. afferent pathway
    b. reflex   e. none of the above
    c. coordinating center

12. Taxonomically, the first evidence of associative activity in the nervous system is seen in
    a. cnidarians   d. flatworms
    b. humans   e. fish
    c. sponges

13. Neurons that carry impulses away from the central nervous system are called
    a. sensory nerves   d. interneurons
    b. afferent nerves   e. extensors
    c. efferent nerves

14. Which of the following types of organisms does not have a central nervous system?
    a. annelids   d. cephalopods
    b. arthropods   e. cnidarians
    c. vertebrates

15. When you look at an intact human brain, what you see the most is a large, highly convoluted outer surface. This is the
    a. cerebral cortex   d. reticular system
    b. medulla   e. viscera
    c. cerebellum

16. Which of the following is an example of an antagonistic control system?
    a. flexors and extensors   c. both of the above
    b. sympathetic and parasympathetic   d. none of the above
       nervous systems

17. What neurotransmitter is released in the ganglia of the sympathetic nervous system?
    a. serotonin   d. all of the above
    b. acetylcholine   e. none of the above
    c. adrenaline or noradrenaline

18. The parasympathetic nervous system has what effect on the heart's pacemaker?
    a. excites it
    b. inhibits it
    c. kills it
    d. has no effect at all
    e. has a variable effect; sometimes excites it, sometimes inhibits it

19. Which of the following is part of the central nervous system?
    a. the spinal cord   d. a and b
    b. the autonomic nervous system e. all of the above
    c. motor pathways

20. Which of the following statements about nervous systems is true?
   a. As nervous systems evolved, there was a trend toward a decreasing number of interneurons.
   b. As nervous systems evolved, the hindbrain and especially the cerebellum played an increasingly more dominant role.
   c. The autonomic nervous system stimulates normal internal body functions and inhibits alarm responses, while the somatic nervous system does the opposite.
   d. Memories appear to be stored in more than one part of the brain.
   e. The two hemispheres of the brain carry out identical functions.

B. Provide the appropriate term to complete each statement.

   1. Maintaining physiological conditions within relatively narrow bounds is called _____.
   2. Clusters of neuron cell bodies in the peripheral nervous system are called _____.
   3. Information is carried to the central nervous system by _____ pathways.
   4. In the central nervous system, the _____ matter is made up of bundles of axons.
   5. Another name for the voluntary nervous system is the _____ nervous system.
   6. Another name for the rhombencephalon is the _____.
   7. The reticular system of the brain is repressed by the neurotransmitter _____.
   8. The _____ and the _____ are the two divisions of the forebrain in amphibians, reptiles, birds and mammals.
   9. The dominant part of the mammalian brain is the _____.
   10. Neuromuscular feedback loops are established by _____ in the muscles that depolarize when the muscles extend or contract.
   11. _____ and _____ are neurotransmitters of the sympathetic nervous system and have an effect opposite to acetylcholine.
   12. Peptide neuromodulators called _____ and _____ strongly affect the intensity of pain perception.

C. Briefly answer the following question.

   1. If a nerve impulse is an all-or-none phenomenon, how can vertebrates show different levels or intensities of response to different stimuli?

CHAPTER ANSWERS

TOPIC EXERCISES

1. I. Central Nervous System
   I.B. Spinal cord,
   II.A. Sensory (afferent) pathways
   II.B.2. Autonomic (involuntary) nervous system
   II.B.2.b. Sympathetic nervous system

2.
a. ii	b. i	c. i	d. i	e. i	f. ii
g. iii	h. ii	i. ii	j. i		

3.
a. cerebral cortex	b. thalamus	c. cerebellum
d. spinal cord	e. medulla	f. hypothalamus

LEARNING CHECKLIST

1. mechanism = the nerve impulse; basic elements = a central processing region (brain), nerves that bring information to the brain, nerves that transmit commands from the brain (p. 918)

2. brain, spinal cord (p. 918)

3. elaboration of more sophisticated sensory mechanisms; differentiation of nerve network into central and peripheral systems; differentiation of afferent and efferent fibers; increased complexity of association; elaboration of the brain (pp. 920-921)

4. hindbrain (rhombencephalon), midbrain (mesencephalon) forebrain (prosencephalon); fish = hindbrain; mammals = forebrain (pp. 921, 923-924)

5. frontal lobe, parietal lobe, temporal lobe, occipital lobe (p. 924)

6. motor cortex, sensory cortex, associative cortex; human = associative (p. 928)

7. neuromuscular control, neurovisceral control, neuroendocrine control (p. 930)

8. flexors and extensors (p. 933)

9. feedback loops, antagonistic controls (p. 935)

10. parasympathetic nervous system, sympathetic nervous system; parasympathetic: ganglia near target organs, effect is to stimulate normal body functions, neurotransmitter = acetylcholine; sympathetic: ganglia near spine, effect is to stimulate alarm responses, neurotransmitter = adrenaline or noradrenaline (pp. 935-936)

MINI EXAM

A.
1. b	2. d	3. e	4. e	5. c	6. a
7. c	8. d	9. e	10. a	11. b	12. d
13. c	14. e	15. a	16. c	17. b	18. b
19. a	20. d				

B.
1. homeostasis	2. ganglia	3. sensory (afferent)
4. white	5. somatic	6. hindbrain
7. serotonin	8. diencephalon, telencephalon	9. cerebrum
10. stretch receptors	11. Adrenaline, noradrenaline	12. enkephalins, endorphins

C. 1. Each individual neuron fires in an all-or-none response, but billions of neurons exist and interconnect in the vertebrate body. Integration of excitatory and inhibitory signals, and associative activities by the neuron cell bodies and central nervous system, plus the sheer number of neurons involved and the frequencies with which they fire result in different levels of response. (p. 921)

46: SENSORY SYSTEMS

IN THE GRAND SCHEME

The nervous system of vertebrates is a communications and control device. The functioning of the vertebrate body is controlled by the nervous system as it receives information, integrates it, and signals some response. The central nervous system is the information-processing center and the command post for sending out responsive orders. But sensory systems provide the information to the brain in the first place. Without sensory systems, the central nervous system would receive no data upon which to act. Sensory neurons monitor both the internal and external environments of the organism and relay this information to the brain. Sensory neurons differ in the stimuli they respond to and in their degrees of complexity, but they all work in the same basic way. When they are stimulated, they depolarize and send a nerve impulse to the central nervous system. The brain builds a complete picture of the internal and external environments by monitoring the pattern of which sensory neurons are active and how frequently they fire.

FOR REVIEW

Carotene: Carotene is a type of carotenoid pigment. Carotenoids are composed of carbon rings linked to chains with alternating single and double bonds. They serve as accessory pigments in photosynthesis and absorb a wide range of wavelengths of light. Beta-carotene can be split to form vitamin A, which can be oxidized to form retinal. Retinal is the pigment used in vertebrate vision, as well as in annelid, mollusk, and arthropod vision.

Depolarization: When a nerve is stimulated by an appropriate stimulus, the voltage-gated Na^+ ion channels in the membrane open and Na^+ floods into the cell. This destroys the polarized resting potential and is called depolarization. The depolarization spreads in a wave and becomes the nerve impulse. Depolarization is the basis for the functioning of neurons and the entire nervous system. It is thus the mechanism by which the central nervous system receives information from the sensory neurons.

Sensory neuron: Neurons are cells that are specialized for conducting electric current (i.e., waves of depolarization). Sensory neurons are part of the peripheral nervous system and conduct electric currents or impulses from the body's internal or external environment to the central nervous system. They are stimulated to send impulses (depolarize) by various sensory stimuli, either directly, or via specialized sensory receptor cells.

CHAPTER OUTLINE

KEY TERMS

p. 941: stimulation, sensory receptor, transduction, transmission, exteroception, free nerve endings

p. 942: taste, smell, chemoreceptors, hearing, mechanoreceptors, vision, photoreceptors, interoception, baroreceptors, nociceptors, proprioceptors

p. 943: stimulus-sensitive receptor proteins, generator potentials (receptor potentials)

p. 944: depolarization, modality

p. 945: receptive field, maps, summate, spatial summation, temporal summation

p. 946: linear receptors, logarithmic receptors, tonic (non-adapting), phasic (rapidly adapting), thermoreceptors, cold receptors, warm receptors

p. 947: epidermis, dermis, subcutaneous tissue, fine touch, hair follicle receptors, Meissner's corpuscles, touch dome endings (Merkel's discs), Ruffini endings, Pacinian corpuscles, muscle spindles

p. 948: stretch receptors, Golgi tendon organs, carotid arteries, carotid sinus, statocysts, saccule, utricle, statolith, hair cells

p. 949: semicircular canals, ampulla, cupula, macula, otolith, stereocilia

p. 950: lateral line organs, taste, smell (olfaction), taste buds, salty, sweet, sour, bitter

p. 951: carotid bodies, hypoxia, peripheral chemoreceptors, papillae

p. 952: central chemoreceptors, ear, tympanic membrane (eardrum), ossicles, hammer, anvil, stirrup, oval window, cochlea, middle ear, Eustachian tube

p. 953: basilar membrane, tectorial membrane, organ of Corti, resonance, resonant frequency, sympathetic resonance

p. 954: sonar, eye

p. 955: eyespot

p. 956: cornea, lens, ciliary muscles, iris, pupil, rods, cones, retina, fovea
p. 957: chromatic aberration, <u>cis</u>-retinal, carotene, opsin, rhodopsin, outer segment, inner segment
p. 958: transducin, phosphodiesterase, bipolar cell, ganglion cell
p. 959: parallax, stereoscopic vision
p. 960: pit organs
p. 961: electroplates, ampullae of Lorenzini

TOPIC EXERCISES

1. Complete the following chart by listing each of the following stimuli in their proper class:

   electricity, gravity, heat, humidity, inertia, light, magnetism, pressure, smell, sound, taste, touch, vibration.

Electromagnetic	Mechanical Forces	Chemicals	Energy

2. Match the following sensory receptors with the appropriate stimulus or condition they detect and monitor.

   a. pain
   b. levels of O_2 and CO_2 in the blood
   c. blood pressure
   d. fine touch in surface areas without hair
   e. duration and extent of touch pressure
   f. limb position, muscle length
   g. changes in electrical currents
   h. vibration
   i. heat
   j. gravity

   i.   Merkel cells (discs)
   ii.   baroreceptors
   iii. ampullae of Lorenzini
   iv.   Meissner's corpuscles
   v.   Pacinian corpuscles
   vi.   nociceptors
   vii. pit organs
   viii. proprioceptors
   ix.   statocysts
   x.   carotid bodies

3. Many people claim to have a "sixth sense" they call ESP, extrasensory perception. How would you design a sensory system for ESP? What would be its components and how would they function? (Hint: what are the basic components of all sensory systems?)

LEARNING CHECKLIST

1. List the three elements involved in sending sensory information to the central nervous system.
2. Name the three classes of environmental stimuli to which sensory receptors respond.
3. What are the simplest type of sensory receptors?
4. What are the three levels of information that different sensory systems can provide about external stimuli?
5. What four types of information can be encoded in sensory information?
6. List the seven different mechanical forces to which our receptors respond. Name the general type of receptor that does the responding.
7. What are the four classes of stimuli to which your different taste buds respond?
8. Where are the auditory sensory receptors located in the ear (be specific)?
9. Name four types of mammals that use sonar.

10. List the four phyla of animals that have evolved well-developed image-forming eyes. Name the visual pigment that they all use.
11. Name the two types of specialized receptor cells found in vertebrate eyes.
12. List three other environmental stimuli to which some vertebrates can respond.

MINI EXAM

A. Circle the letter of the one best answer for each question.

1. The amount of light entering the eye is determined by the size of the
   a. retina
   b. cornea
   c. pupil
   d. fovea
   e. optic nerve

2. The cells responsible for color vision in vertebrates are called
   a. rod cells
   b. cone cells
   c. bipolar cells
   d. cupula cells
   e. ampullae

3. Which of the following substances is involved in the electromagnetic and chemical events of vision?
   a. rhodopsin
   b. transducin
   c. phosphodiesterase
   d. all of the above
   e. none of the above

4. Which of the following is not a mechanical stimulus?
   a. gravity
   b. sound
   c. touch
   d. vibration
   e. smell

5. Nerve impulses are carried from the eye to the brain by the
   a. optic nerve
   b. cornea
   c. bipolar cells
   d. rod and cone cells
   e. suspensor ligaments

6. The membrane that separates the outer ear from the middle ear of mammals is called the
   a. foveal membrane
   b. basilar membrane
   c. oval window
   d. tectorial membrane
   e. tympanic membrane

7. Which of the following is not one of the four taste classes that taste buds respond to?
   a. bitter
   b. salty
   c. spicy
   d. sweet

8. Rod cells and cone cells are located in the
   a. organ of Corti
   b. retina
   c. iris
   d. cornea
   e. pupil

9. Which of the following sensory systems is not found in fish?
   a. ampullae of Lorenzini
   b. lateral line system
   c. pit organs
   d. taste buds
   e. all of the above are found in fish

10. The simplest sensory receptors in a nervous system are
    a. found only in invertebrates
    b. nerve endings that depolarize in response to direct physical stimulation
    c. mechanical receptors that employ a lever device
    d. auditory receptors

11. Which of the following sensory systems of vertebrates did <u>not</u> evolve first in an aquatic environment?
    a. infrared vision   c. electric organs
    b. taste   d. regular vision

12. The most sensitive vertebrate chemoreceptors known are the
    a. rod and cone cells of mammals
    b. taste and olfactory receptors of fishes
    c. organs of Corti of humans
    d. taste and olfactory receptors of mammals
    e. organs of Corti of bats

13. Compared with chemical stimuli, auditory stimuli
    a. travel farther
    b. travel more quickly
    c. provide better directional information
    d. all of the above
    e. none of the above

14. The Eustachian tube connects the
    a. outer ear and middle ear
    b. middle ear and inner ear
    c. inner ear and throat
    d. cochlea and semicircular canals
    e. middle ear and throat

15. Which of the following sensory receptors function via hyperpolarization rather than depolarization?
    a. rod and cone cells   d. all of the above
    b. organs of Corti   e. none of the above
    c. proprioceptors

16. The fovea is part of the
    a. cornea   d. retina
    b. iris   e. organ of Corti
    c. papillae

17. Which of the following is <u>not</u> one of the ossicles in the middle ear of humans?
    a. stirrup   c. saddle
    b. anvil   d. hammer

18. Which of the following stimuli can be detected by a proprioceptor?
    a. taste   d. gravity
    b. pain   e. all of the above
    c. color

19. Information transmitted from the pit organs of a snake is processed by
    a. modified muscles
    b. the auditory center of the snake's brain
    c. electroplates
    d. the visual center of the snake's brain
    e. magnetic receptors

B. Provide the appropriate term to complete each statement.

1. The cupulae that detect motion or angular momentum are located in the _____ of the inner ear.

2. A(n) _____ is a small pebble of calcium carbonate that bends cilia and helps a vertebrate detect gravity or which way is up.

3. The tightly coiled chamber of the inner ear where hearing actually takes place is called the _____.

4. All image-forming eyes, such as those of the vertebrates, mollusks, arthropods, and annelids, use the visual pigment _____.

5. Inner perception or the sensing of internal body conditions is called _____.

6. The voltage changes that occur in stimulated sensory receptors are called _____.

7. The receptors used for hearing in terrestrial vertebrates are thought to have evolved from the _____ system of fish.

8. Olfactory receptors are involved in the sense of _____.

9. _____ is the sense that provides the most detailed information about an external stimulus.

10. A _____ sensory receptor continues to produce action potentials at the same rate no matter how long the stimulus lasts.

C. Briefly answer each of the following questions.

1. Athletes such as boxers, football players, and rugby players often suffer a detached retina - where a sharp blow to the head causes a piece of the retina to detach or break loose from the back of the eye. How would this affect their vision? Why?

2. How is the electrical sensory system of electric fish analogous to the sonar system of some mammals? Is it similar to the lateral line system of fishes?

3. Why can dogs hear dog whistles and people can't?

4. If the nerve impulse of any neuron is identical to any other neuron, in terms of its depolarization, how can we perceive the vast array of sensory sensations that we do?

CHAPTER ANSWERS

TOPIC EXERCISES

1. Mechanical Forces = gravity, inertia, pressure, sound, touch, vibration; Chemicals = humidity, smell, taste; Electromagnetic Energy = electricity, heat, light, magnetism

2.
a. vi	b. x	c. ii	d. iv	e. i
f. viii	g. iii	h. v	i. vii	j. ix

3. There would have to be sensory receptors of some sort to receive the stimuli, whatever its form. The receptors would have to connect to sensory neurons that would conduct impulses to the brain, where the information would be processed and integrated. Use your imagination in supplying details about the structure, location, and functioning of the ESP receptors (e.g., what class of stimuli do they detect; are there any structural adaptations for amplifying the stimulus; etc.)!

LEARNING CHECKLIST

1. stimulation of sensory receptor, transduction of signal from receptor to sensory neuron, transmission of signal to CNS by sensory neuron (p. 941)

2. mechanical forces, chemicals, electromagnetic energy (p. 941)

3. free nerve endings (p. 941)

4. attention, location, imaging (p. 942)

5. what? where? how much? when? (pp. 944-946)

6. touch, vibration, pain, pulling, pressure, gravity, equilibrium (motion); mechanoreceptors (pp. 946-949)

7. salt, sweet, sour, bitter (p. 950)

8. the organ of Corti (hair cells between the basilar and tectorial membranes) in the cochlea of the inner ear (pp. 952-953)

9. bats, shrews, whales, dolphins (p. 954)

10. annelids, mollusks, arthropods, vertebrates; pigment = cis-retinal (pp. 955, 957)

11. rod cells, cone cells (p. 956)

12. heat, electricity, and magnetism reception (pp. 960-962)

MINI EXAM

A.   1. c   2. b   3. d   4. e   5. a   6. e
     7. c   8. b   9. c   10. b   11. a   12. b
     13. d   14. e   15. a   16. d   17. c   18. d
     19. d

B.   1. semicircular canals   2. statolith   3. cochlea
     4. <u>cis</u>-retinal   5. interoception   6. generator or receptor potentials
     7. lateral line   8. smell   9. Vision
     10. tonic or non-adapting

C. 1.   Depending on how much of the retina was detached, they would lose all or part of their vision in the affected eye. If the retina is detached, the necessary connections between rod cells, cone cells, bipolar cells, ganglion cells, and the optic nerve may be destroyed, and nerve impulses cannot be transmitted from the eye to the brain. (pp. 956-959)

   2.   Electrical fishes discharge electricity and then monitor disturbances in the electric field that are caused by environmental objects. In sonar, the mammals use sound waves to establish a picture of their environment. They emit sound waves and monitor the pattern with which they return after bouncing off objects in the environment. Fishes do not emit anything with their lateral line system, but instead monitor changes in water pressure or movement as they or other objects move through the water. (pp. 949-950; 954; 960-961)

   3.   A dog's auditory receptors are more sensitive to high-pitched sounds than are a human's auditory receptors. The ability to hear a particular pitch depends on the flexibility of the basilar membrane in the cochlea of the inner ear; the less flexible it is, the less the mammal will hear. Children can hear high-pitched sounds up to 20,000 cycles per second, but this activity declines with age as the basilar membrane becomes less flexible and the ear becomes less efficient at amplifying sound waves. Dogs, on the other hand, can hear frequencies as high as 40,000 cycles per second because of the greater sensitivity (flexibility) of their basilar membranes. (pp. 953-954)

   4.   The brain perceives the difference between different senses (e.g., between pain and vision and taste) and between different input of the same sense strictly on the basis of which neuron is providing the impulse and how frequently that neuron fires. Remember, different areas of the brain are "wired" to different sensory receptors. An impulse arriving in the auditory region of the cerebral cortex, for example, is perceived as a sound, not a temperature or a smell or a sight. All of the sensations we experience are a result of the integration and processing of nerve impulses that go on in our brains, not to any character inherent in the nerve impulse itself. (p. 941)

47: HORMONES

IN THE GRAND SCHEME

We have seen how the body receives information about its internal and external environments through its various sensory systems. We also have examined how the central nervous system processes all the incoming information it receives and then sends out appropriate response commands via its autonomic nervous system (affecting smooth muscles and organs) or its voluntary nervous system (affecting skeletal muscles). This chapter completes the circuit by addressing how longer-term orders are given by the central nervous system and carried out by hormones produced by endocrine glands. The net result of all this activity is that the central nervous system regulates essentially all body activities and unites a diverse collection of cells, tissues, and organs into a smoothly functioning, unified, single organism. The functioning of each organ system is controlled by feedback loops and antagonistic mechanisms, thus maintaining the homeostasis necessary for life. Hormones are chemical extensions of the nervous system and bring about long-term changes or responses within the organism's body.

FOR REVIEW

Membrane transport: Cell membranes are lipid bilayers that are selectively permeable. Some substances simply diffuse across like water (osmosis) or by passing through a transmembrane protein channel. Some protein channels have carriers that help transport substances; this is facilitated diffusion. Some channels transport substances against their concentration gradients by expending energy and carrying out active transport. The sodium-potassium pump and the proton pump are examples of such channels and are often coupled to the transport of other substances or the synthesis of ATP.

Operation of neurons: At rest, neurons are polarized as a result of an uneven concentration of Na^+ and K^+ ions inside and outside the cell membrane. This polarization is maintained by active transport. When a neuron receives a signal or stimulus above threshold value, it causes a sudden and massive movement of ions into and out of the neuron. This depolarization spreads along the neuron as an electric impulse. When it reaches the axon, it stimulates the vesicles there to release their neurotransmitter into the synaptic cleft. The neurotransmitter diffuses across the cleft and binds to receptors on the postsynaptic membrane, which may be part of a muscle cell, another neuron, or an endocrine gland. Depending on the type of neurotransmitter, the recipient cell or organ will be stimulated or inhibited.

Central nervous system: The nervous system of a vertebrate is divided into two major components, the central nervous system and the peripheral nervous system. The central nervous system consists of the brain and the spinal cord. It receives information from sensory neurons in the peripheral system, processes all the incoming information, and then sends out responsive commands to muscles and organs and glands via motor neurons in the peripheral nervous system.

CHAPTER OUTLINE

NEUROENDOCRINE CONTROL (pp. 966-967)
THE IMPORTANCE OF CHEMICAL MESSENGERS (pp 967-968)
    The Role of Receptors
    How Molecular Signals are Sent
    Factories for Making Molecular Messengers: Endocrine Glands
HOW HORMONES WORK (pp. 969-973)
    Steroid Hormones Enter Cells
    Peptide Hormones Do Not Enter Cells

KEY TERMS

TOPIC EXERCISES

1. Hormones that have opposite effects are called antagonistic. Arrange the following six hormones into their three proper antagonistic pairs. For each pair, indicate what body parameter the pair affects.

    Hormones: calcitonin, GHRH, glucagon, insulin, parathyroid hormone, somatostatin.

    Pairs   Affects

    a.

    b.

    c.

2. Complete the following table by filling in the blanks with the appropriate term.

Hormone	Where Produced	Function
Aldosterone	a. _____	Maintain proper Na^+ and K^+ balance
ACTH	b. _____	c. _____
d. _____	e. _____	Stimulate uterine contractions and milk ejection
Insulin	f. _____	g. _____

3. Indicate the hormonal chain of command by using the following terms to fill in the blanks. Each blank should contain the name of the endocrine gland and, in parentheses, the hormone it produces.

    Terms: anterior pituitary, hypothalamus, luteinizing hormone (LH), ovary, progesterone, releasing hormone

    Chain of Command:

    a. _____ --> b. _____ --> c. _____

LEARNING CHECKLIST

1. List the three separate motor command systems employed by the central nervous system.
2. List the four steps involved in hormonal communication in the vertebrate body.
3. What type of molecules recognize and bind to hormones? Where are they located?
4. Name the two general chemical categories of hormones. Which type uses second messengers?
5. Name two hormones released by the posterior pituitary. Where are these hormones produced?
6. List seven hormones released by the anterior pituitary. Where are these hormones produced? What stimulates their production?
7. List the two components of the adrenal gland and the hormones each produces.
8. What two hormones control the level of glucose in the blood?

9. What organ or part of an organ is at the top of the chain of command and controls the neuroendocrine system?
10. Name the two control mechanisms used by the hypothalamus to regulate production of anterior pituitary hormones.
11. Name three types of nonendocrine hormones.

MINI EXAM

A. Circle the letter of the one best answer for each question.

1. Releasing hormones are produced by
   a. the hypothalamus
   b. the anterior pituitary
   c. the posterior pituitary
   d. the ovaries and testes
   e. it depends on which releasing hormone you're talking about

2. Releasing hormones directly affect
   a. the hypothalamus
   b. the anterior pituitary
   c. the posterior pituitary
   d. the ovaries and testes
   e. it depends on which releasing hormone you're talking about

3. Which two hormones in your body are absolutely essential for survival?
   a. calcitonin and insulin
   b. parathyroid hormone and aldosterone
   c. estrogen and testosterone
   d. somatotropin and cortisol
   e. vasopressin and thyroxine

4. Which of the following statements about prostaglandins is true?
   a. they are one of the types of receptor proteins found in many cells
   b. they are produced by endocrine glands
   c. they travel throughout the body by circulating in the blood
   d. all of the above are true
   e. none of the above are true

5. Robert Wadlow grew to a gigantic size because of a tumor in his
   a. adrenal glands
   b. thyroid gland
   c. hypothalamus
   d. parathyroid glands
   e. pituitary gland

6. The hypothalamus is connected to the anterior pituitary by
   a. neural connections
   b. sinuses
   c. short blood vessels
   d. membrane receptors
   e. none of the above

7. The target tissue for luteinizing hormone is the
   a. liver
   b. kidneys
   c. pancreas
   d. thyroid gland
   e. gonads

8. Which of the following hormones has no known function in mammals?
   a. MSH
   b. GHRH
   c. PRL
   d. calcitonin
   e. vasopressin

9. Insulin and glucagon are produced in the
   a. hypothalamus
   b. anterior pituitary
   c. liver
   d. pancreas
   e. adrenal gland

10. Diabetes is caused by a deficiency of
    a. protein
    b. glucagon
    c. glucose
    d. glycogen
    e. insulin

11. Noradrenaline and adrenaline are produced by the
    a. anterior pituitary
    b. pancreas
    c. adrenal cortex
    d. adrenal medulla
    e. gonads

12. Noradrenaline and adrenaline are not only hormones, but are also
    a. neurotransmitters in the somatic nervous system
    b. neurotransmitters in the sympathetic nervous system
    c. digestive enzymes
    d. all of the above
    e. none of the above

13. Which of the following is not a peptide hormone?
    a. insulin
    b. endorphins
    c. testosterone
    d. ADH
    e. all of the above are peptide hormones

14. How many amino acid units are in an enkephalin hormone?
    a. 1
    b. 5
    c. 32
    d. hundreds
    e. thousands

15. What type of hormone appears to regulate emotional responses in the brain?
    a. prostaglandins
    b. enkephalins
    c. endorphins
    d. atrial peptides
    e. gastrin

16. What type of hormones enter their target cells, bind with a receptor protein, penetrate the nucleus, and influence the transcription of genes?
    a. steroid hormones
    b. peptide hormones
    c. both of the above
    d. none of the above

17. Which of the following statements about how insulin works is true?
    a. most vertebrate cells have glycoprotein receptors for insulin on their cell membranes
    b. insulin binding causes phosphorylation of tyrosine and production of cyclic AMP
    c. inositol phosphates amplify the insulin signal
    d. all of the above
    e. none of the above

18. Which of the following statements is true?
    a. one hormone can play different roles in different parts of the body
    b. one cell may use more than one second messenger
    c. both of the above
    d. none of the above

19. Which of the following is not a steroid hormone?
    a. thyroid hormone (TH)
    b. cortisol
    c. estrogen
    d. progesterone
    e. all of the above are steroid hormones

20. Gastrin is produced by the
    a. liver
    b. large intestine
    c. pancreas
    d. brain
    e. stomach

B. Provide the appropriate term to complete each statement.

1. In the early 1960s, cyclic AMP was described as a second messenger by Earl _____.

2. All steroid hormones are derived from _____.

3. Hormones are chemical extensions of the _____ system.

4. Aspirin inhibits production of _____.

5. In the neuroendocrine chain of command, the anterior pituitary receives orders from the _____.

6. _____ are chemicals that are made at one place in the body and exert their influence at another place in the body.

7. Another name for antidiuretic hormone (ADH) is _____.

8. Neural connections run from the hypothalamus to the _____.

9. Another name for growth hormone (GH) is _____.

10. Lack of iodine in your diet may lead to a greatly enlarged thyroid gland which is called a _____.

C. Briefly answer the following question.

1. Persons with diabetes have high levels of glucose in their blood. People with hypoglycemia have the opposite problem: low blood glucose levels. Besides fasting, what might be a cause of hypoglycemia, and why can it be a serious problem?

CHAPTER ANSWERS

TOPIC EXERCISES

1. a. calcitonin and parathyroid hormone   blood calcium levels
   b. GHRH and somatostatin   release of GH from anterior pituitary
   c. glucagon and insulin   blood glucose levels

2. a. adrenal cortex
   b. anterior pituitary
   c. stimulate production of adrenal cortex hormones
   d. oxytocin
   e. hypothalamus
   f. beta cells in islets of Langerhans in pancreas
   g. decrease blood glucose level

3. a. hypothalamus (releasing hormone)
   b. anterior pituitary (luteinizing hormone, LH)
   c. ovary (progesterone)

LEARNING CHECKLIST

1. autonomic nervous system, voluntary nervous system, neuroendocrine system (p. 966)

2. issuing the command, transporting the signal, hitting the target, having an effect (p. 968)

3. receptor proteins; in target cell membranes or cytoplasm (pp. 967, 969-970)

4. steroid hormones and peptide hormones; peptide hormones (pp. 969-971)

5. vasopressin (antidiuretic hormone, ADH) and oxytocin; produced in hypothalamus (pp. 974-975)

6. thyroid-stimulating hormone (TSH), luteinizing hormone (LH), follicle-stimulating hormone (FSH), adrenocorticotropic hormone (ACTH), somatotropin (growth hormone, GH), prolactin (PRL), and melatonin (melanocyte-stimulating hormone, MSH); all produced in anterior pituitary; production stimulated by specific releasing hormone from hypothalamus (pp. 977, 981-983)

7. adrenal medulla: produces epinephrine and norepinephrine; adrenal cortex: produces cortisol and aldosterone (p. 979)

8. insulin and glucagon (p. 980)

9. the hypothalamus (part of the diencephalon of the forebrain) (p. 981)

10. CNS control, feedback control (p. 983)

11. neurohormones, prostaglandins, atrial peptides (pp. 983-984)

MINI EXAM

A.
1. a	2. b	3. b	4. e	5. e	6. c
7. e	8. a	9. d	10. e	11. d	12. b
13. c	14. b	15. c	16. a	17. d	18. c
19. a	20. e				

B.
1. Sutherland	2. cholesterol	3. nervous
4. prostaglandins	5. hypothalamus	6. Hormones
7. vasopressin	8. posterior pituitary	9. somatotropin
10. goiter		

C. 1. Hypoglycemia can be caused by overly active beta cells in the islets of Langerhans in the pancreas secreting too much insulin and overbalancing glucagon production or by underactive alpha cells in the islets of Langerhans secreting too little glucagon. Hypoglycemia can be serious because glucose is the main fuel source for cells; it is the oxidation of glucose that provides the ATP necessary to keep the cells running. (p. 980 and Chapter 8)

48: LOCOMOTION

IN THE GRAND SCHEME

Of the three kingdoms of multicellular organisms, animals are by far the most active. Plants and fungi are sedentary, growing in one spot. If they move, it is passively as a result of being blown by the wind or carried along by moving water. Some animals are also sedentary and passive movers, but the vast majority of animals exhibit locomotion. They actively move their body parts and actively move from place to place. Such movement has resulted in the active lifestyle we associate with animals - the running, swimming, flying, hopping, crawling, walking and other motions that are employed to migrate, obtain food, flee from danger, and so on. All animal locomotion follows the same basic principle: muscles contract and work against an internal or external skeleton, which results in particular body parts being moved. For vertebrates, the skeleton is internal and is composed of bone and/or cartilage. The microscopic anatomy of skeletal muscles results in contractions that can generate significant force. The contracting of muscles is not random, but is under the control of the central nervous system.

FOR REVIEW

Actin: All eukaryotic cells have a network of protein fibers that crisscross their cytoplasm. Actin filaments, microtubules, and intermediate filaments are the three types of protein fibers that comprise this cytoskeleton. Actin molecules spontaneously form their filament structures. These actin filaments are also called microfilaments and play a major role in determining cell shape. Actin filaments also function in cell movement and the contraction of muscle cells.

ATP: ATP, adenosine triphosphate, is the universal energy currency of all living organisms and cells. Energy must be supplied if work is to be done, and whenever work is performed by a cell, the necessary energy is supplied by breaking one of the high-energy phosphate bonds of ATP. This releases energy (to do work) and leaves ADP (adenosine diphosphate) and P_i (inorganic phosphate). There is a continual cycling between ATP and ADP + P_i in living cells. Cellular respiration uses the energy released by oxidizing foodstuffs to synthesize ATP from ADP + P_i. Without ATP, a cell could not work and therefore the organism could not live; it could not carry out active transport or contract muscles, for example.

Bone: Bone is a type of structural connective tissue. Connective tissue, in turn, is one of the four major types of vertebrate tissues. Bone is essentially a special type of cartilage (another type of structural connective tissue). In bone, the collagen fibers are coated with calcium phosphate salts, so that bone is strong without being brittle.

Striated muscle: Striated muscle is one of the three types of muscle found in vertebrates. It is also called skeletal muscle and is under voluntary or conscious control. It is responsible for movement of the vertebrate skeleton. Striated muscle cells are formed by the fusion of several cells during development. The resulting fiber can contract simultaneously and exert considerable force.

Neuromuscular junction: The synapse between a neuron and a muscle cell is called a neuromuscular junction. The neurotransmitter released by the neuron axon is acetylcholine. It binds to receptors in the postsynaptic membrane of the muscle cell and triggers contraction of the muscle.

CHAPTER OUTLINE

KEY TERMS

p. 1003: summation, recruitment
p. 1004: tetanus, motor unit, isometric tension, isotonic
p. 1005: oxygen debt, Cori cycle, fatigue
p. 1006: dense bodies, fiber types, slow oxidative, fast oxidative, fast glycolytic, myosin isozymes, myoglobin, hypertrophy, disuse atrophy
p. 1007: calmodulin, myosin light chain kinase (MLCK)

TOPIC EXERCISES

1. Match each of the following organisms with the type of skeleton it has. Skeleton terms may be used more than once.

   a. clam   i. no skeleton

   b. shark   ii. hydroskeleton

   c. jellyfish   iii. exoskeleton

   d. human   iv. endoskeleton

   e. earthworm

   f. grasshopper

2. Label the following parts on the sarcomere drawn below: actin filament, myosin filament, S-1 head, Z line.

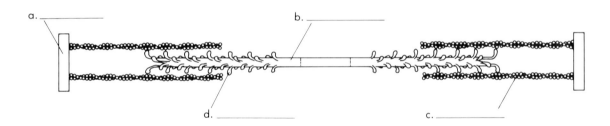

a. _____   b. _____

d. _____   c. _____

3. The sarcomere illustrated in the previous question is at rest. In the space below, draw what the same sarcomere would look like if it was contracted.

LEARNING CHECKLIST

1. Name the force that tends to hold objects in one place.
2. What are bone cells called? Name the 2 structural elements of which vertebrate bones are composed.
3. Name the three kinds of joints.
4. Name the three types of skeleton found in animals and state what each is composed of.
5. Name the two subdivisions of the human skeleton.
6. List the three types of vertebrate muscle cells.
7. Name the five proteins that are found in myofilaments. Which two are the major components?
8. Describe how actin and myosin filaments move relative to each other when a muscle cell contracts. What role do the myosin heads play in this movement?
9. Describe, in general terms, what happens when a neuron stimulates a striated muscle to contract. Your answer should mention what roles are played by the neurotransmitter, the calcium ions and their channels, the sarcoplasm and sarcoplasm reticulum, and the myofilament proteins.
10. What two factors determine the total amount of force developed by skeletal muscles?
11. Distinguish between isometric and isotonic muscle contractions.
12. How do cardiac muscle contractions differ from skeletal muscle contractions?

MINI EXAM

A. Circle the letter of the one best answer for each question.
   1. When a muscle is at rest, Ca^{++} ions are concentrated within the spaces of the
      a. actin filaments
      b. myosin filaments
      c. Z lines
      d. sarcoplasmic reticulum

   2. During muscle contraction, Ca^{++} ions bind to
      a. troponin
      b. tropomyosin
      c. alpha-actinin
      d. acetylcholine
      e. cyclic AMP

   3. When a muscle is at rest, what blocks myosin from binding to actin?
      a. inositol triphosphate
      b. alpha-actinin
      c. Ca^{++}
      d. troponin
      e. tropomyosin

   4. During muscle contraction, which of the following shortens?
      a. Z lines
      b. sarcomere
      c. actin and myosin filaments
      d. all of the above
      e. none of the above

   5. Z lines are composed of
      a. actin
      b. alpha-actinin
      c. myosin
      d. myofilaments
      e. motor end plates

   6. Which of the following statements about muscle contraction is true?
      a. Action potentials last longer in skeletal muscle than in cardiac muscle.
      b. In isometric contractions of skeletal muscle, muscle tension remains constant and the muscle shortens.
      c. When the flexor muscle of your leg contracts, your lower leg moves closer to your thigh.
      d. all of the above
      e. none of the above

7. How much energy is released when a mole of ATP is split into ADP and P_i?
   a. O.73 kcal
   b. 0.0073 kcal
   c. 73 kcal
   d. 730 kcal
   e. 7.3 kcal

8. The muscles of a jellyfish exert their force against
   a. incompressible water
   b. an exoskeleton
   c. an endoskeleton
   d. none of the above; jellyfish don't have muscles

9. How many bones are in the human body?
   a. 26
   b. 73
   c. 118
   d. 206
   e. 481

10. Arthropods have skeletons that are made of
    a. body fluids
    b. bone
    c. cartilage
    d. chitin
    e. actin and myosin

11. Muscles are connected to bones by
    a. crossbridges
    b. ligaments
    c. tendons
    d. sutures
    e. marrow

12. Which of the following substances is most brittle?
    a. muscle
    b. cartilage
    c. bone
    d. chitin

13. An actin filament consists of how many strings of actin proteins wrapped around each other?
    a. 2
    b. 4
    c. 10
    d. hundreds
    e. thousands

14. What process converts lactic acid to glucose and returns it to the muscle?
    a. fatigue
    b. the Cori cycle
    c. summation
    d. tetanus
    e. recruitment

15. What changes shape when myofilaments contract?
    a. actin filaments
    b. Z lines
    c. myosin heads
    d. all of the above
    e. none of the above

16. What is attached to Z lines in a sarcomere?
    a. myosin heads
    b. actin filaments
    c. myosin tails
    d. crossbridges
    e. neurons

17. The contracting units of a myofibril are called
    a. muscle cells
    b. flexors
    c. extensors
    d. sarcoplasms
    e. sarcomeres

18. Which of the following is believed to be a chemical messenger that might link the muscle cell membrane with the sarcoplasmic reticular membrane?
    a. inositol triphosphate
    b. acetylcholine
    c. calmodulin
    d. cyclic AMP
    e. collagen fibers

19. New bone is formed by cells called
    a. osteocytes
    b. lamellae
    c. osteoblasts
    d. Haversians
    e. fontanels

20. Which of the following is <u>not</u> part of the appendicular skeleton?
    a. pectoral girdle
    b. pelvic girdle
    d. cranium
    e. all of the above are c.clavicleappendicular

B. Provide the appropriate term to complete each statement.

1. _____ is the neurotransmitter that is released at neuromuscular junctions with striated muscle.

2. The energy needed to counteract the force of gravity and move an object is provided by molecules of _____.

3. Bone contains crystals of _____, a mineral that contains calcium.

4. _____ are skeletons composed of internal body fluids.

5. Arthropod exoskeletons are made of _____, which is relatively brittle.

6. During contraction of smooth muscles, Ca^{++} binds with a protein called _____.

7. A(n) _____ is the set of muscle fibers innervated by all the branches of the axon of a single motor neuron.

8. In striated muscles, the cytoplasm is called the _____.

9. In striated muscles, the endoplasmic reticulum is called the _____.

10. The signal for a striated muscle to contract comes from the _____ via motor neurons.

C. Briefly answer the following question.

1. The exoskeleton of arthropods limits the body size that can be achieved because of its brittleness and subsequent need for bulk. Why do you suppose the largest arthropods (e.g., lobsters, crabs) occur in the oceans, not on land?

CHAPTER 48 ANSWERS

TOPIC EXERCISES

1. a. iii   b. iv   c. ii
    d. iv   e. ii   f. iii

2. a. Z line   b. myosin filament
    c. actin filament d. S-1 head

3.

Note: Overall sarcomere length has decreased so that myosin filaments are closer to Z line and unattached ends of actin filaments are closer together, but length of the Z lines, myosin filaments and actin filaments have not changed.

LEARNING CHECKLIST

1. gravity (p. 988)

2. osteoblasts and osteocytes; spongy bone tissue and compact bone tissue (pp. 989-990)

3. sutures, cartilaginous joints, freely movable joints (p. 990)

4. hydroskeleton: composed of internal body fluids; exoskeleton: composed of chitin (arthropod skeleton); endoskeleton: composed of cartilage and/or bone (pp. 991-994)

5. axial skeleton, appendicular skeleton (p. 994)

6. smooth muscle, striated muscle, cardiac muscle (p. 996)

7. actin, myosin, tropomyosin, troponin, alpha-actinin; two major components = actin and myosin (pp. 998-999)

8. Actin and myosin filaments are interdigitated and slide past each other during contraction. The movement is caused by a change in shape of the myosin heads which temporarily attach to and "walk" or ratchet along the actin filament. (pp. 999-1001)

9. The neuron releases a neurotransmitter, which causes calcium ion channels to open in the muscle cell membrane and in the sarcoplasmic reticulum membrane. This causes Ca^{++} ions to flood into the sarcoplasm (cytoplasm) of the muscle and interact with the sarcomeres. The Ca^{++} ions bind with one of the myofilament proteins and cause conformational changes that allow the myosin heads to bind to the actin filament; thus contraction occurs. (p. 1002)

10. summation, recruitment (p. 1003)

11. isometric = muscle length stays constant, but tension increases; isotonic = muscle length decreases, but tension is constant (pp. 1004-1005)

12. cardiac muscle contracts as a unit, action potential lasts longer, individual contractions cannot summate (p.1005)

MINI EXAM

A.

1. d	2. a	3. e	4. b	5. b	6. c
7. e	8. a	9. d	10. d	11. c	12. d
13. a	14. b	15. c	16. b	17. e	18. a
19. c	20. d				

B.

1. Acetylcholine	2. ATP	3. hydroxyapatite
4. Hydroskeletons	5. chitin	6. calmodulin
7. motor unit	8. sarcoplasm	9. sarcoplasmic reticulum
10. central nervous system		

C. The sea water provides buoyancy and helps support the arthropod. It can grow to larger size without as thick an exoskeleton as it would need on land for the same size. It can grow larger without having to become so thick that it loses the ability to move (p. 991)

49: FUELING BODY ACTIVITIES: DIGESTION

IN THE GRAND SCHEME

All organisms require energy to live and to carry out their life functions. ATP, the energy currency of organisms, is obtained from the oxidation of energy-rich organic compounds. Since vertebrates cannot synthesize these organics from inorganic sources, they must obtain them preformed by eating other organisms. Vertebrates have evolved highly efficient digestive systems to process their food. Various chambers along the one-way tract are specialized for functions such as obtaining the food, mechanically breaking the food into small pieces, temporarily storing it, using acids and enzymes to break it into molecular fragments, absorbing the small building-block molecules, and passing the unabsorbed waste materials outside the body. Our digestive systems process our food - our fuel - and make it available to be utilized by our cells. Without such a system our cells, and thus ourselves, would starve to death. In processing our food, our digestive systems also provide us with the necessary raw materials to make new macromolecules, cells, and tissues.

FOR REVIEW

Acid: Acids are substances that dissociate to form H^+ ions when they are dissolved in water. The higher the concentration of H^+ ions, the stronger the acid. Acid strength is indicated by the pH scale, which is inversely proportional to the H^+ concentration. Pure water has a pH of 7; the stronger the acid, the lower the pH value. All acids have pH values somewhere between 0 and 7.

Glycogen: Organisms store glucose in an insoluble form by converting it to polysaccharides called starches. In animals, the starch molecule is composed of highly branched chains of amylose. Each amylose chain consists of hundreds of glucose molecules linked together. The specific name for this animal starch is glycogen. Glucose is converted to glycogen in the liver.

Lysosome: Cells package their digestive enzymes in vesicles called lysosomes. These vesicles are formed from the Golgi complex and isolate the digestive enzymes so that they can be transported to where they are needed inside or outside the cell while at the same time preventing the enzymes from digesting the cell itself. Maintaining the lysosome membrane requires a constant expenditure of energy. If an adequate supply of ATP is not available, the lysosome membrane is digested and then the rest of the cytoplasm is attacked by the digestive enzymes, killing the cell.

Phagocytosis: During phagocytosis, a cell surrounds and engulfs solid particles such as other cells or food fragments. The particles wind up inside the cell, enfolded in a vesicle. This vesicle can then fuse with a lysosome, and particles can be digested. Phagocytosis is common in protists and in cells lining the digestive tracts of many animals.

Enzyme action: Enzymes are biological catalysts. They catalyze or speed up chemical reactions in living organisms by lowering the activation energies of the reactions. Enzymes are globular proteins with complex three-dimensional shapes that determine their ability to function. An enzyme can only bind with a specific substrate if there is a match between the shape of the enzyme's active site and the shape of the substrate molecule. Any factor that changes or destroys the shape of the enzyme (e.g., such as pH or temperature changes, or inhibitors) decreases the ability of the enzyme to function properly.

Oxidative respiration: Oxidative respiration is the process that provides the energy that is required to keep living organisms alive. All organisms obtain energy to perform work by oxidizing organic compounds and using the energy released during the oxidation to synthesize ATP via proton pumps. Vertebrates eat food to obtain the necessary energy-rich organic compounds, such as sugars and fats, that will be oxidized.

CHAPTER OUTLINE

KEY TERMS

p. 1010: digestion, phagocytosis, food vacuole
p. 1011: digestive cavity, pharynx, extracellular digestion
p. 1012: crop, gizzard, intestine, foregut, midgut, hindgut,
p. 1013: pancreas, proteases, amylases, lipases, duodenum
p. 1014: mastication, teeth, carnivores, herbivores, omnivores
p. 1015: incisors, canines, premolars, molars, saliva, salivary glands, amylase, pulp, enamel, dentin
p. 1016: palate, trachea, larynx, glottis, epiglottis, esophagus
p. 1017: peristalsis, sphincter, mucosa, gastric pits, parietal cells, chief cells, pepsinogen, pepsin, mucus
p. 1018: gastrin, duodenal ulcers
p. 1019: pyloric sphincter
p. 1020: jejunum, ileum, villi, microvilli, lacteals
p. 1021: bicarbonate, liver, bile salts, micelles, emulsification, lecithin, gallbladder, chyme, cholecystokinin (CCK)
p. 1022: portal vein, sinuses, hepatic vein
p. 1023: deamination, ammonia, urea, uric acid, colon, rectum, feces, anus, cloaca
p. 1024: cellulase, lagomorphs, cecum, rumen, ruminant, reticulum
p. 1027: vitamins, ascorbic acid (vitamin C), scurvy, essential amino acids
p. 1028: essential minerals, trace elements, anorexia nervosa, bulimia

TOPIC EXERCISES

1. Match each of the following types of organisms with the type of digestive system they have. A choice may be used more than once.

   a. nematode   i. digestive tract with two openings

   b. cnidarian   ii. food vacuole

   c. earthworm   iii. blind sac with one opening

   d. vertebrate

   e. protist

   f. flatworm

2. Complete the chart below by listing the following terms in their proper sequence to depict the flow of food through an earthworm's digestive system (a = the first chamber the food enters) and state the function of each chamber.

   Terms: crop, gizzard, intestine, pharynx

Chamber	Function
a.	
b.	
c.	
d.	

3. List the following terms in their proper sequence to depict the pathway of food and wastes through the human digestive system.

Terms	Proper Sequence
anus	
colon	
duodenum	
esophagus	
mouth	
pharynx	
rectum	
rest of small intestine	
stomach	

LEARNING CHECKLIST

1. What two types of digestive structures are associated with intracellular digestion? What one type is associated with extracellular digestion?
2. What two types of agents carry out digestion?
3. Name the three general types of enzymes and the substances they digest.
4. Name the four types of teeth that humans have. Which are adapted to our carnivorous diet? Which are adapted to our herbivorous diet?
5. What three things happen when food moves to the back of the mouth in a mammal?
6. Name the two types of secretory cells found in the exocrine glands of the mucosa of the stomach. What substance does each produce?
7. What is the one type of organic molecule that is digested in the stomach?
8. Which single portion of the vertebrate digestive tract carries out the most digestion and absorption of nutrients?
9. Name two structures that greatly increase the surface area of the human intestine.
10. Name four digestive substances (not hormones) produced by the pancreas.
11. Name two functions of the liver.
12. What is the primary function of the large intestine?
13. Name two digestive pouches in mammals that contain bacteria that can digest cellulose. Which does a horse have? Which does a cow have?
14. What is the formula for nutrition?
15. How many different vitamins are required by humans? How many essential amino acids?
16. What are the two most common eating disorders in the United States?

MINI EXAM

A. Circle the letter of the one best answer for each question.
1. Vertebrates store feces in their
    a. rectum
    b. rumen
    c. cecum
    d. crop
    e. sphincter

2. Which of the following does <u>not</u> occur in the mouth?
    a. lubrication of the food
    b. beginning of protein digestion
    c. breaking the food into small fragments
    d. all of the above <u>do</u> occur in the mouth
    e. none of the above occur in the mouth

3. Animals that eat both plant and animal material are called
    a. herbivores
    b. mesentaries
    c. incisors
    d. carnivores
    e. omnivores

4. Which of the following would you be <u>least</u> likely to find in an herbivore?
    a. a rumen or cecum
    b. molars
    c. bacteria in the gut
    d. canine teeth
    e. a large intestine

5. The vast majority of the absorption of nutrients occurs in the
   a. esophagus
   b. colon
   c. small intestine
   d. duodenum
   e. stomach

6. Which of the following statements about digestion is true?
   a. All animals have a digestive cavity with two openings.
   b. Cellulose is easily digested by most animals.
   c. Most vertebrates obtain their nutrients by phagocytosis.
   d. It is normal and healthy for vertebrates to have colonies of bacteria living in their digestive tracts.
   e. Digestion occurs in only one chamber or region of the vertebrate digestive system.

7. Villi and microvilli are found in the
   a. esophagus
   b. stomach
   c. crop
   d. large intestine
   e. small intestine

8. Most ulcers occur in the
   a. colon
   b. duodenum
   c. esophagus
   d. stomach
   e. pancreas

9. Which of the following passageways is part of the cloaca of vertebrates?
   a. the rectum
   b. the reproductive tract
   c. the urinary tract
   d. all of the above
   e. none of the above

10. Enzymes that break up starches and other carbohydrates are called
    a. proteases
    b. lipases
    c. amylases
    d. triglycerides
    e. cholecystokinin

11. The pancreas produces digestive enzymes and releases them into the
    a. colon
    b. esophagus
    c. liver
    d. stomach
    e. duodenum

12. How many canine teeth does an adult human have?
    a. 0
    b. 2
    c. 4
    d. 6
    e. 8

13. The lubricating fluid that is released into the mouth is called
    a. saliva
    b. mucus
    c. gastrin
    d. HCl
    e. pepsin

14. When a mammal swallows, the nasal cavities are closed off by the
    a. esophagus
    b. palate
    c. glottis
    d. larynx
    e. peristalsis

15. A ring of muscle that closes off a passageway is called a
    a. reticulum
    b. villi
    c. gastric pit
    d. cecum
    e. sphincter

16. In the stomach, pepsinogen is converted into
    a. pepsin
    b. bicarbonate
    c. HCl
    d. glycogen
    e. vitamins

17. Bicarbonate is produced by the
    a. duodenum
    b. liver
    c. stomach
    d. pancreas
    e. salivary glands

18. Bile salts are produced by the
    a. stomach
    b. liver
    c. pancreas
    d. gall bladder
    e. duodenum

19. Blood is taken from the stomach and small intestine to the liver via the
    a. portal vein
    b. sinuses
    c. hepatic vein
    d. pyloric sphincter
    e. microvilli

20. Which of the following substances is not produced as a result of deamination?
    a. urea
    b. ammonia
    c. uric acid
    d. HCl
    e. all of the above are produced by deamination

21. Which of the following is not an enzyme?
    a. cellulase
    b. pepsin
    c. gastrin
    d. all of the above are enzymes
    e. none of the above is an enzyme

22. Which of the following is not a function of the liver?
    a. convert glucose to glycogen
    b. convert glycogen to glucose
    c. remove amino groups from amino acids
    d. form urea
    e. all of the above are functions of the liver

23. Which of the following substances cannot be absorbed across the wall of the stomach?
    a. alcohol
    b. water
    c. protein fragments
    d. all of these can be absorbed
    e. none of these can be absorbed

24. Which of the following animals is mismatched with its digestive system characteristic?
    a. sponge - has no digestive cavity
    b. roundworm - carries out extracellular digestion
    c. earthworm - has a crop and a gizzard
    d. cnidarian - has a digestive cavity with two openings
    e. flatworm - has a pharynx

B. Provide the appropriate term to complete each statement.

1. The _____ of earthworms has the same function as the teeth of vertebrates.

2. _____ is a digestive enzyme produced in the salivary glands and the pancreas.

3. Gastrin is produced in the _____.

4. _____ neutralizes acidity in the small intestine.

5. Lysine and tryptophan are examples of essential _____ for humans.

6. The process of degrading or breaking down a complex macromolecule to its simpler components is called _____.

7. Food particles in a food vacuole are digested when a _____ fuses with the vacuole and releases its digestive enzymes.

8. The first part of the small intestine is called the _____.

C. Briefly answer each of the following questions.

1. Commercials on television commonly advertise products that will cure acid stomachs. Are acid stomachs good or bad? Why?

2. Carnivores have stomachs that can distend and hold much more food than our stomachs can. Why is this advantageous?

3. Bacteria and protozoans living in the digestive tracts of animals are examples of a symbiotic relationship that is mutually beneficial. The animals benefit by having the microorganisms digest cellulose and synthesize compounds such as vitamin K for them. How do the bacteria and protozoans benefit?

4. Kwashiorkor is a disease caused by protein deficiency and is common in malnourished people. There has been a surprising increase of kwashiorkor in the United States, not just among poor people but among college students as well. Can you think of an explanation? (Hint: in general, animal material contains a greater diversity of amino acids than does plant material).

CHAPTER 49 ANSWERS

TOPIC EXERCISES

1. a. i   b. iii   c. i
    d. i   e. ii   f. iii

2.

Chamber	Function
a. pharynx	acquisition (obtain food)
b. crop	temporary storage of food
c. gizzard	fragmentation (mechanically break down food)
d. intestine	extracellular digestion (enzymatic digestion and absorption)

3. Proper sequence = mouth, pharynx, esophagus, stomach, duodenum, rest of small intestine, colon, rectum, anus

LEARNING CHECKLIST

1. intracellular: food vacuole, blind sac with one opening; extracellular: digestive tract with two openings (pp. 1010-1012)

2. hydrochloric acid (HCl), specific enzymes (p. 1013)

3. proteases digest proteins; amylases digest starches and other carbohydrates, lipases digest lipids and fats (p. 1013)

4. incisors, canines, premolars, molars; carnivorous = incisors and canines; herbivorous = premolars and molars (p. 1015)

5. the palate closes off the nasal cavities; the swallowing center in the brain is stimulated; respiration is inhibited and the trachea is sealed off (p. 1016)

6. parietal cells - produce HCl; chief cells - produce pepsinogen (p. 1017)

7. protein (pp. 1017-1019)

8. small intestine (pp. 1020-1021)

9. villi, microvilli (p. 1020)

10. proteases, lipases, carbohydrate enzymes, bicarbonate (p. 1021)

11. produce bile salts, regulate blood glucose level; deaminate amino acids (pp. 1021-1023)

12. act as a refuse dump; compacting, storing, and eliminating waste material (pp. 1023-1024)

13. cecum; rumen; horse = cecum; cow = rumen (p. 1024)

14. food - exercise = fat (p. 1025)

15. at least 13 vitamins; 8 essential amino acids (p. 1027)

16. anorexia nervosa and bulimia (p. 1028)

MINI EXAM

A.
1. a	2. b	3. e	4. d	5. c	6. d
7. e	8. b	9. d	10. c	11. e	12. c
13. a	14. b	15. e	16. a	17. d	18. b
19. a	20. d	21. c	22. e	23. c	24. d

B.
1. gizzard	2. Amylase	3. stomach
4. Bicarbonate	5. amino acids	6. digestion
7. lysosome	8. duodenum	

C. 1. A low pH level in the stomach is normal and good; it allows pepsin to function and digest protein, and it physically breaks apart food. Problems arise when the stomach secretes too much acid and when not enough bicarbonate is produced to neutralize it in the duodenum. If the lining of the digestive tract is exposed to too much acid, ulcers can form. Acid in the stomach also helps kill harmful bacteria. (pp. 1017-1019).

2. Finding and catching animals for food is more difficult and less reliable than eating plants. By gorging, carnivores are able to take advantage of a successful kill and utilize it before it can spoil or be eaten by other competitors. (p. 1019)

3. The gut provides a protected, relatively stable environment in which the microorganisms are literally surrounded by their food (pp. 1024-1025)

4. There has been an increase in vegetarianism, and it is difficult to obtain a balanced, complete diet with all the necessary essential amino acids from plants alone. Eating disorders such as anorexia nervosa and bulimia also contribute to malnutrition. (pp. 1027-1028)

50: RESPIRATION

IN THE GRAND SCHEME

All vertebrates carry out aerobic oxidative metabolism. The living cells of vertebrates must obtain oxygen if they are to carry out this metabolism, synthesize ATP, and continue to live. At the same time, the cells must be able to get rid of the carbon dioxide they produce as a by-product of their metabolism. The respiratory systems of vertebrates, whether gills or lungs, are simply mechanical devices that ensure that an adequate exchange of gas can occur: enough oxygen can be taken into the body to meet the metabolic demands of all its cells, and carbon dioxide can be removed. This chapter examines the details of vertebrate respiratory systems (i.e., the mechanics of gas exchange and the anatomy and functioning of the various types of vertebrate respiratory systems). The next chapter deals with the circulatory system, the mechanism for transporting gases between the respiratory organs and the rest of the cells of the body.

FOR REVIEW

Chemistry of carbon dioxide: Carbon dioxide (CO_2) is one of the inorganic compounds thought to have been common on the early earth. All of the carbon atoms found in organic molecules today have come from CO_2 molecules. Carbon dioxide is produced as a by-product of aerobic cellular respiration and some forms of anaerobic respiration. Carbon dioxide is not polar, but reacts with water to form carbonic acid (H_2CO_3).

Diffusion: Unless at a temperature of absolute zero, molecules do not sit still, but move about randomly because of thermal agitation. Over time, there is a net movement of molecules from areas where they are more concentrated to areas of lower concentration. If no other factors interfere, the end result is a uniform distribution or concentration of the molecules throughout the whole system or area in question.

Oxidative respiration: Oxidative respiration is the process by which all vertebrates (and almost all other organisms) obtain the energy they need to survive. Energy-rich organic compounds such as glucose are oxidized, and the energy that is released is used to drive proton pumps and thus synthesize ATP. This is an aerobic process - the energy that drives the proton pump is supplied by electron transport, and oxygen is the ultimate electron acceptor. Cells must obtain oxygen if they are to carry out aerobic oxidative respiration. If oxygen is not available, anaerobic respiration occurs (i.e., fermentation) and there is a much lower yield of ATP per initial molecule of glucose. Carbon dioxide is produced as a by-product of oxidative respiration.

Adaptation of vertebrates to terrestrial living: Vertebrates first evolved in the seas. During the course of their evolution they achieved many adaptations that allowed them to live successfully on land. These adaptations included the amniotic egg and placenta, efficient locomotion, dry skin, and efficient lungs.

Red blood cells: Erythrocytes (red blood cells) are the most common type of blood cells. They produce and are packed with many molecules of hemoglobin that bind and carry oxygen. Because of this, red blood cells are classified as sequestering connective tissue; they sequester or accumulate hemoglobin.

CHAPTER OUTLINE

KEY TERMS

TOPIC EXERCISES

1. For each of the following pairs, circle the member of the pair that would have the higher concentration of oxygen dissolved in it. In each case, the pools are the same size, shape, and temperature, unless otherwise indicated.

    a. At sea level: a salt water swimming pool and a freshwater swimming pool

    b. Freshwater pools: one in Miami (sea level) and one in Denver (over 5200 feet altitude)

    c. Freshwater pools: one at 15°C and one at 27°C

2. Distinguish between the two respiratory terms below by completing the following chart.

Terms	Type of Organism Found in	What it is	What it does
tracheae	a.	b.	c.
trachea	d.	e.	f.

3. Arrange the following terms in their proper sequence to show the pathway that air follows when a human inhales through his or her nose.

Terms	Inhalation Pathway
alveoli	
bronchi	
bronchioles	
glottis	
larynx	
nostrils	
pharynx	
trachea	

LEARNING CHECKLIST

1. List the four main components of air and their percentage composition.
2. What four factors determine how many molecules of a particular gas will be present in water?
3. State Fick's Law of Diffusion and define each term.
4. What are the three general tendencies that have occurred during the evolution of respiratory systems that have increased or optimized the rate of diffusion?
5. How do sponges and cnidarians increase ∆p?
6. Name four different types of respiratory structures found in higher animals. Which is the most efficient?
7. What mechanism makes fish gills so efficient? What two substances are involved in this mechanism and what is their relationship to each other?
8. List the two principal reasons that terrestrial animals do not have gills.
9. Compare the lungs of amphibians, reptiles, and mammals in terms of surface area.
10. How do bird lungs differ from the lungs of amphibians, reptiles, and mammals in terms of air-flow patterns and associated blood vessels? Do these arrangements make bird lungs more or less efficient than the lungs of other terrestrial vertebrates?

11. What happens to the size (volume) of the thoracic cavity when a person inhales? The movement of what two structures causes this volume change, and what directions do they move? Why does this cause the lungs to inflate?
12. Name two carrier proteins that transport oxygen in circulatory systems and state what types of organism have each one.
13. Name three gases that bind to hemoglobin.
14. What part of the brain controls breathing? What is the primary factor being monitored by receptors that determines breathing rate?

MINI EXAM

A. Circle the letter of the one best answer for each question.
1. The most common gas found in air is
   a. oxygen
   b. argon
   c. nitrogen
   d. carbon dioxide
   e. carbon monoxide

2. Which of the following animals have air sacs attached to their lungs?
   a. birds
   b. amphibians
   c. reptiles
   d. mammals
   e. all of the above

3. A countercurrent flow system between substance A and substance B
   a. maximizes the exchange by having A and B flow in the same direction
   b. minimizes the exchange by having A and B flow in the same direction
   c. maximizes the exchange by having A and B flow in opposite directions
   d. minimizes the exchange by having A and B flow in opposite directions

4. Carbon dioxide is converted into carbonic acid in the cytoplasm of red blood cells by the enzyme
   a. hemoglobin
   b. carbonic anhydrase
   c. DPG
   d. carbon monoxide
   e. hemocyanin

5. Which of the following is not a way to increase the efficiency of a respiratory system?
   a. increase the surface area available for diffusion of gases
   b. decrease the distance over which the gases must diffuse
   c. increase the concentration differences of gases inside and outside the system
   d. dry the system out so the gases do not have to diffuse through water
   e. all of the above will increase efficiency

6. Oxygen and carbon dioxide move in and out of cells by
   a. diffusion
   b. active transport
   c. both of the above
   d. none of the above

7. Which of the following respiratory systems is most efficient at obtaining oxygen from the surrounding environment?
   a. mammal lungs
   b. reptile lungs
   c. amphibian lungs
   d. bird lungs
   e. fish gills

8. During exhalation in humans, air moves from the bronchus into the
   a. bronchioles
   b. alveoli
   c. nostrils
   d. pharynx
   e. trachea

9. The majority of carbon dioxide is transported in the blood
   a. attached to hemoglobin
   b. bound to oxygen
   c. dissolved in the plasma
   d. as carbon monoxide in the red blood cells
   e. as bicarbonate ions in the red blood cells

10. The Bohr effect explains why
    a. hemoglobin binds carbon monoxide more readily than oxygen
    b. hemoglobin unloads its oxygen when it encounters low pH
    c. diffusion occurs so slowly over long distances
    d. oxygen is present in the atmosphere in relatively low concentrations
    e. some introductory biology students don't like their instructor

11. Hemocyanin
    a. uses iron to bind oxygen
    b. turns blue when it combines with oxygen
    c. is found in invertebrate erythrocytes
    d. all of the above
    e. none of the above

12. One atmosphere of pressure equals
    a. 1 mm Hg
    b. 380 mm Hg
    c. 600 mm Hg
    d. 760 mm Hg
    e. 1000 mm Hg

13. Which of the following is the most soluble in water?
    a. carbon dioxide
    b. oxygen
    c. nitrogen
    d. they all have the same solubility

14. In the formula for Fick's Law of Diffusion, the distance a molecule must travel is symbolized as
    a. D
    b. A
    c. d
    d. R
    e. none of the above

15. Diffusion alone is effective only over distances less than approximately
    a. 0.5 mm
    b. 5.0 mm
    c. 0.5 cm
    d. 5.0 cm
    e. 0.5 m

16. Which of the following animals have tracheae?
    a. earthworms
    b. grasshoppers
    c. cnidarians
    d. all of the above
    e. none of the above

17. Mollusks have
    a. no specialized respiratory organ
    b. lungs
    c. tracheae
    d. gills

18. Gas exchange in birds occurs in the
    a. pharynx
    b. operculum
    c. air sacs
    d. alveoli
    e. parabronchi

19. Which of the following would have the highest concentration of oxygen?
    a. a liter of sea water
    b. a liter of fresh water
    c. a liter of air at sea level
    d. a liter of air at the top of Mt. Everest
    e. all would have equal amounts of oxygen

20. The residual volume in adult bird lungs is
    a. 0
    b. about 500 ml
    c. about 800 ml
    d. about 1200 ml
    e. about 3000 ml

21. When a bird breathes, air moves from the lung into the
    a. posterior air sac
    b. anterior air sacs
    c. trachea
    d. pharynx
    e. it depends if the bird is inhaling or exhaling

22. The respiratory control center of humans is located in the
    a. blood-brain barrier
    b. alveoli
    c. erythrocytes
    d. brainstem
    e. trachea

23. The volume of air that remains in your lungs after a normal resting expiration is called the
    a. expiratory reserve
    b. respiratory minute volume
    c. functional residual capacity
    d. vital capacity
    e. residual volume

B. Provide the appropriate term to complete each statement.

1. In mammals, the site of gas exchange is the _____ of the _____.

2. The _____ is a sheet-like muscle that separates the chest cavity from the abdominal cavity in a mammal.

3. Another name for the windpipe is the _____.

4. The lungs and the chest cavity are covered with a thin smooth membrane called the _____.

5. The voice box of humans is also called the _____.

6. Another name for the chest cavity is the _____ cavity.

7. The water formed during aerobic oxidative respiration is called _____ water.

8. The weight or pressure of the air around us is measured as _____ pressure.

9. _____ flow describes the flow pattern of air and capillary blood in bird lungs.

10. _____ is the process of forcing air out of our lungs and bodies.

C. Briefly answer each of the following questions.

1. Why isn't it efficient for aquatic animals such as fish and amphibian larvae to move their gills through the water? Why do they do it?

2. Are there any terrestrial animals that are truly independent of water?

CHAPTER 50 ANSWERS

TOPIC EXERCISES

1. a. freshwater swimming pool
   b. one in Miami
   c. one at 15°C

2. a. insects (arthropods)
   b. network of passageways leading from body surface to interior cells
   c. provides air passageway for direct diffusion of O_2 into and CO_2 out of interior cells
   d. vertebrates
   e. windpipe, connects larynx and bronchi
   f. provides passageway for movement of air into and out of lungs

3. nostrils, pharynx, glottis, larynx, trachea, bronchi, bronchioles, alveoli

LEARNING CHECKLIST

1. Nitrogen = 78.09%; oxygen = 20.95%; noble gases = 0.93%; carbon dioxide = 0.03% (p. 1032)

2. Composition of the air in contact with the water; solubility of the gas; temperature of the air and water; solute concentration of the water (p. 1033)

3. R = D x A x Δp/d; R = rate of diffusion, D = diffusion constant, A = area across which diffusion occurs, Δp = difference in concentration or partial pressures, d = distance molecule must travel (p. 1034)

4. Increasing A (surface area available for diffusion); decreasing d (distance traveled); increasing Δp (concentration difference) (p. 1035)

5. By creating a water current (p. 1035)

6. External gills, tracheae, branchial gills, lungs; branchial gills are the most efficient (pp. 1035-1038)

7. Countercurrent flow (or exchange); water and blood flow past each other in opposite directions (pp. 1036-1038)

8. Air is less buoyant than water and cannot adequately support the gill tissue; water diffuses into air via evaporation and too much water would be lost from gills exposed to air (p. 1038)

9. There is increasing internal surface area going from amphibians to reptiles to mammals. (pp. 1039-1040)

10. Amphibians, reptiles, and mammals have saclike lungs with a two-way flow of air; air comes in and goes out the same passageway and there is always a residual volume. Because of the arrangement of bird lungs with posterior and anterior air sacs, there is a one-way flow of air through the lungs and no residual volume. In addition, the blood vessels are arranged so that there is a cross-current flow of blood past the air spaces in the lungs. These arrangements make bird lungs more efficient than the other lungs (pp. 1039-1041)

11. It increases; rib cage moves up and out, diaphragm moves down (flattens out); air sucked into lungs because of lower pressure there (pp. 1041-1044)

12. Hemoglobin - found in vertebrates and some invertebrates; hemocyanin - found in invertebrates (p. 1046)

13. Oxygen, carbon dioxide, carbon monoxide (p. 1046-1047)

14. Respiratory control center in the brainstem; level of CO_2 and thus pH of the blood (pp. 1048-1049)

MINI EXAM

A.
1. c	2. a	3. c	4. b	5. d	6. a
7. e	8. e	9. e	10. b	11. b	12. d
13. a	14. c	15. a	16. b	17. d	18. e
19. c	20. a	21.b	22. d	23. c	

B.
1. alveoli, lungs
2. diaphragm
3. trachea
4. pleural membrane
5. larynx
6. thoracic
7. metabolic
8. barometric
9. Cross-current
10. Exhalation (Passive expiration)

C. 1. Gills are highly branched and provide a lot of resistance to being swept through water; therefore the animal expends a lot of energy in the process. Gills are also delicate and are exposed to potential damage when waving around in the water. But animals that wave their gills do not have branchial chambers to pump water, and waving is better than having no movement of water across the gills at all. Although energetically costly and potentially dangerous, waving at least prevents depleted water (oxygen-poor, carbon dioxide-rich) from building up around the gills. It helps increase Δp. (pp. 1035-1036)

2. Many terrestrial animals are independent of water in terms of being able to reproduce on land and being able to live in very dry environments. By using metabolic water and/or eating food with a high water content, some animals can even survive without ever drinking water. But no animals are truly independent of water. The membranes of cells must be kept moist to retain their integrity, and water is the major constituent of all living cells and bodies (pp. 1032-1033)

51: CIRCULATION

IN THE GRAND SCHEME

Complex, three-dimensional, multicellular animals could not exist without some sort of circulatory system. The circulatory system transports needed materials such as food, oxygen, and water to cells and at the same time removes waste materials from them. In a multicellular animal, the distances that materials have to move are too great to be covered by simple diffusion. Cells in your brain and arms and legs would starve to death before glucose could reach them by diffusing from the intestine, or they would suffocate from lack of oxygen or die from the buildup of toxic waste materials that were not removed quickly enough. Blood travels close to every living cell in the body and helps integrate all the different parts into one functional whole. All of the other organ systems interact with the circulatory system in one way or another. Blood not only carries gases, nutrients, and wastes, it also transports hormones and distributes heat. By monitoring and regulating where the blood goes and what it contains, vertebrates can fine-tune and coordinate the efficient operation of all their organs.

FOR REVIEW

Erythrocytes: Red blood cells (erythrocytes) are one of the types of sequestering connective tissues found in vertebrate bodies. They are the most common type of blood cell, and they are packed with molecules of hemoglobin. The hemoglobin is produced in the erythrocytes and is used to transport both oxygen and carbon dioxide in the blood.

Cardiac muscle: Muscle is one of the four basic types of vertebrate tissue, and cardiac (heart) muscle is one of the three types of muscle. In cardiac muscle, the contracting fibers are interconnected and form a latticework. Because of the direct electrical junction between fibers, depolarization of one fiber causes a wave of contraction to spread throughout the whole heart muscle and the heart contracts as a unit rather than a little bit at a time.

Depolarization: Depolarization is responsible for the contraction of cardiac muscle and for the transmission of nerve impulses. During depolarization there is a change in cell membrane charges as transmembrane channels open and ions flood into and out of the cells.

How hemoglobin carries oxygen: Hemoglobin is a protein that is composed of four polypeptide chains. Each chain has an iron ion that can reversibly bind oxygen. Thus each hemoglobin molecule can carry up to four oxygen molecules. Factors such as the partial pressure of oxygen, temperature, and pH will determine how much oxygen is bound to the hemoglobin at any one time.

CHAPTER OUTLINE

KEY TERMS

TOPIC EXERCISES

1. Match the following components of the circulatory system with their proper functions.

   a. arteries

   b. capillaries

   c. erythrocytes

   d. heart

   e. leukocytes

   f. platelets

   g. veins

   i. contain hemoglobin

   ii. help initiate blood clotting

   iii. carry blood toward the heart

   iv. site of gas and metabolite exchange

   v. carry blood away from the heart

   vi. defend body against invading bacteria and other foreign substances

   vii. pumping device for moving blood

2. Use the following terms to construct the heart of a fish, a frog, a lizard, and a bird. Indicate the components of each of these types of hearts by placing the appropriate letter in the chart below.

   Parts:
   a. conus arteriosus
   d. left ventricle
   g. single atrium
   j. sinus venosus

   b. conus arteriosus with septum
   e. right atrium
   h. single ventricle

   c. left atrium
   f. right ventricle
   i. single ventricle with septum

   Animal   Heart Components

   fish

   frog

   lizard

   bird

3. Trace the pathway of blood through an adult human heart by arranging the following terms in their proper sequence, beginning with the right atrium.

   Terms   Pathway

   aortic valve   right atrium
   bicuspid valve
   left atrium
   left ventricle
   pulmonary valve
   right atrium
   right ventricle
   tricuspid valve

LEARNING CHECKLIST

1. Name the two types of circulatory systems. Which type do vertebrates have?
2. What are the four principal functions of the vertebrate circulatory system?
3. Name the three basic elements of the vertebrate circulatory system.
4. List the five types of vessels found in the vertebrate cardiovascular system, their function, and the number of tissue layers of which they are composed.
5. What role does the lymphatic system play in helping maintain the body's water balance?
6. Name the four components of blood plasma.
7. List the three principal types of cells in the blood.
8. Name the four chambers of the fish heart. How are they arranged?
9. During the evolution of vertebrate hearts from fish, through amphibians and reptiles, to birds and mammals, what trends can be seen (e.g., what happened to each of the four fish heart chambers)?
10. Name the four chambers of the human heart.
11. When the heart contracts, where does the depolarization begin? To what two other tissues does it travel?
12. What are three ways that the heart's performance can be monitored?
13. Name the two separate factors that control arteriolar smooth muscle tension.
14. Name two types of receptors that monitor physical characteristics of the blood in the circulatory system.

MINI EXAM

A. Circle the letter of the one best answer for each question.

1. Which of the following contains oxygenated blood in an adult human?
   a. right atrium
   b. pulmonary artery
   c. pulmonary vein
   d. all of the above
   e. none of the above

2. The sinoatrial node is derived from the more primitive
   a. ventricle
   b. bundle of His
   c. conus arteriosus
   d. tricuspid valve
   e. sinus venosus

3. If you have your blood pressure read and it is 115/75, your diastolic pressure is:
   a. 115
   b. 75
   c. 190
   d. 40
   e. 1.5

4. Water that diffuses out of the blood plasma is returned to the cardiovascular system by the
   a. hepatic vein
   b. aorta
   c. lymphatic system
   d. megakaryocytes
   e. septum

5. In adult humans, blood flows from the left atrium into the
   a. right atrium
   b. pulmonary veins
   c. aorta
   d. left ventricle
   e. right ventricle

6. Heart murmurs are caused by
   a. leaky valves
   b. emphysema
   c. erythropoiesis
   d. atherosclerosis
   e. through-flow channels

7. Systolic blood pressure is read when the
   a. ventricles are relaxed
   b. ventricles are contracted
   c. heart is not beating
   d. none of the above

8. Which of the following is the most muscular chamber in a bird's heart or a mammal's heart?
   a. the right atrium
   b. the left atrium
   c. the left ventricle
   d. the right ventricle
   e. all are equally muscular

9. In which type of heart is there mixing of oxygenated and deoxygenated blood?
   a. fish
   b. frog
   c. crocodile
   d. all of the above
   e. none of the above

10. Which of the following statements about circulatory systems is true?
    a. Hormones are transported in the blood.
    b. All invertebrates have an open circulatory system.
    c. Capillaries have thicker walls than veins do.
    d. The systemic circulation carries blood to and from the lungs.
    e. All of the above are true

11. The pumping devices of circulatory systems are called
    a. arteries
    b. veins
    c. capillaries
    d. valves
    e. hearts

12. Materials are exchanged between the blood and the surrounding tissues in the
    a. arteries
    b. veins
    c. capillaries
    d. all of the above
    e. none of the above

13. Oxygenated blood leaves the heart via the
    a. pulmonary vein
    b. pulmonary artery
    c. vena cava
    d. aorta
    e. respiratory circuit

14. The innermost tissue layer of arteries is composed of
    a. smooth muscle
    b. Purkinje fibers
    c. connective tissue
    d. elastic fibers
    e. endothelial cells

15. Blood flow to a capillary can be shut off by a(n)
    a. erythropoietin
    b. precapillary sphincter
    c. through-flow channel
    d. aortic valve
    e. granulocyte

415

16. The lymphatic system
    a. is an open circulatory system
    b. contains one-way valves
    c. returns fluids to the bloodstream
    d. all of the above
    e. none of the above

17. The major component of blood plasma is
    a. water
    b. proteins
    c. salts and ions
    d. metabolites and wastes
    e. platelets

18. Which of the following is a type of leukocyte?
    a. macrophage
    b. eosinophil
    c. monocyte
    d. all of the above
    e. none of the above

19. When the inner walls of arteries accumulate fat deposits, the condition is called
    a. fibrillation
    b. angina pectoris
    c. atherosclerosis
    d. thrombus
    e. arteriosclerosis

20. What type of tissue is found in human infants only for the first year or so of life and is used to generate heat rapidly since the infant cannot regulate body temperature efficiently by sweating or shivering?
    a. smooth muscle
    b. erythropoietin
    c. Purkinje fibers
    d. basophils
    e. brown fat

21. The main cardiovascular cause of death in the United States is
    a. heart attacks
    b. strokes
    c. angina pectoris
    d. hypertension
    e. vasoconstriction

B. Provide the appropriate term to complete each statement.

1. Each contraction of the heart is initiated by the _____ node.

2. The _____ valve closes the opening between the left atrium and the left ventricle in the human heart.

3. The _____ drains blood from the upper body back to the right atrium.

4. The _____ valve prevents blood from flowing backwards into the left ventricle.

5. The bundle of _____ conducts depolarization over both ventricles.

6. The most common protein in blood plasma is _____.

7. _____ refers to the fraction of the total blood volume that is occupied by red blood cells.

8. The process by which red blood cells accumulate hemoglobin and lose their nuclei is called _____.

9. The cardiovascular control center which monitors and regulates blood pressure is located in the _____.

C. Briefly answer each of the following questions.

1. What is the advantage and disadvantage to mammals of having no nuclei in their mature erythrocytes?

2. Why is it advantageous to be able to restrict the flow of blood to the extremities during periods of low temperatures or stress (e.g., why do you turn pale when you are scared)?

3. Both elephantiasis and radical mastectomies interfere with the lymphatic system. In elephantiasis, parasitic worms called filaria get into the lymph vessels and block them. When a woman has a radical mastectomy, the lymph glands and vessels are commonly removed from the chest, armpit, and upper arm on the same side from which the cancerous breast is removed. What symptoms would you expect to see in people with elephantiasis or who have had a radical mastectomy?

4. You have been asked by a science fiction fan club to design a large, multicellular animal with no circulatory system. Describe the animal you design -what is its shape? Where does it live? How active is it? Is it ectothermic or endothermic? Explain your answer.

CHAPTER 51 ANSWERS

TOPIC EXERCISES

1.
| a. v | b. iv | c. i | d. vii |
| e. vi | f. ii | g. iii | |

2.

Animal	Heart Components
fish	j, g, h, a
frog	j, e, h, c, b
lizard	j, e, i, c
bird	e, f, c, d

3. right atrium -> tricuspid valve -> right ventricle -> pulmonary valve -> left atrium -> bicuspid valve -> left ventricle -> aortic valve

LEARNING CHECKLIST

1. Closed system and open system; vertebrates have closed system (pp. 1053-1054)

2. Nutrient and waste transport, oxygen and carbon dioxide transport, temperature maintenance, and hormone circulation (pp. 1054-1055)

3. The heart, the blood vessels, and the blood (p. 1056)

4. Arteries and arterioles: carry blood away from the heart, composed of four tissue layers; capillaries: site of gas exchange and metabolite exchange between blood and surrounding tissue, one tissue layer; venules and veins: carry blood back to the heart, four tissue layers (pp. 1056-1060)

5. Lymphatic system returns water that has escaped from capillaries to the blood circulatory system (p. 1060)

6. Water; dissolved metabolites and wastes; dissolved salts and ions; dissolved proteins (pp. 1060-1063)

7. Erythrocytes, leukocytes, and platelets (pp. 1063-1064)

8. Sinus venosus, atrium, ventricle, conus arteriosus; arranged linearly (p. 1065)

9. Conversion of sinus venosus to SA node, separation of atrium into right and left chambers, separation of ventricle into right and left chambers, loss of conus arteriosus (becomes trunks of major arteries leaving heart) (pp. 1065-1068)

10. Left atrium, left ventricle, right atrium, right ventricle (pp. 1069-1071)

11. Begins at SA (sinoatrial) node; travels to AV (atrioventricular) node and then the bundle of His and Purkinje fibers (pp. 1071-1072)

12. Listen to the heart working, monitor blood pressure, measure depolarization waves (pp. 1072-1074)

13. Extrinsic control by autonomic nervous system, intrinsic control (autoregulation) by chemical factors produced nearby (p. 1074)

14. Baroreceptors measure blood pressure, stretch receptors measure blood volume (pp. 1075-1076)

MINI EXAM

A.

1. c	2. e	3. b	4. c	5. d	6. a
7. b	8. c	9. b	10. a	11. e	12. c
13. d	14. e	15. b	16. d	17. a	18. d
19. c	20. e	21. a			

B.

1. sinoatrial (SA)	2. bicuspid (mitral)	3. superior vena cava
4. aortic	5. His	6. serum albumin
7. Hematocrit	8. erythropoiesis	9. medulla

C. 1. The advantage is that there is more room to pack in more hemoglobin molecules and thus increase the oxygen-carrying capacity. The disadvantage is that without a nucleus the cell cannot repair damage to itself and thus has a relatively short life span (approximately four months); new red blood cells must be made constantly to replace dying ones. (p. 1063)

2. Closing off surface capillaries prevents loss of heat to the environment, thereby conserving body heat. It also maximizes blood flow to critical organs that may be needed to meet the emergency (e.g., heart and skeletal muscles for running away, liver to convert glycogen to glucose). (pp. 1057-1059)

3. With the lymph vessels blocked or removed, water that diffuses out of the blood plasma cannot be returned to the cardiovascular system. Instead it accumulates in the surrounding tissues, causing edema, or swelling of the tissue. The affected area appears bloated. (p. 1060)

4. To be large and multicellular and have no circulatory system, the animal would have to be aquatic and essentially two-dimensional (analogous to the giant kelp). This way, each cell could be in direct contact with the environment, and exchange of material could take place by direct diffusion. Being aquatic would avoid desiccation problems. Diffusion is a fairly slow process, so the animal would have to be fairly inactive; it could not meet the energetic demands of an active life style. It would most likely be ectothermic. Because of its two-dimensionality, it would have an extremely large surface-area-to-volume ratio, and it would be almost impossible for the animal to maintain a body temperature much different from that of its surrounding environment. (pp. 1053-1055)

52: THE IMMUNE SYSTEM

IN THE GRAND SCHEME

Every organism's body is being attacked and invaded constantly by viruses and by living organisms such as bacteria, protists, fungi, and multicellular parasites. Without defenses against the damage, diseases, and infections caused by the invaders, the attacked organism would soon die. Organisms have evolved myriad defensive mechanisms to protect themselves from the invaders; vertebrates have evolved an extremely sophisticated defense system called the immune system, which is based on several types of highly specialized white blood cells that search out and destroy foreign materials that have entered the host's body. Some of the cells even supply long-term, future protection against reinvasion by a previously defeated attacker. The recognition of an invading substance (or organism) by the immune system cells occurs at the molecular level and is based on the three-dimensional shapes of particular molecules. The ability to recognize so many different types of invaders is conferred upon the immune system by a unique form of gene processing. A disease such as AIDS, which destroys the immune system, makes us realize with brutal clarity the importance of the immune system - without it we cannot live. We succumb to the hordes of attackers.

FOR REVIEW

Phagocytosis: During phagocytosis a cell engulfs food particles (such as another cell or fragments of an organism) by enfolding it within extensions of its cell membrane. As a result the food particles wind up inside the cell in a vesicle where they can be broken down by digestive enzymes. Phagocytosis allows the bulk passage of material into the cell, material that is too large to enter the cell by diffusion or through transmembrane channels.

Recombination: Recombination is the architect of the genome. Mutation is the ultimate source of new genetic material, but recombination is responsible for the reshuffling of existing genetic material that results in the genetic diversity and myriad of allele combinations that we see in species. Recombination can occur by the exchange of entire chromosomes, as occurs during meiosis and sexual reproduction, and it can occur by the exchange of parts of chromosomes (e.g., crossing-over, gene transfer) or rearrangement within a single chromosome.

Macrophage: Macrophages are one of the types of defensive connective tissues. They are specialized types of white blood cells that are phagocytic. They circulate throughout the body and engulf and digest invading bacteria, foreign material, and cellular debris. They will phagocytize any cell coated with antibodies and can thus detect and remove diseased cells that are carrying antibodies.

Lymphocyte: Lymphocytes are another type of specialized white blood cell that are part of the defensive connective tissue. They circulate in the blood and produce antibodies in response to the presence of foreign material. The antibodies are a crucial component in the body's defense against disease.

The lymphatic system: The closed circulatory system of vertebrates is not completely closed - fluid diffuses out of the plasma as the blood passes through the capillaries. This fluid is collected by the lymphatic system, which returns it to the bloodstream near the heart. Defensive connective tissue cells are also found in the lymphatic system.

CHAPTER OUTLINE

KEY TERMS

p. 1081: skin, nonspecific defenses, the immune system, epidermis, dermis, subcutaneous tissue, stratum corneum
p. 1082: stratum basal layer, psoriasis
p. 1084: macrophages, neutrophils, phagocytes, natural killer (NK) cells, autoimmune diseases, MHC (major histocompatibility complex) marker
p. 1086: complement system, membrane attack complex (MAC), interferons, inflammatory response, pus
p. 1087: pyrogens, fever, smallpox, cowpox, variola, vaccination, vaccinia
p. 1088: antigens, antibodies, immune response, primary immune response, secondary immune response
p. 1090: hemopoietic stem cells, monocytes, T cells
p. 1091: helper T cells, cytotoxic T cells, inducer T cells, suppressor T cells, B cells, plasma cells

p. 1092: cell surface receptor
p. 1093: CD3, MHC-I, MHC-II, B receptors, T receptors, somatic rearrangement, CD4, CD8
p. 1094: HLA genes
p. 1096: monokines, gamma-interferon, interleukin-1
p. 1097: cell-mediated immune response, humoral (antibody) immune response, lymphokines, interleukin-2 (T cell growth factor), macrophage migration inhibition factor
p. 1098: cyclosporine, memory cells, immunoglobulins
p. 1099: class M, class G, killer (K) cells
p. 1100: light chains, heavy chains, hypervariable segments
p. 1101: IgM, IgG, IgA, IgD, IgE, histamines
p. 1102: beta-microglobin
p. 1103: human leukocyte-associated antigen (HLA) complex, instructional theory, clonal selection theory
p. 1104: somatic mutation
p. 1105: acquired immunological tolerance, natural immunological tolerance
p. 1106: autoimmune diseases, myasthenia gravis, allergic reactions, mediators, anaphylactic shock, allergens, desensitization
p. 1107: rheumatoid arthritis, systemic lupus erythematosus (SLE), trypanosomes
p. 1108: determinant, polyclonal, monoclonal antibody, myelomas, hybridomas
p. 1109: human immunodeficiency virus (HIV)

TOPIC EXERCISES

1. The cells of the immune system have different types of cell surface proteins that are crucial in the functioning of the immune systems. Some of these proteins are receptors, some are MHC (major histocompatibility complex) proteins. Complete the following chart by using a "+" sign or "-" sign to indicate which type of cell has which type of surface protein.

Cell Type	T Receptor	B Receptor	MCH-I	MCH-II
B cells				
T$_4$ cells				
T$_8$ cells				
Macrophages				

2. Match each of the following type of cell with its proper function in the immune system.

a. B cells
b. Cytoxic T cells
c. Helper T cells
d. Inducer T cells
e. Macrophages
f. Mast cells
g. Plasma cells
h. Suppressor T cells

i. lyse infected body cells
ii. initiate the inflammatory or allergic response
iii. decrease or terminate the immune response
iv. precursors of plasma cells
v. engulf cells and present antigens
vi. an antibody "factory"
vii. cause maturation of T cells
viii. initiate the immune response

WHO'S WHO

Complete the following chart.

Scientists	Contribution to Biology
a. _____	Began the study of immunology using cowpox vaccination against smallpox
b. _____	Demonstrated that immunity was invoked by injected material, not created by it (used fowl cholera)
Milstein and Kohler	c. _____

LEARNING CHECKLIST

1. Name the body's first line of defense against invading microbes and the three layers of which it is composed.
2. List the four most important nonspecific chemical and cellular defenses of the body.
3. Distinguish between antigens and antibodies.
4. What are the three principal kinds of white blood cells?
5. What are the four principal kinds of T cells?
6. Distinguish between a negative test and a positive test in immune surveillance for recognizing foreign tissue.
7. Name the three general types of cell surface proteins.
8. What type of white blood cell carries out an immediate response to infection? What type of white blood cell initiates the immune response?
9. Name the two types of immune responses.
10. What are the six basic steps in the chain of events of the cell-mediated immune response?
11. What are the five basic steps in the chain of events of the humoral immune response?
12. What three mechanisms do antibodies use to destroy foreign material?
13. How many polypeptide chains make up an antibody? What are the types of chains and how many are there of each?
14. Name the five classes of heavy chains found in mammalian antibodies.
15. What two theories have been proposed to explain how the great diversity of receptors and antibodies is generated? Which one is correct?
16. What three processes generate the tremendous diversity of B and T cells?
17. What is the difference between acquired immunological tolerance and natural immunological tolerance? What is the basis for both forms of tolerance?
18. Name three autoimmune diseases.
19. Name two disease-causing agents that carry out antigen shifting.
20. List three ways that T_4 cells are altered when they are infected with HIV (AIDS virus).

MINI EXAM

A. Circle the letter of the one best answer for each question.

1. AIDS is such a deadly disease because the AIDS virus attacks and destroys
    a. T_4 cells
    b. B cells
    c. T_8 cells
    d. macrophages
    e. myelomas

2. Which of the following statements about AIDS is true?
   a. the disease is highly infectious
   b. the fatality rate is low if the disease is detected in its early stages
   c. both of the above
   d. none of the above

3. Smallpox is caused by a virus called
   a. vaccinia
   b. cowpox
   c. variola
   d. jenneri
   e. cyclosporin

4. Circulating forms of B receptors that have been secreted by plasma cells are called
   a. T receptors
   b. complement
   c. antigens
   d. monokines
   e. antibodies

5. In which of the following places would you not expect to find white blood cells?
   a. thymus
   b. liver and spleen
   c. blood and lymph
   d. you would expect to find white blood cells in all of these places
   e. you would not expect to find white blood cells in any of these places

6. Both white and red blood cells are produced in bone marrow by
   a. hemopoietic stem cells
   b. phagocytic cells
   c. erythrocytic stem cells
   d. memory cells
   e. plasma cells

7. Precursors of macrophages are called
   a. T cells
   b. killer cells
   c. B cells
   d. plasma cells
   e. monocytes

8. The immune response is terminated or decreased by
   a. suppressor B cells
   b. suppressor T cells
   c. both of the above
   d. none of the above; the immune response can only be stimulated, not terminated

9. Which type of T cell lyses cells that have been infected with viruses?
   a. inducer T cells
   b. helper T cells
   c. cytotoxic T cells
   d. suppressor T cells
   e. none of the above

10. When a B cell encounters antigen to which it is targeted, it divides rapidly and produces
    a. more antigen
    b. plasma cells
    c. T_4 cells
    d. killer cells
    e. interferons

11. A cell surface receptor
    a. is always a protein
    b. extends across a cell membrane and has an end that protrudes outside the cell
    c. both of the above
    d. none of the above

12. All human T lymphocytes have a glycoprotein cell identity marker that is designated
    a. HLA
    b. HIV
    c. MHC-II
    d. IgM
    e. CD3

13. Your body has millions of different immune receptors for detecting millions of different antigens because
    a. you have millions of different immune receptor genes
    b. immune receptor genes undergo somatic rearrangement
    c. immune receptor genes undergo antigen shifting
    d. all of the above
    e. none of the above

14. Helper T cells and inducer T cells are also called _____ cells because of the cell-type marker protein they both have.
    a. T_4
    b. T_8
    c. T_{16}
    d. T_{12}

15. Which type of surface marker is present on every nucleated cell in your body?
    a. B receptor
    b. T receptor
    c. MHC-I
    d. MHC-II
    e. all of the above

16. MHC surface markers are specified in humans by
    a. ABC genes
    b. HIV genes
    c. mediator genes
    d. HLA genes
    e. hybridoma genes

17. Macrophages respond to a virus by secreting soluble proteins called
    a. histamines
    b. antibodies
    c. monokines
    d. lymphokines
    e. complement

18. Memory cells
    a. produce cyclosporine
    b. are responsible for acquired immunological tolerance
    c. prevent an animal from encountering certain antigens
    d. provide an accelerated immune response upon second exposure to a particular antigen
    e. all of the above

19. What holds together the four polypeptide chains of an antibody?
    a. disulfide bonds
    b. light chains
    c. heavy chains
    d. complement proteins
    e. MHC proteins

20. Of the five classes of antibody heavy chains, which one's function is still unclear?
    a. E
    b. M
    c. G
    d. A
    e. D

21. Diseases in which a person's immune system attacks the person's own normal tissue are called
    a. secondary immune diseases
    b. autoimmune diseases
    c. antigen shifting diseases
    d. polyclonal diseases
    e. hybridoma diseases

22. The cells that you see when you look at your skin were produced in the
    a. dermis
    b. psoriasis layer
    c. subcutaneous tissue
    b. stratum basal layer
    e. stratum corneum layer

B. Provide the appropriate term to complete each statement.

1. Your body uses its _____ system to resist infection and defend itself against diseases.

2. _____ is the process of injecting a person with a harmless microbe to confer resistance to a dangerous microbe.

3. "Not-self" molecules that trigger an immune response are called _____.

4. _____ are large, irregularly shaped phagocytic white blood cells.

5. Phagocytes, T cells, and B cells all arise from stem cells in the _____.

6. Invertebrates use a _____ test to recognize foreign tissue.

7. _____ is an enzyme that digests bacterial cell walls and is found in vertebrate mucus and saliva.

8. The MHC in MHC cell surface proteins stands for _____.

9. Of the two immune responses, the more long-range defense carried out by B cells is called the _____ immune response.

10. Antibody molecules are also called _____.

11. When they detect a bacterial cell wall, proteins of the complement system form a(n) _____ that will form a hole in the bacterium's cell membrane.

C. Briefly answer the following question.

1. Why is antigen shifting so good from the pathogen's point of view and so bad from your point of view if you are invaded by the pathogen?

427

CHAPTER 52 ANSWERS

TOPIC EXERCISES

1.

Cell Type	T Receptor	B Receptor	MCH-I	MCH-II
B cells	-	+	+	+
T_4 cells	+	-	+	+
T_8 cells	+	-	+	-
Macrophages	-	-	+	+

2.
a. iv	b. i	c. viii	d. vii
e. v	f. ii	g. vi	h. iii

WHO'S WHO

a. Jenner
b. Pasteur
c. developed monoclonal antibodies

LEARNING CHECKLIST

1. skin; epidermis, dermis, subcutaneous tissue (p. 1081)

2. cells that kill invading microbes, proteins that kill invading microbes, inflammatory response, temperature response (p. 1083)

3. Antigens are "not-self" or foreign molecules that cause an immune response in a vertebrate. Antibodies are proteins that are produced by the immune system as part of the immune response in battling antigens. (p. 1088)

4. phagocytes, T cells, and B cells (p. 1090)

5. helper T cells, cytoxic T cells, inducer T cells, suppressor T cells (p. 1091)

6. negative test: cells <u>lacking</u> a specific cell surface protein are presumed to be foreign and are attacked and destroyed; positive test: cells <u>with</u> a specific cell surface molecule not found on normal vertebrate cells are presumed to be foreign and are attacked and destroyed (p. 1092)

7. cell identity markers (glycoproteins), MHC proteins, immune receptor proteins (p. 1093)

8. macrophage; helper T cells (p. 1094)

9. cell-mediated response; humoral response (p. 1097)

10. proliferation, activation, induction, attack, suppression, memory (pp. 1097-1098)

11. proliferation, differentiation and secretion, attack, suppression, memory (pp. 1098-1099)

12. complement, macrophages, killer (K) cells (p. 1099)

13. four; two identical light chains and two identical heavy chains (p. 1100)

14. IgM, IgG, IgA, IgD, IgE (p. 1101)

15. instructional theory, clonal selection theory; clonal selection theory is correct (p. 1103)

16. somatic rearrangement, shifting of the reading frame by misalignment, random mistakes in base pairing (somatic mutation) (pp. 1103-1104)

17. Acquired tolerance occurs when foreign tissue is introduced into an embryonic animal before its immune system has developed; natural tolerance refers to the phenomenon that a mature animal's immune system does not attack its own tissue. Both are based on elimination or suppression of particular clones of lymphocytes. (p. 1105)

18. myasthenia gravis, rheumatoid arthritis, systemic lupus erythematosus (SLE) (pp. 1106-1107)

19. influenza viruses, parasitic trypanosomes (p. 1107)

20. they release progeny viruses before dying; they secrete a soluble suppressing factor that blocks other T cells from responding to antigen; they stop transcribing MHC genes (p. 1109)

MINI EXAM

A.

1. a	2. d	3. c	4. e	5. d	6. a
7. e	8. b	9. c	10. b	11. c	12. e
13. b	14. a	15. c	16. d	17. c	18. d
19. a	20. e	21. b	22. d		

B.

1. immune	2. Vaccination	3. antigens
4. Macrophages	5. bone marrow	6. negative
7. Lysozyme	8. major histocompatibility complex (MHC)	9. humoral
10. immunoglobulins	11. membrane attack complex (MAC)	

C. 1. Antigen shifting makes it difficult if not impossible for your immune system to mount a successful attack and defense against the pathogen. If the pathogen invades your body with antigen 1 on its surface, your immune system will trigger a response to seek out and destroy all cells with antigen 1 on them. But if the pathogen has shifted antigens and now bears antigen 2 on its surface it will not be attacked by the antibodies and other defenses directed against antigen 1. By the time your body musters its defenses against antigen 2, the pathogen may have shifted antigens again. Antigen shifting not only short circuits your body's immune response, but also makes it difficult if not impossible to develop a successful vaccine against the pathogen. (p. 1107)

53: KIDNEYS AND WATER BALANCE

IN THE GRAND SCHEME

Unless they are isotonic with their surrounding environments, all organisms tend to gain water and lose salts or lose water and gain salts, depending on the relative osmolality of the organism and the environment. Such gains and losses can be lethal to the organism if they are too extreme. To remain alive and functioning properly, living cells require homeostasis. They also need to be able to dispose of nitrogenous waste products. In the vertebrates, osmoregulation and excretion of nitrogenous wastes are both carried out by the kidney. Nitrogenous wastes are filtered from the blood in the kidney and the kidney actively controls how much water and solutes are excreted with the nitrogenous wastes. The functioning of the kidney is regulated by the central nervous system and hormones, another example of integration and feedback processes in the vertebrate body.

FOR REVIEW

Sodium chloride: Sodium chloride, NaCl, is a molecule made up of one sodium atom ionically bonded to one chlorine atom. In satisfying the octet rule, the sodium atom (atomic number 11) donates one electron to the chlorine atom (atomic number 17). As a result, the sodium becomes a positive ion (Na^+), the chlorine becomes a negative ion (Cl^-), and the two ions are attracted to each other by their opposite charges. Thus the ionic bond is formed. Common table salt consists of crystals of sodium chloride. When put in water, sodium chloride dissociates or dissolves into its individual ions as a result of the polarity of the surrounding water molecules.

Membrane transport: The lipid bilayer membranes of cells are selectively permeable. Some materials can enter or leave the cell by simple diffusion, some by facilitated diffusion, and some are pumped against their concentration gradients by active transport. Facilitated diffusion and active transport require the use of specific transmembrane proteins and channels.

Hormones: Hormones are chemical messengers that are produced in one part of the organism's body and have their affect on target cells in a different part of the organism's body. They are transported in the circulatory system and tend to bring about slower, more long-term changes than do the electrical signals of the nervous system. Many hormones are part of a hormonal chain of command that is controlled by the hypothalamus. Hormones are a key element in helping the body maintain homeostasis by using feedback systems and antagonistic controls.

Nitrogenous wastes: The liver carries out deamination, removing the amino group from excess amino acids. The nitrogen in the amino group cannot be utilized by the animal, so it is excreted as nitrogenous waste. The amino group is converted to ammonia; in some animals the ammonia is further converted to urea or uric acid. The liver releases the nitrogenous waste into the bloodstream, where it is transported, eventually filtered out in the kidney, and then excreted.

Countercurrent exchange: In a countercurrent exchange system, the exchange of a substance between A and B is maximized because A and B flow in opposite directions. Fish gills are extremely efficient at obtaining oxygen from the surrounding water because they are countercurrent systems: the water flows past them in the opposite direction of the blood flowing in them. The blood is able to pick up the maximum amount of oxygen possible from the surrounding water. The nephron tubules in the mammalian kidney also act as a countercurrent system, maximizing the amount of water that is reabsorbed from the urine, resulting in concentrated urine.

CHAPTER OUTLINE

OSMOREGULATION (pp. 1115-1117)
    The Problems Faced by Osmoregulators
    How Osmoregulation is Achieved
THE ORGANIZATION OF THE VERTEBRATE KIDNEY (pp. 1117-1118)
    Filtration
    Reabsorption
    Excretion
THE EVOLUTION OF KIDNEYS AMONG THE VERTEBRATES (pp. 1118-1120)
    Freshwater Fishes
    Marine Fishes
    Sharks
    Amphibians and Reptiles
    Mammals and Birds
HOW THE MAMMALIAN KIDNEY WORKS (pp. 1120-1123)
EXCRETION OF NITROGENOUS WASTES (pp. 1123-1125)
THE KIDNEY AS A REGULATORY ORGAN (pp. 1125-1126)
    Regulation of Kidney Function

KEY TERMS

p. 1115: osmoconformers, osmolality, osmoregulators, hyperosmotic, hypoosmotic
p. 1116: nephrid organs, Malpighian tubules, urine
p. 1117: kidney, nephrons, Malpighian corpuscle, Bowman's capsule, glomerulus
p. 1118: glomerular filtrate
p. 1119: salt glands
p. 1120: renal tubule, loop of Henle
p. 1122: cortex, medulla
p. 1124: urea, uric acid, dialysis, hemodialysis, catheters, continuous ambulatory peritoneal dialysis, histocompatibility antigens
p. 1125: guano, homeostasis, vasopressin (antidiuretic hormone, ADH)
p. 1126: aldosterone

TOPIC EXERCISES

1. Complete the following chart by answering each question for both freshwater fishes and marine fishes (bony fishes, not sharks or other members of the class Chondrichthyes).

Questions	Freshwater Fishes	Marine Fishes
a. Are they hyperosmotic or hypoosmotic relative to their environment?		
b. Do they drink a lot or very little?		
c. Do they produce a lot of dilute urine or less urine, less dilute?		
d. Do their gills pump solutes into or out of the blood?		

432

2. Use the following terms to label the parts of the nephron diagrammed below: ascending arm, Bowman's capsule, collecting duct, descending arm, distal segment, glomerulus, loop of Henle, proximal segment, urine.

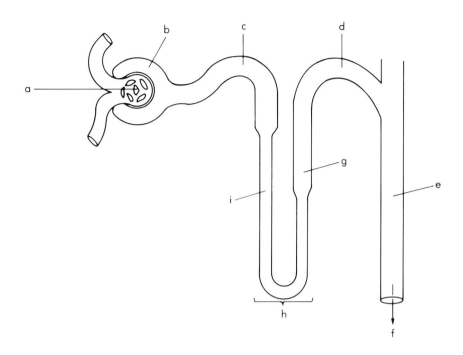

LEARNING CHECKLIST

1. What are the two options possible for any organism with regard to its water balance relative to the surrounding environment? Which option do most vertebrates follow?
2. Name four types of osmoregulatory organs and the types of organisms that have them.
3. Name the three different functions of all vertebrate kidneys.
4. List the nitrogenous waste product found in the urine of a freshwater fish.
5. What is one structural and functional difference between the kidneys of freshwater fishes and marine bony fishes?
6. How do sharks solve their problems of water and salt balance?
7. What is the single most important structural reason for the increase in the efficiency of bird and mammal kidneys compared with other vertebrates?
8. What are the five stages of the countercurrent flow process in the mammalian kidney?
9. What are the names of the two zones seen in a longitudinal section of the kidney?
10. What three general solutions have evolved in response to the combined problem of ammonia being toxic unless greatly diluted in water and the need to conserve water in terrestrial animals and marine fishes?
11. Name two hormones that influence the functioning of the kidney and indicate where each is produced.

MINI EXAM

A. Circle the letter of the one best answer for each question.

1. Which of the following animals have loops of Henle?
   a. insects
   b. fish
   c. birds
   d. all of the above
   e. none of the above

2. Aquatic organisms that are hypoosmotic relative to the surrounding water tend to
   a. gain water from the environment
   b. gain salts from the environment
   c. both of the above
   d. none of the above

3. Which of the following is an osmoconformer?
   a. a shark
   b. a human
   c. all vertebrates are osmoconformers
   d. no vertebrates are osmoconformers

4. Nephrid organs are found in
   a. insects
   b. fish
   c. sponges
   d. many freshwater invertebrates
   e. amphibians

5. The excretory organs of insects are called
   a. nephrid organs
   b. contractile vacuoles
   c. collecting ducts
   d. nephron tubules
   e. Malpighian tubules

6. Which of the following would be least likely to be found in the glomerular filtrate?
   a. plasma proteins
   b. glucose and amino acids
   c. water
   d. urea
   e. all of the above are likely to be found in the glomerular filtrate

7. Urea is formed in the
   a. loop of Henle
   b. collecting duct
   c. glomerulus
   d. liver
   e. bladder

8. The tube that leads from the kidney to the bladder is called the
   a. loop of Henle
   b. collecting duct
   c. nephron
   d. renal tubule
   e. ureter

9. Filtrate moves into the Bowman's capsule from the
   a. collecting duct
   b. loop of Henle
   c. glomerulus
   d. proximal segment
   e. distal segment

10. Urine is stored in the
    a. glomerulus
    b. bladder
    c. loop of Henle
    d. all of the above
    e. none of the above

11. Freshwater fish excrete
    a. ammonia
    b. uric acid
    c. urea
    d. all of the above
    e. no nitrogenous waste product

12. Which nitrogenous waste is concentrated in a shark's blood?
    a. ammonia
    b. uric acid
    c. nitrate
    d. N_3
    e. urea

13. Marine reptiles eliminate excess salts through their
    a. salt glands in their heads
    b. kidneys
    c. general body surface (skin)
    d. all of the above
    e. none of the above; marine reptiles don't eliminate excess salts

14. Which of the following animals has the most concentrated urine relative to its blood plasma?
    a. sea turtle
    b. bird
    c. human
    d. camel
    e. sponge

15. The urine of a pocket mouse, compared to its blood plasma, is
    a. the same concentration
    b. 4 times as concentrated
    c. 14 times as concentrated
    d. 22 times as concentrated
    e. 38 times as concentrated

16. How many nephrons does the typical human have?
    a. 2
    b. 20
    c. about 200
    d. about 20 thousand
    e. about 2 million

17. The more concentrated the urine that a mammal can produce, the longer are its
    a. glomeruli
    b. proximal segments
    c. loops of Henle
    d. Bowman's capsule
    e. Malpighian tubules

18. The part of the kidney that is least permeable to water is the walls of the
    a. collecting duct
    b. ascending arm
    c. glomerulus
    d. descending arm
    e. Bowman's capsule

19. The lower portions of the loops of Henle and the collecting ducts are located in the kidney's
    a. cortex
    b. medulla
    c. neck
    d. renal artery
    e. bladder

20. Which of the following statements is true?
    a. ADH makes the collecting duct more permeable to urea
    b. guano contains high concentrations of urea
    c. aldosterone is produced by the hypothalamus in response to high levels of sodium ions in the blood
    d. uric acid is the most soluble of the nitrogenous waste products
    e. all of the above

B. Provide the appropriate term to complete each statement.

    1. Organisms that maintain the total ionic concentration of their body fluids at the same level as their surrounding environment are called _____.

    2. The total ionic concentration of an organism's body fluids is defined as the organism's _____.

    3. Freshwater fishes are _____-osmotic relative to their environment.

    4. The excretory and osmoregulatory organs of vertebrates are called _____.

    5. The tubular units of kidneys, which form the urine, are called _____.

    6. The _____ is the bed of capillaries in the kidney from which fluids and solutes are forced.

    7. In the ascending limb of the loop of Henle, _____ diffuses and is actively transported out of the tubule into the surrounding tissue.

    8. Sharks and rays belong to the class _____.

    9. The hairpin loop of the nephron tube in mammalian kidneys is called the loop of _____.

    10. This hairpin loop sets up a _____ flow system.

    11. Ammonia is flushed into the surrounding water in the _____ of fishes.

C. Briefly answer each of the following questions.

    1. What is the advantage and disadvantage of being an osmoregulator as opposed to an osmoconformer?

    2. Explain what is meant by the statement that insects <u>pull</u> their blood through the filter that removes nitrogenous wastes and other substances while vertebrates <u>push</u> their blood through the filter. How is this related to the type of circulatory system they have?

    3. How would blood pressure disorders (e.g., high pressure or low pressure) affect the functioning of the kidney?

CHAPTER 53 ANSWERS

TOPIC EXERCISES

1.

Questions	Freshwater Fishes	Marine Fishes
a.	hyperosmotic	hypoosmotic
b.	very little	a lot
c.	a lot, dilute	less
d.	into	out of

2. a. glomerulus   b. Bowman's capsule   c. proximal segment
    d. distal segment   e. collecting duct   f. urine
    g. ascending arm   h. loop of Henle   i. descending arm.

LEARNING CHECKLIST

1. Osmoconforming or osmoregulating; most vertebrates = osmoregulators (p. 1115)

2. Contractile vacuoles: many protists and sponges; nephrid organs: many freshwater invertebrates; Malpighian tubules: insects; kidneys: vertebrates (p. 1116)

3. Filtration of blood, reabsorption of desirable ions and metabolites, secretion and excretion of certain materials (p. 1117)

4. Ammonia (ammonium ion, NH_5) (p. 1118)

5. Marine: active ion transport channels pump ions into tube instead of out (p. 1118)

6. Sharks become essentially isotonic with surrounding water (and thus essentially osmoconformers) by maintaining high levels of urea in their bodies (pp. 1118-1119)

7. The intermediate segment of the nephron tube is bent into a hairpin loop called the loop of Henle (p. 1120)

8. i. water diffuses out of the descending arm of the loop of Henle; ii. at beginning of ascending arm, salt diffuses out of tube; iii. higher in ascending arm, salt actively transported out; iv. urea diffuses out of the collecting duct, v. water diffuses out of the collecting duct (pp. 1121-1122)

9. Cortex, medulla (p. 1122)

10. Flushing ammonia from the gills into the surrounding water; detoxifying ammonia by converting it to urea; converting ammonia to insoluble uric acid (pp. 1124-1125)

11. Vasopressin (antidiuretic hormone, ADH): produced by hypothalamus; aldosterone: produced by adrenal gland (pp. 1125-1126)

MINI EXAM

A.
1. c	2. b	3. a	4. d	5. e	6. a
7. d	8. e	9. c	10. b	11. a	12. e
13. a	14. d	15. d	16. e	17. c	18. b
19. b	20. a				

B.
1. osmoconformers 2. osmolality 3. hyper
4. kidneys 5. nephrons 6. glomerulus
7. salt 8. Chondrichthyes 9. Henle
10. countercurrent 11. gills

C. 1. advantage: maintaining a constant internal solute concentration has permitted vertebrates to evolve complex patterns of internal metabolism; disadvantage: animal must spend energy to constantly regulate the osmolality and maintain it at a fairly constant level (pp. 1115-1116)

2. Potassium ions are secreted into the Malpighian tubules, the excretory organs of insects. This establishes a high osmotic concentration in the tubules and water is "pulled" into the tubules from the surrounding blood. The water diffuses into the tubules as a result of the concentration gradient. The walls of the Malpighian tubules act as the filter, allowing some substances in, but not others. In the vertebrate kidney, water and dissolved substances are forced out of the blood (in the glomerulus) and into the nephrons. The substances are pushed out of the glomerular capillaries by the high blood pressure. The capillary walls act as the filter, letting some substances through into the nephron and retaining some in the blood. The difference in these two systems is related to the open versus closed circulatory system. The closed system of vertebrates maintains a high blood pressure as the blood is pumped through the arteries and into the capillaries. There is no such comparable high blood pressure with the open circulatory system of the insect. (pp. 1116-1117)

3. Blood pressure is the driving force for pushing the glomerular filtrate out of the glomerulus and into the Bowman's capsule. High blood pressure would tend to force more filtrate out, whereas low blood pressure would result in less filtrate. It probably also would affect the solutes in the filtrate: high pressure would force out more and bigger molecules, whereas low pressure would force out fewer and only the smaller molecules. All of this would affect the overall salt and water balance of the body. (pp. 1116-1117, 1120-1123)

54: SEX AND REPRODUCTION

IN THE GRAND SCHEME

Reproduction - passing your genes to the next generation - is the name of the game in evolution. If your genes are not passed on, your reproductive fitness is zero. Sexual reproduction is a very old phenomenon; it evolved in the sea, long before the vertebrates. Almost all vertebrates reproduce sexually and sex is one of the most powerful of all drives. (In browsing through this book, you probably turned to this chapter before any other, right?) Sexual reproduction ensures high levels of genetic diversity in the offspring and thus provides the raw material upon which natural selection can act. Sexual reproduction on land has desiccation constraints not found with aquatic sex, and terrestrial vertebrates have evolved various strategies to protect their eggs and developing embryos. In this chapter we examine how vertebrates reproduce sexually, and in the next chapter we will see how the fertilized egg develops into an adult.

FOR REVIEW

Meiosis: Meiosis is the process in diploid organisms that results in the formation of haploid gametes: the egg cells and sperm cells. The pairing and crossing-over that occur between homologous chromosomes during meiosis, plus the random assortment of chromosomes among the daughter cells, result in tremendous genetic diversity in the gametes and then individual variation among the offspring formed from the union of two gametes. Meiosis is the cellular mechanism behind sexual reproduction.

Evolution of sexual reproduction: Many organisms can reproduce asexually, without sex, and scientists have often wondered why sexual reproduction evolved since it involves definite costs to an individual as well as potential benefits. Many scientists now believe that meiosis with its synapsis of homologous chromosomes evolved initially as a mechanism to repair chromosomal damage rather than as a mechanism for sexual reproduction per se.

Adaptation: Features that promote the likelihood of survival and reproduction of an organism in a particular environment are called adaptations. Over many generations, changes in gene frequencies occur in populations as individuals with favored characteristics reproduce more than do individuals with less favored or unfavored characteristics. Gradually the favored characteristics become more common in the population. This process of adaptation results in the formation (evolution) of new species.

Amniotic egg: The evolution of the amniotic egg was critical in helping the vertebrates successfully colonize land. Amniotic eggs protect the developing embryo from drying out in the dry terrestrial environment and also supply the necessary nutrients, water, and oxygen while removing or storing waste materials. Amniotic eggs first evolved in the reptiles, and are also found in birds and monotremes.

Mammals: The mammals evolved from the reptiles approximately 200 million years ago and have become an extremely diversified and successful class of vertebrates. Evolutionary advances such as homeothermy, a four-chambered heart, efficient locomotion, a large brain, and extensive care of their young have contributed to their success.

Hormones: Hormones are the chemical messengers of the vertebrate body. They are produced by numerous glands and have a multitude of long-term effects. Most hormones are under the hierarchial control of the central nervous system; the chain of command goes from the hypothalamus to the pituitary gland to various other endocrine glands. Acting in concert, the central nervous system and the hormonal system help maintain proper homeostasis, growth, and development (including sexual development and reproductive cycles).

CHAPTER OUTLINE

KEY TERMS

p. 1129: external fertilization, desiccation
p. 1130: ovipary, ovovivipary, viviparous, parthenogenesis, protogyny, protandry, hermaphrodites
p. 1131: tadpoles, metamorphosis, penis
p. 1132: amniotic eggs, chorion, amnion, monotremes, marsupials, placenta, copulation
p. 1134: sperm, testes, scrotum, seminiferous tubules, spermatogenesis, spermatogonia, primary spermatocytes, spermatids, spermatozoa, acrosome
p. 1135: testosterone, epididymis, vas deferens, urethra
p. 1136: ejaculation, semen, seminal fluid, ovaries, oocytes
p. 1137: primary oocytes, ova, polar bodies, oviducts (fallopian tubes)
p. 1138: vagina, uterus, cervix, endometrium, pheromones
p. 1139: estrus, estrous cycle, menstrual cycle, gametogenesis
p. 1140: gonadotropin-releasing hormone (GRH), follicle-stimulating hormone (FSH), follicles
p. 1141: follicular phase, luteal phase, estrogen, luteinizing hormone (LH), ovulation, corpus luteum, progesterone
p. 1142: menstruation, prolactin, oxytocin
p. 1143: coitus, excitement, plateau, orgasm, resolution, clitoris, labia
p. 1144: prostate gland, pair bonding, birth control

p. 1146: rhythm method, coitus interruptus, condom, cervical cap, diaphragm, douche, jellies, sponges, foams, birth control pills

p. 1147: acquired immune deficiency syndrome (AIDS), human immunodeficiency virus (HIV)

p. 1148: ELISA (Enzyme Linked Immuno-Sorbent Assay) antibody test, Western blot

p. 1150: vasectomy, tubal ligation, hysterectomy

p. 1151: intrauterine devices (IUDs), "morning after" pill, aborted, vacuum suction, dilation and curettage, curette, RU 486

TOPIC EXERCISES

1. Complete the following chart by writing in the specific part of the male or female body where each of the following events takes place in humans.

	Event	Location
a.	fertilization of egg cell	
b.	production of FSH and LH	
c.	production of GRH	
d.	production of progesterone	
e.	release of sperm into female during normal intercourse	
f.	sperm cells become motile	
g.	spermatogenesis	

2. Trace the pathway of a human male gamete from its site of production to its release from the body by arranging the following terms in their proper sequence.

Terms	Sequence
epididymis	
seminiferous tubules	
urethra	
vas deferens	

3. Trace the pathway of a human female gamete from its site of production to its release from the body (either as a developed baby or an unfertilized egg) by arranging the following terms in their proper sequence.

Terms	Sequence
cervix	
fallopian tube	
follicle	
uterus	
vagina	

LEARNING CHECKLIST

1. In what type of environment did sex first evolve?
2. What is the most common reproductive strategy of fish and amphibians?
3. List the three kinds of internal fertilization strategies.
4. What type of reproductive strategy do reptiles and birds have? What type of eggs do they produce?
5. Name the three types of mammals based on their reproductive strategies.
6. What are the two phases of spermatogenesis? Name the four different types of cells that are involved (in their proper sequence).
7. Name the three stop-and-go stages that occur during the process of meiosis in human egg cells.
8. List the two distinct phases of the female mammal's reproductive cycle. How long does a typical cycle last in women?
9. What are the four physiological phases that occur during human intercourse?
10. Name seven different methods of birth control.

MINI EXAM

A. Circle the letter of the one best answer for each question.

1. The first organisms to engage in sexual reproduction were
   a. primitive terrestrial vertebrates
   b. advanced terrestrial vertebrates
   c. marine vertebrates
   d. primitive marine organisms

2. Which of the following animals has an amniotic egg?
   a. a frog
   b. a sea turtle
   c. a fish
   d. all of the above
   e. none of the above

3. Which mammals are oviparous?
   a. marsupials
   b. placental mammals
   c. monotremes
   d. no mammals are oviparous
   e. all mammals are oviparous

4. Some fish are
   a. viviparous
   b. ovoviviparous
   c. oviparous
   d. all of the above
   e. none of the above

5. Compared with fish, most amphibians have
   a. internal fertilization rather than external
   b. much longer development time
   c. very few numbers of eggs produced during each reproductive cycle
   d. all of the above
   e. none of the above

6. Progesterone is produced by the
   a. corpus luteum
   b. hypothalamus
   c. seminiferous tubules
   d. pituitary gland
   e. oviduct

7. Ovulation is caused by the hormone
   a. FSH
   b. progesterone
   c. GRH
   d. estrogen
   e. LH

8. How many chromosomes does a normal, mature, human sperm cell contain?
   a. 1
   b. 2
   c. 23
   d. 46

9. Mature sperm cells are called
   a. spermatogenesis
   b. spermatids
   c. spermatogonia
   d. primary spermatocytes
   e. spermatozoa

10. What is the name of the vesicle at the tip of a sperm cell that contains enzymes that will help the sperm cell penetrate an egg cell it encounters?
    a. scrotum
    b. amnion
    c. chorion
    d. prostate gland
    e. acrosome

11. During the excitement phase of intercourse, what makes the human penis enlarge and become rigid?
    a. blood
    b. semen
    c. bone
    d. contracted muscles

12. Which of the following is the largest in size?
    a. mature sperm cell
    b. mature egg cell
    c. polar body
    d. they are all approximately the same size

13. The lining or inner layer of the uterus is called the
    a. cervix
    b. vagina
    c. labia
    d. endometrium
    e. epididymis

14. How long is the refractory period for men after intercourse?
    a. men don't have a refractory period
    b. about 20 seconds
    c. about 2 minutes
    d. about 20 minutes
    e. about 2 hours

15. Which of the following forms of birth control does not prevent conception (fertilization)?
    a. an IUD
    b. a condom
    c. a diaphragm
    d. a vasectomy
    e. all of the above do prevent conception

16. Which of the following is the most reliable form of birth control?
    a. the rhythm method
    b. a douche
    c. birth control pills
    d. coitus interruptus
    e. they are all equally reliable

17. What structure is cut and tied off in a vasectomy?
    a. the penis
    b. the epididymis
    c. the urethra
    d. the seminiferous tubules
    e. the vas deferens

18. Vasectomies and tubal ligations make the person
    a. sterile
    b. unable to produce sex hormones
    c. lose their sex drive
    d. all of the above
    e. none of the above

19. Which of the following statements is true?
    a. in the United States, the annual abortion rate is greater than the annual birthrate
    b. most male birds do not have a penis
    c. sexual reproduction increases genetic diversity
    d. all of the above
    e. none of the above

B. Provide the appropriate term to complete each statement.

1. The scientific study of the physiology of human intercourse was begun in the 1960s by William _____ and Virginia _____.

2. Ilya _____ was one of the first to report parthenogenesis in vertebrates, in small lizards of the genus Lacerta.

3. The larval stage of frogs and toads are called _____; to become adults they will undergo _____.

4. The development of an adult from an unfertilized egg is called _____.

5. Most vertebrates that utilize internal fertilization use a _____ to inject or insert sperm into the female.

6. The duck-billed platypus and the echidna are the only two types of living primitive mammals called _____.

7. When a female mammal is sexually receptive, she is said to be "in heat" or in _____.

8. After ovulation has occurred, the ruptured follicle is converted into the _____.

9. Ejaculation releases _____, which is a mixture of sperm cells and seminal fluids.

10. Withdrawing the penis from the vagina before ejaculation is an unreliable form of birth control called _____.

11. _____ is a chemical that causes abortion early in the first trimester of pregnancy that is in use in France and China.

C. Briefly answer each of the following questions.

1. There has been an evolutionary trend among the vertebrates towards increasing protection of the developing embryo, going from the "naked" eggs of fishes and amphibians, to the amniotic eggs of reptiles and birds, to the increasingly long retention of the offspring inside the mother's womb in mammals. What are some advantages and disadvantages (benefits and costs) for the mothers as well as their offspring of such increasing protection? Do you think there is a limit to how far this trend can or will proceed?

2. The older a woman is when she becomes a mother, the greater the chance that her child will suffer a genetic defect. Do you think the same relationship holds with the age of the father? Why or why not?

CHAPTER 54 ANSWERS

TOPIC EXERCISES

1. Location:
   a. oviduct (fallopian tube)
   b. pituitary gland (anterior portion)
   c. hypothalamus
   d. corpus luteum
   e. vagina
   f. epididymis
   g. seminiferous tubules

2. Sequence: seminiferous tubules --> epididymis --> vas deferens --> urethra

3. Sequence: follicle --> fallopian tube --> uterus --> cervix --> vagina

LEARNING CHECKLIST

1. In the sea (p. 1129)

2. External fertilization (pp. 1129-1131)

3. Ovipary, ovovivipary, viviparous (p. 1130)

4. Internal fertilization; amniotic eggs (pp. 1131-1132)

5. Monotremes, marsupials, placental mammals (p. 1132)

6. Meiosis, development; cells = spermatogonia, primary spermatocytes, spermatids, spermatozoa (p. 1134)

7. Developmental arrest, ovulation, fertilization (p. 1137)

8. Follicular phase, luteal phase; 28 days (p. 1141)

9. Excitement, plateau, orgasm, resolution (p. 1143)

10. Abstinence, sperm blockage, sperm destruction, prevention of egg maturation, surgical intervention, prevention of embryo implantation, abortion (pp. 1146-1151)

MINI EXAM

A.

1. d	2. b	3. c	4. d	5. b	6. a
7. e	8. c	9. e	10. e	11. a	12. b
13. d	14. d	15. a	16. c	17. e	18. a
19. d					

B.

1. Masters, Johnson
2. Darevsky
3. tadpoles, metamorphosis
4. parthenogenesis (asexual reproduction)
5. penis
6. monotremes
7. estrus
8. corpus luteum
9. semen
10. coitus interruptus
11. RU 486

C. 1. Disadvantages: higher energy costs for mother to make an amniotic egg rather than a naked egg; energetically costly for mother to carry around developing embryo and provide it with nutrients; limits clutch or litter size. Potential disadvantage for a mammalian embryo being inside mother: if mother is injured or killed, offspring will be too. Advantages: greater protection means greater chance of survival, good not only for offspring itself but also for mother in terms of successfully passing her genes on to future generations; offspring more developed, better able to take care of itself when finally hatched or born. Limits: mammalian mother cannot retain fetus too long or it will impose too large an energetic drain and physical impediment; offspring might also become too large to pass through birth canal. (pp. 1129-1132, plus many other chapters and common sense)

2. No, not likely. Men do not maintain their gametes from the time they are born the way women do, but rather make them fresh every day, so sperm cells do not accumulate mutations the way oocytes do. (pp. 1134-1138)

55: DEVELOPMENT

IN THE GRAND SCHEME

Embryonic development converts a single-celled zygote into a complex, multicellular organism with specialized tissues and organs. Whether this development takes place rapidly or slowly, and whether in a naked egg, an amniotic egg, or within the mother's body, the process involves a sequence of similar steps in all vertebrates. We began our examination of vertebrate biology by looking at the diversity of vertebrates that have evolved on the earth, and then the structure and functioning of their various tissues and organ systems. This chapter explains how each vertebrate winds up with particular tissues, organs, and body parts arranged the way they are. Sexual reproduction produces a new vertebrate; development molds it into its proper form and function.

FOR REVIEW

Terrestrial reproductive strategies: The single biggest problem facing all terrestrial organisms is drying out. Plants were the first organisms to colonize the land about 410 million years ago. Fungi and arthropods soon followed, and ancestral amphibians moved on to the land about 360 million years ago. The truly terrestrial vertebrates - the reptiles, birds, and mammals - have evolved various adaptations or strategies such as internal fertilization, the amniotic egg, and the placenta for solving the problems of reproducing in a terrestrial, desiccating environment. A suite of life history traits helps maximize the organism's reproductive success.

Ectoderm, mesoderm, endoderm: Ectoderm, mesoderm, and endoderm are the three primary tissue layers of all vertebrates. They are the first three tissues to form as the embryo develops and they represent the outer, middle, and inner tissue layers respectively. All other tissues and organs are derived from these initial three.

Coelom: A coelom is the type of body cavity found in the more advanced invertebrates and the vertebrates. It is completely surrounded or bounded by mesoderm tissue. This makes it different from the pseudocoel of lower invertebrates that develops between the mesoderm and endoderm. The animal's internal organs (e.g., digestive, reproductive) develop within or around the margins of the coelom, and hang down into it, suspended by double layers of mesoderm called mesentaries.

Radial and spiral cleavage: Radial and spiral cleavage describe two different patterns of cell division that occur during cleavage in an embryo. Deuterostomes, organisms such as echinoderms, chordates, arrow worms, and acorn worms, undergo radial cleavage. All other animals with a coelom are called protostomes and undergo spiral cleavage. The cleavage pattern is one of several fundamental embryological differences between the protostomes and deuterostomes.

Chordates: Three characteristics distinguish the chordates from all other animals: (1) a single, dorsal, hollow nerve cord; (2) a notochord; and (3) pharyngeal slits. These traits appear during the embryological development of the chordate, and in some cases are retained permanently. There are three subphyla of chordates: the lancelets, the tunicates, and the vertebrates.

The amniotic egg: The evolution of the amniotic egg was a major advance for terrestrial vertebrates. It has helped the reptiles and birds become extremely successful terrestrially. Besides protecting the embryo from desiccation, the egg contains a large yolk to nourish the developing embryo. The presence of this yolk influences the cleavage and development patterns that take place.

Amnion and chorion: The amnion and the chorion are two of the internal cell layers or membranes that form in the amniotic egg. The chorion is the outermost layer that lines the inner shell membrane, and the amnion is the innermost layer, forming a sac around the embryo. The amnion and chorion are retained in mammalian embryology; the amnion again encloses the embryo and the chorion helps form part of the placenta.

CHAPTER OUTLINE

INITIAL STAGE OF REPRODUCTION: FERTILIZATION (pp. 1155-1157)
    Penetration
    Activation
    Fusion
SETTING THE STAGE FOR DEVELOPMENT: CELL CLEAVAGE (pp. 1158-1160)
    Cell Cleavage Patterns
        Primitive aquatic vertebrates
        Amphibians and advanced fishes
        Reptiles and birds
        Mammals
    The Blastula
THE ONSET OF DEVELOPMENTAL CHANGE: GASTRULATION (pp. 1160-1162)
    Alternative Patterns of Gastrulation
        Aquatic vertebrates
        Reptiles, birds, and mammals
THE DETERMINATION OF BODY ARCHITECTURE: NEURULATION (pp. 1162-1163)
EVOLUTIONARY ORIGIN OF THE VERTEBRATES: THE NEURAL CREST (pp. 1163-1165)
    Structures Derived from the Neural Crest
        The gill chamber
        Elaboration of the nervous system
        Skull and sensory organs
    The Role of the Neural Crest in Vertebrate Evolution
HOW CELLS COMMUNICATE DURING DEVELOPMENT (pp. 1165-1167)
            induction
THE NATURE OF DEVELOPMENTAL DECISIONS (pp. 1167-1168)
THE EVOLUTION OF DEVELOPMENT (p. 1168)
THE COURSE OF HUMAN DEVELOPMENT (pp. 1168-1173)
    First Trimester
        The first month
        The second month
        The third month
    Second Trimester
        Placental development
    Third Trimester
    Birth
    Nursing
POSTNATAL DEVELOPMENT (pp. 1173-1174)
        allometric growth

KEY TERMS

p. 1155: zygote, development, fertilization, zona pellucida
p. 1156: acrosome, egg activation
p. 1157: gray crescent, in vitro fertilization

TOPIC EXERCISES

1. Arrange the following stages of vertebrate development in their proper sequence.

Stages	Sequence
blastula	
cleavage	
fertilization	
gastrula	
morphogenesis	
neural crest formation	
neurulation	
organogenesis	
zygote	

2. Match the following tissues and organs with the primary tissue type from which they are derived. Each primary tissue may be used more than once.

a. heart

b. skin

c. lungs

d. central nervous system

e. digestive tract

f. muscles

i. endoderm

ii. ectoderm

iii. mesoderm

3.   Label the following parts on the gastrula diagram below: archenteron, blastocoel, ectoderm, endoderm, mesoderm, yolk.

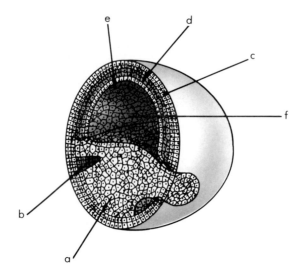

LEARNING CHECKLIST

1.   Name the six stages of vertebrate development.
2.   What are the three stages of fertilization?
3.   What three effects does the entry of the sperm cell have on the egg cell?
4.   List the two cleavage patterns found in vertebrates.
5.   In what three ways do blastula cells differ from each other?
6.   Name the three primary tissue layers formed during gastrulation. What new cavity is formed during gastrulation?
7.   What two characteristic features of chordates are formed during neurulation?
8.   Name eight vertebrate structures that arise from neural crest cells or placodes.
9.   What two types of induction occur during development? What type of signal is used during induction?
10. Distinguish between a cell that is determined versus one that is committed. Which comes first?
11. What major developmental event characterizes the first, second, third, and fourth weeks of human pregnancy? The last six months?
12. What growth pattern characterizes human postnatal development?

MINI EXAM

A. Circle the letter of the one best answer for each question.

1.   Ectoderm cells associated with anterior neural crest cells thicken and form
     a. the archenteron   d. blastomeres
     b. the primitive streak   e. placodes
     c. the dorsal lip

2.   The lining of the uterus in which the mammalian embryo implants itself is called the
     a. coccyx   d. yolk plug
     b. trophoblast   e. lanugo
     c. endometrium

450

3. In humans, organogenesis in the embryo is essentially complete by which stage of the pregnancy?
   a. first week
   b. first trimester
   c. second trimester
   d. third trimester

4. When central nervous system tissue causes nearby ectoderm tissue to form an eye lens, it is an example of
   a. egg activation
   b. meroblastic cleavage
   c. primary induction
   d. secondary induction
   e. allometric growth

5. The cavity inside the blastula is called the
   a. gastrula
   b. archenteron
   c. gill chamber
   d. blastomere
   e. blastocoel

6. What does the father contribute to his offspring?
   a. a haploid nucleus
   b. many cytoplasmic signals
   c. both of the above
   d. none of the above

7. The first "test-tube baby" produced by in vitro fertilization is now more than 10 years old. The child's name is
   a. Jane Doe
   b. Hilde Mangold
   c. Emily Haeckel
   d. Louise Brown

8. The outer membrane that surrounds an egg cell is called the
   a. acrosome
   b. morula
   c. zona pellucida
   d. gray crescent
   e. trophoblast

9. When does a human egg cell complete its meiotic division?
   a. before the female is even born
   b. just before ovulation
   c. after sperm penetration
   d. after cleavage has begun
   e. after implantation in the uterus

10. Cleavage is characterized by
    a. rapid cell division
    b. rapid growth in the size of the embryo
    c. each cell having the same components as its neighbors
    d. all of the above
    e. none of the above

11. In meroblastic cleavage, cleavage occurs only in the
    a. placodes
    b. blastodisc
    c. trophoblast
    d. yolk

12. What type of animal forms a trophoblast during its early development?
    a. mammal
    b. amphibian
    c. bird
    d. reptile
    e. fish

13. During what stage of development do the three primary tissue layers first appear?
    a. cleavage
    b. blastulation
    c. neurulation
    d. fertilization
    e. gastrulation

14. The gut or digestive tract of a vertebrate arises from the
    a. vegetal pole
    b. primitive streak
    c. archenteron
    d. blastocoel
    e. somites

15. Which of the following is not associated with the site of invagination during gastrulation?
    a. dorsal lip
    b. blastopore
    c. primitive streak
    d. all of the above are associated with the site
    e. none of the above are associated with the site

16. What type of tissue gives rise to the notochord?
    a. ectoderm
    b. mesoderm
    c. endoderm
    d. all of the above

17. The segmented blocks of tissue that develop on each side of the notochord are called the
    a. somites
    b. neural tube
    c. neural crest
    d. adrenal medulla
    e. alveolar ducts

18. The first truly vertebrate phase of development is marked by the formation of the
    a. archenteron
    b. primitive streak
    c. coccyx
    d. notochord
    e. neural crest

19. When does neurulation occur during human pregnancy?
    a. first week
    b. second week
    c. third week
    d. fourth week
    e. second trimester

20. What chemical messenger is associated with human birth?
    a. oxytocin
    b. fetal ACTH
    c. prostaglandins
    d. all of the above
    e. none of the above

21. A newborn infant obtains maternal antibodies from the
    a. lanugo
    b. colostrum
    c. rubella
    d. afterbirth
    e. thalidomide

22. During gestation and the first six months of life, what is the estimated rate at which the human brain generates neurons?
    a. 250 per day
    b. 250,000 per minute
    c. 25,000,000 per minute
    d. 25,000 per second

B. Provide the appropriate term to complete each statement.

1. Hans _____ and Hilde _____ helped solve the mystery of how embryos form.

2. The notochord and hollow dorsal nerve cord are formed during _____.

3. During early development, the solid ball of cells that is produced during cleavage is called a _____.

4. When one tissue's development is determined by another tissue, _____ is occurring.

5. When two haploid gametes fuse, a single diploid cell called a _____ is formed.

6. In frogs, a _____ appears opposite the point where the sperm cell penetrated the egg cell.

7. When eggs contain little or no yolk, _____ cleavage occurs.

8. Once a cell's developmental fate becomes fixed and irreversible, the cell is said to be _____.

9. The biogenic law that ontogeny recapitulates phylogeny was first proposed by Ernst _____.

10. When different parts of an organism's body grow at different rates, it is referred to as _____ growth.

C. Briefly answer the following question.

1. The placenta was a significant evolutionary advancement, and is a highly complex as well as crucial structure. Describe its primary function and structure. What endocrine role does it play?

CHAPTER 55 ANSWERS

TOPIC EXERCISES

1. Sequence: fertilization --> zygote --> cleavage --> blastula --> gastrula --> neurulation --> neural crest formation --> organogenesis --> morphogenesis

2. a. iii   b. ii   c. i
   d. ii   e. i   f. iii

3. a. yolk   b. blastocoel   c. ectoderm
   d. mesoderm   e. endoderm   f. archenteron

LEARNING CHECKLIST

1. Fertilization, cleavage, gastrulation, neurulation, neural crest formation, organogenesis (p. 1155)

2. Penetration, activation, fusion (pp. 1155-1157)

3. Changes in the cell membrane; completion of meiosis; rearrangement of egg cytoplasm (pp. 1156-1157)

4. Holoblastic, meroblastic (pp. 1158-1159)

5. Cytoplasmic contents, size (yolk content), neighboring cells (p. 1160)

6. Ectoderm, endoderm, mesoderm; archenteron (pp. 1160-1161)

7. Notochord; hollow dorsal nerve cord (p. 1163)

8. Gill chamber, sensory ganglia and neurons, Schwann cells, adrenal medulla, sense organs, teeth, cranial bones (p. 1164)

9. Primary, secondary; chemical signal (p. 1167)

10. A cell is determined when you can predict its developmental fate; it is committed when that fate cannot be changed. Determination comes first (p. 1168)

11. First week = cleavage; second week = gastrulation; third week = neurulation; fourth week = organogenesis; last 6 months = growth (pp. 1169-1172)

12. Allometric growth (p. 1173)

MINI EXAM

A.

1. e	2. c	3. b	4. d	5. e	6. a
7. d	8. c	9. c	10. a	11. b	12. a
13. e	14. c	15. d	16. b	17.a	18. e
19. c	20. d	21. b	22. b		

B.

1. Spemann, Mangold
4. induction
7. holoblastic
10. allometric

2. neurulation
5. zygote
8. committed

3. morula
6. gray crescent
9. Haeckel

C. 1. The placenta is composed of both fetal and maternal tissue, the fetal trophoblast enlarged and embedded in the maternal uterine wall. The placenta is highly vascularized with both maternal and fetal blood vessels, but the two circulatory systems do not mix directly. Materials such as oxygen and nutrients from the mother and wastes from the fetus are exchanged by diffusion between the two circulatory systems. During the course of its development and functioning, the placenta secretes estrogen, progesterone, human placental lactogen (HPL), antidiuretic hormone (ADH), aldosterone, renin, and prostaglandins. (pp. 1159, 1170, 1172)

56: ANIMAL BEHAVIOR

IN THE GRAND SCHEME

Of all the living organisms on earth, only multicellular animals show complex behavioral responses to external stimuli. They possess all the parts necessary to do so: a nervous system to receive and process stimuli and send out commands, and a muscular and skeletal system that makes quick and diverse movements possible. Vertebrates have the most complex nervous systems, and, not surprisingly, they also have the most complex behavior of all animals. The ability of animals to learn and to modify their behavior is directly related to how large the associative areas of their brains are and is extremely great in mammals, especially primates. There are limits, however, to what an animal can learn and when it can learn. All behavior also has a genetic component. Both nature and nurture are important in determining how an animal behaves. Much of the behavior of animals centers on communication. The actual form of the communication may vary widely from species to species, but the end results are usually similar and vital. Without communication systems, many animals would be unable or less likely to find mates, reproduce, care for young, locate food, or avoid predators.

FOR REVIEW

Neurons and interneurons: Neurons are the cells of the nervous system that are specialized for transmitting nerve impulses or electrical signals. Receptor cells respond to stimuli from the animal's external and internal environment and trigger sensory neurons that carry signals from the receptors to the central nervous system. Motor neurons carry signals from the central nervous system to effectors such as muscles and glands. Interneurons connect the sensory and motor neurons and comprise the central nervous system. They process all the incoming signals and determine appropriate responses. Animals could not behave without their neurons and nervous systems. They would not be able to perceive stimuli nor respond to them.

Memory and learning: The exact mechanisms of how memory and learning occur are still not known. It appears, however, that short-term memory works by short-term excitation of specific neurons (i.e., an electrical basis), whereas long-term memories involve actual structural changes in the neural connections in parts of the brain. There is no single part of the brain in which memories appear to reside.

Reproductive isolation: There are many different mechanisms that prevent hybridization between species. These mechanisms are classified in general on the basis of whether they prevent the formation of a zygote. Prezygotic isolating mechanisms include geographic isolation, ecological isolation, temporal isolation, behavioral isolation, mechanical isolation, and prevention of gamete fusion. Postzygotic isolating mechanisms include failure of the hybrid zygote to develop normally and hybrids being less fit or even sterile. Most courtship behavior is species-specific and helps maintain reproductive isolation between species.

Sensing the environment: Animals have numerous sensory systems that are specialized for perceiving different stimuli or aspects of the environment. Each system has the same basic components: receptor cells for perceiving the information, sensory neurons to carry the nerve impulses to the brain, and a brain to process the incoming information and formulate an appropriate response. There must also be motor neurons to carry the brain's commands to appropriate effectors. Different receptor cells are specialized to respond to such diverse stimuli as temperature, mechanical forces, chemicals, sound waves, light, electricity, and magnetism. Without sensory systems, animals could not respond to environmental stimuli; in other words, they could not behave.

Hormonal control of physiological processes: Hormones are chemical messengers that are produced in one part of the body by endocrine glands and have their effects on target cells in different parts of the body. Many hormones are under the control of the central nervous system via the hypothalamus and its releasing hormones. Most physiological processes are controlled by varying levels of specific hormones. Fine-tuned control is maintained by feedback mechanisms. The hormonal system provides slower, but longer lasting effects on body functionings than does the nervous system. Hormone levels influence an animal's behavior as well as its physiology.

CHAPTER OUTLINE

KEY TERMS

p. 1177: behavior, proximate causation, ultimate causation, nature, nurture
p. 1178: ethology, stereotyped, sign stimulus, innate releasing mechanism, fixed action pattern
p. 1180: audition, vision, olfaction, neuroethology, escape response
p. 1181: mechanoreceptors, comparative psychologists, learning, nonassociative learning, associative learning, habituation
p. 1182: sensitization, conditioned, classical conditioning (Pavlovian conditioning), operant conditioning, conditioned stimulus
p. 1183: learning preparedness
p. 1184: mantle, siphon
p. 1185: nature versus nurture controversy, imprinting, filial imprinting, sensitive phase, critical period
p. 1186: sexual imprinting, cross-fostering studies, genetic template
p. 1187: hypothalamus, pituitary, ovaries, testes, testosterone, androgens, behavioral endocrinology, brood parasite
p. 1188: exogenous, endogenous, biological clock, free-running rhythms, circadian rhythms, crop milk
p. 1189: suprachiasmatic nuclei, melatonin, pineal gland, photoperiod, circannual behaviors, social releasers, stimulus/response chain, conspecific
p. 1190: species-specific, dewlap, pheromones, bombykol, chemoreceptors
p. 1192: alarm call, alarm pheromones, trail pheromones, dance language
p. 1193: worker bees, scout bees, waggle dance
p. 1194: taxis, phototactic, kinesis, migrations
p. 1195: orientation, navigation, magnetite, cognitive behavior
p. 1196: cognitive maps

TOPIC EXERCISES

1. Explain, in your own words, the difference between instincts and learned behaviors. Which is more important in determining animal behavior?

2. Behavioral research has been conducted on many different species of animals and it is useful to know the names of the different species. Match the following scientific names with the proper type of animal

a. <u>Agapornis</u>   i.   lizard

b. <u>Aplysia</u>   ii. lovebird

c. <u>Anolis</u>   iii. bee

d. <u>Bombyx</u>   iv. moth

e. <u>Apis</u>   v.   slug

WHO'S WHO

Complete the following chart.

Scientist	
Lorenz, von Frisch, and Tinbergen	a. _____
b. _____	Studied the genetic basis of "maze-bright" and "maze-dull" rats
Dilger	c. _____
Pavlov	d. _____
e. _____	Developed special apparatus to study operant conditioning in rats
f. _____	Studied the neurological basis of learning in the sea slug
Harlow	g. _____
h. _____	Studied the roles of instinct and learning in the development of song in male white-crowned sparrows
i. _____	Studied hormonal control of reproductive behavior in ring doves
von Frisch, Wenner, and Gould	j. _____
Morgan	k. _____

LEARNING CHECKLIST

1. What are the two different ways (perspectives) of explaining behavior?
2. The nature versus nurture controversy sums up what two viewpoints?
3. Name the two broad catagories of learned behavior and two examples of each type.
4. Name the two types of imprinting that occur.
5. List two patterns (lengths of time) for behavioral rhythms. How long does each last?
6. List the five sensory channels through which animal communication can occur.
7. What two traits apply to courtship behaviors?
8. List the three stages of language learning.
9. Name three types of movement behavior in animals.

MINI EXAM

A. Circle the letter of the one best answer for each question.

1. Which of the following is an example of a question about the ultimate causation of a behavior?
   a. What muscles are involved when a hummingbird hovers over a flower?
   b. When is the critical period for imprinting to occur in young goats?
   c. Which hormones must be present at what levels to make a female lizard rective to male courtship?
   d. All of the above
   e. None of the above

2. Which of the following involves trial-and-error learning?
   a. habituation
   b. classical conditioning
   c. sensitization
   d. operant conditioning
   e. all of the above

3. Human behavior, like other mammalian behavior, is determined
   a. strictly by the genes
   b. strictly by learning
   c. by a mixture of genes and learning
   d. none of the above

4. Learning to not respond to a stimulus is called
   a. imprinting
   b. sensitization
   c. kinesis
   d. habituation
   e. altruism

5. A goose retrieving a stray egg and rolling it back into its nest is an example of
   a. instinctive behavior
   b. operant conditioning
   c. associative behavior
   d. learning preparedness
   e. kinesis

6. A "Skinner box" is used for experiments in
   a. classical conditioning
   b. operant conditioning
   c. migration
   d. taxis
   e. aggression

7. Which of the following statements is true?
   a. animals can learn to associate any stimuli using classical conditioning
   b. animals are innately programmed to learn some things more easily than others
   c. instinctive learning programs explain why most people speak only one language
   d. all of the above
   e. none of the above

8. The time at which a fruit fly pupa hatches is determined by
   a. when the egg was laid
   b. how much light is present
   c. a single gene
   d. where the egg is laid
   e. no one knows

9. A rat that is "maze-dull"
   a. will pass on that trait to its offspring
   b. can never learn anything else either
   c. both of the above
   d. none of the above

10. Chemical signals between individuals of the same species are called
    a. endogenous
    b. hormones
    c. kinesis
    d. electricity
    e. pheromones

11. The component of an animal's nervous system that provides the instruction for carrying out a particular fixed action pattern is called a(n)
    a. sign stimulus
    b. social releaser
    c. innate releasing mechanism
    d. suprachiasmatic nuclei
    e. exogenous biological clock

12. All the thousands of human languages are based on the same set of how many consonant sounds?
    a. 26
    b. 40
    c. 4
    d. 260
    e. 12

13. How many of the basic consonant sounds can a normal human baby distinguish?
    a. all of them
    b. half of them
    c. only 1
    d. it depends on the child's ethnic background

14. A sensitive phase and critical period are associated with what type of behavior?
    a. cognitive
    b. kinesis
    c. taxis
    d. imprinting
    e. conspecific

15. Which of the following animals is a brood parasite?
    a. lovebirds
    b. Anolis lizards
    c. fruit flies
    d. geese
    e. cuckoo

16. Circadian rhythms are based on approximately a
    a. 2-hour period
    b. 24-hour period
    c. 7-day period
    d. 30-day period
    e. 365-day period

17. The biological clock of mammals is located in the
    a. suprachiasmatic nuclei of the hypothalamus
    b. suprachiasmatic nuclei of the pineal gland
    c. melatonin of the pineal gland
    d. androgens of the gonads
    e. all of the above

18. Nonoriented changes in activity level or movement are called
    a. exogenous
    b. taxis
    c. kinesis
    d. migration
    e. conspecific

19. How is the distance to a food source communicated by a dancing honeybee?
    a. by the direction it waggles its abdomen
    b. by how far it moves during the straight run portion of the dance
    c. by which direction it turns after making the straight run
    d. by the tempo or degree of vigor of the dance
    e. none of the above - bees can't communicate the distance

B. Provide the appropriate term to complete each statement.

1. _____ describes behavior that suggests the animal has reasoning ability or is capable of thinking.

2. Something that is external is said to be _____.

3. _____ is the study of the neural basis of behavior.

4. Habituation is a type of _____ learning.

5. _____ refers to a young animal following and forming a bond with the first moving object it sees and hears.

6. The study of the natural history of behavior is called _____.

7. Pavlov's experiments with dog salivation are an example of _____ conditioning.

8. The way an organism responds to stimuli is the basic definition of _____.

9. The modification of behavior as a result of experience is defined as _____.

10. The sex pheromone of silkworm moths is called _____.

C. Briefly answer each of the following questions.

1. Why might it be advantageous for a song sparrow not to be able to learn the song of another type of bird, even if it hears it during the critical song imprinting period?

2. What type of newborn animals do you think would be most likely to exhibit imprinting on their parents (i.e., what general characteristics would they have)? Do you think imprinting is always adaptive or advantageous? Why or why not?

CHAPTER 56 ANSWERS

TOPIC EXERCISES

1. An instinct is a behavior that is genetically programmed and appears in a relatively complete and functional form the first time the animal performs it. Learned behaviors are modified in response to what the animal experiences; they are not genetically "hardwired," but develop with use. Animal behavior is not all instinct or all learning. Instinct and learning represent two ends of a spectrum. Each may play a more important role in certain animals or in certain types of behavior. Basically, all behavior has some genetic component to it (the genes, after all, determine the structure of the brain and other neural circuits), but most behaviors can be modified to at least some extent over time.

2.   a. ii   b. v   c. i   d. iv   e. iii

WHO'S WHO

   a. Won Nobel prize for their pioneering work in ethology
   b. Tryon
   c. Studied the genetic basis of carrying nesting material in lovebirds
   d. First to describe classical conditioning in dogs
   e. Skinner
   f. Kandel
   g. Studied social interactions in rhesus monkeys using infants and model surrogate mothers
   h. Marler
   i. Lehrman
   j. Studied the dance language of honeybees
   k. A behaviorist skeptical of conscious thought in animals

LEARNING CHECKLIST

   1. Explanations involving proximate causation (how the behavior works) and explanations involving ultimate causation (why the behavior evolved) (p. 1177)

   2. The importance of genetics versus learning in determining how an animal behaves (p. 1177)

   3. Nonassociative learning, e.g., habituation and sensitization; associative learning, e.g., classical conditioning and operant conditioning (pp. 1181-1183)

   4. Filial imprinting and sexual imprinting (pp. 1185-1186)

   5. Circadian rhythms, circannual rhythms; about 24 hours, one year, respectively (pp. 1188-1189)

   6. Visual, acoustical, chemical, tactile, electric (p. 1189)

7. They are species-specific and may have more than one component (p. 1191)

8. Rapid learning of vocabulary, simple sentence construction, learning rules of grammar (p. 1194)

9. Taxis, kinesis, migration (p. 1194)

MINI EXAM

A.
1. e	2. d	3. c	4. d	5. a	6. b
7. b	8. c	9. a	10. e	11. c	12. b
13. a	14. d	15. e	16. b	17. a	18. c
19. d					

B.
1. Cognitive behavior	2. exogenous	3. Neuroethology
4. nonassociative	5. Imprinting (Filial imprinting)	6. ethology
7. classical	8. behavior	9. learning
10. bombykol		

C. 1. Knowing only its own song-sparrow song will help ensure that it mates only with its own species. No time or energy will be wasted on singing the wrong songs and attracting and courting the wrong type of bird. (pp. 1186-1187)

2. Young must be precocial and capable of moving about soon after birth. Animals probably live in groups in which it is important that the young be able to pick out their own parent from among many others. The system is extremely advantageous as long as each youngster imprints on the correct individual. If it imprints improperly it will not receive proper parental protection or feeding, and it may not have the correct species image or identity of itself. This could cause serious problems later when it becomes old enough to reproduce and searches for a mate. (pp. 1185-1187)

57: BEHAVIORAL ECOLOGY

IN THE GRAND SCHEME

The behavior of an animal is crucial in determining the success of that animal. Proper and efficient behavior is necessary if the animal is to obtain food, a nesting site, and a mate or to successfully raise its young or deal with other ecological problems it faces. Behavior is as much of an evolutionary adaptation as the morphology and physiology of the individual are. Behavior can be selected for or against and behavior can evolve. Selection favors those behaviors that increase the individual's fitness, those behaviors that have the greatest benefits and least costs. Individuals with such adaptive behavior will be selected for and will pass on the genetic basis for such behavior to future generations. Different environmental or ecological conditions select for different types of behavior. For example, vertebrates exhibit a vast array and varying degrees of social behavior in dealing with offspring, potential mates, competitors, predators, and prey. The type of behavior exhibited is directly related to the ecological conditions under which the animals live. It seems fitting to end our examination of vertebrate biology with behavior, since behavior cuts across all other aspects of the animal's biology. Behavior is influenced by genetics, development, motivational states determined by hormones and other physiological conditions, the functioning of the nervous system, the anatomical structuring of the body, and, as you will see, the ecology of the animal.

FOR REVIEW

Natural selection: Natural selection is the mechanism behind the process of evolution. Individuals in a population are selected for or against depending on what traits they have. Individuals with traits that make them well adapted to their local environment are selected for. They tend to live longer and produce more successful offspring than those individuals that are less well adapted. As the successful individuals pass on their genes to their offspring, and the unsuccessful ones don't or do so at a slower rate, the proportion of successful or well adapted genes and individuals in the population increases over time and generations. Evolution occurs because of natural selection.

Adaptation: An adaptation is a trait that makes an organism more likely to survive and reproduce in its particular environment. The process of adaptation involves the progressive genetic change in a population over time. As stated above, some members of a population have characteristics that make them able to survive longer and produce more offspring than other members of the population (i.e., they are better adapted). Their offspring inherit these traits, so they too survive longer and reproduce more. Gradually, over many generations, the favored traits become more and more common in the population. This is how new species are formed. Behavioral adaptations can be as important as morphological and physiological adaptations in determining the success of various animals.

Animal behavior: Behavior is defined simply as the way an organism responds to a stimulus in its environment. The behavior of animals, their quick and often complex reactions and interactions, is one of the key features that distinguishes animals from members of the other kingdoms of life and is one of the reasons we find them so fascinating. To understand the behavior of an animal, we must also understand its genetics, its hormonal condition, its physiology, its morphology, and its ecology.

CHAPTER OUTLINE

KEY TERMS

p. 1199: survival value, adaptive, behavioral ecology, adaptive significance, fitness, foraging behaviors
p. 1200: specialists, generalists, net energy, optimal foraging theory
p. 1201: social behavior, home range, territoriality, defense
p. 1202: reproductive strategies, mate choice, parental investment
p. 1203: reproductive competition, sexual selection, sexual dimorphism
p. 1204: intrasexual selection, intersexual selection, secondary sexual characteristics, runaway selection
p. 1205: spermatophore, mating systems, monogamy, polygyny, polyandry
p. 1206: altricial, precocial, society, sociobiology, female defense polygyny
p. 1207: altruism, group selection
p. 1208: reciprocal altruism, unrelated, kin, kin selection, inclusive fitness, coefficient of relatedness
p. 1209: eusocial
p. 1210: haplodiploidy, castes, superorganism, queen substance, drones
p. 1211: larvicide
p. 1212: division of labor, helpers at the nest
p. 1213: alarm call, nepotism, socioecology
p. 1214: ungulates
p. 1215: biological evolution, cultural evolution, tradition

TOPIC EXERCISES

1. Many different species of animals have been studied in the course of investigating behavioral ecology. Match each type of animal with the type of behavior it exhibits which has been studied by researchers.

    a. cliff swallows

    b. ant lions

    c. oystercatchers

    d. vampire bats

    e. gulls

    f. meerkats

    g. naked mole rats

    h. Florida scrubjays

    i. Mormon crickets

    j. sunbirds

    k. deer

    l. Belding's ground squirrels

    m. honeybees

    i.   actively defend a patch of flowers

    ii.   eusocial mammal

    iii. alarm calls represent nepotism

    iv.   males have large parental investment in form of spermatophore

    v.   trap prey in pits

    vi.   remove broken eggshells from nest area

    vii. have helpers at the nest

    viii. maintain a sentinel while rest of group feeds

    ix.   specialists that feed on mussels

    x.   discriminate against cheaters who do not participate in reciprocal altruism

    xi.   sexual selection has resulted in large body and antler size in males

    xii. eusocial insect with haplodiploidy sex determination

    xiii. group living confers benefit of increased feeding rate but cost of increased parasitism of young

2. Complete the following chart on mating systems and reproductive behavior by providing the appropriate term or definition.

Term	Definition
a. _____	The mating of one male with several females
b. _____	The mating of one male with one female
c. _____	The mating of one female with several males

WHO'S WHO

Complete the following chart.

Scientist	Contribution to Biology
a. _____	Studied the adaptiveness of eggshell removal of gulls
b. _____	Developed concepts of parental investment and reciprocal altruism
Fisher	c. _____
d. _____	Initiated the study of sociobiology
e. _____	Proposed theory of group selection
Hamilton	f. _____
Pellissier Scott	g. _____
h. _____	Studied the function of alarm calls in Belding's ground squirrels
i. _____	Wrote Sociobiology: The New Synthesis

LEARNING CHECKLIST

1. Name the three approaches Tinbergen used in studying animal behavior.
2. Name the two broad groups into which animals can be divided on the basis of the range of food they eat.
3. List two reasons why animals may not always maximize energy intake when they feed.
4. What is the difference between a home range and a territory?
5. Name three aspects of reproductive strategies.
6. List two reasons why mate choice may be beneficial.
7. What are the two components of sexual selection?
8. Name the three types of mating systems.
9. Name three factors that affect the type of mating system exhibited by a population.
10. Name two advantages and two disadvantages of group living.
11. What are the two components of fitness?
12. List four characteristics of eusocial insects.
13. Name two bird species that have helpers at the nest.
14. What two processes have led to adaptive change during the course of human evolution and the emergence of civilization?

MINI EXAM

A. Circle the letter of the one best answer for each question.

1. Saving the life of your _____ would do the least for increasing your inclusive fitness.
   a. father
   b. sister
   c. son
   d. cousin
   e. brother-in-law

2. The total number of your alleles that are passed on to the next generation by you and your relatives you have helped is defined as your
   a. individual fitness
   b. inclusive fitness
   c. kin selection
   d. reciprocal altruism
   e. sociality

3. The study of how natural selection shapes behavior is called
   a. sociobiology
   b. socioecology
   c. behavioral ecology
   d. nepotism
   e. cultural evolution

4. Behaviors that influence what an animal eats and how it obtains its food are called
   a. foraging behaviors
   b. social behaviors
   c. territorial behaviors
   d. eusocial behaviors
   e. altricial behaviors

5. Pandas and koalas feed exclusively on bamboo and eucalyptus, respectively. This means they are
   a. eusocial
   b. altruistic
   c. monogamous
   d. specialists
   e. generalists

6. Optimal foraging theory predicts that animals feed in such a way to
   a. maximize energy intake
   b. minimize energy intake
   c. maximize risk of predation
   d. spend as much time as possible feeding
   e. none of the above

7. Which of the following statements about territoriality is true?
   a. territoriality is always beneficial to the animal
   b. territories frequently overlap in time or space
   c. territories rarely contain any resources
   d. all of the above are true
   e. none of the above are true

8. Which sex should show mate choice?
   a. always males
   b. always females
   c. the sex having higher parental investment
   d. the sex having lower parental investment
   e. neither sex

9. Which of the following is <u>not</u> associated with monogamy?
   a. altricial young
   b. sexual dimorphism
   c. one male mating with one female
   d. all of the above are associated with monogamy
   e. none of the above are associated with monogamy

10. Exaggerated secondary sexual characteristics can occur as a result of
    a. intrasexual selection
    b. intersexual selection
    c. runaway selection
    d. all of the above
    e. none of the above

11. Which mating system is most common in birds?
    a. monogamy
    b. polygyny
    c. polyandry
    d. they are all equally common

12. Which mating system is most common in mammals?
    a. monogamy
    b. polygyny
    c. polyandry
    d. they are all equally common

13. Arguments that a particular behavior has been selected for because it benefits the group or species are examples of arguments for
    a. kin selection
    b. sexual selection
    c. group selection
    d. natural selection
    e. artificial selection

14. What type of selection is most likely responsible for the large antlers seen on male elk?
    a. kin selection
    b. group selection
    c. territorial selection
    d. intrasexual selection
    e. intersexual selection

15. In haplodiploidy sex determination
    a. males are sterile
    b. males are haploid
    c. males are diploid
    d. males are either haploid or diploid
    e. males do not exist

16. In leafcutter ants, division of labor among workers is related to the
    a. worker's sex
    b. number of workers
    c. worker's size
    d. all of the above
    e. none of the above

17. In most vertebrates, group members share a maximum of _____ of their genes while naked mole rats share up to _____.
    a. 10, 20
    b. 20, 10
    c. 30, 60
    d. 80, 50
    e. 50, 80

18. Which of the following Belding's ground squirrels is most likely to give an alarm call?
    a. a female with no kin nearby
    b. a female with kin nearby
    c. a male with no kin nearby
    d. a male with kin nearby
    e. they are all equally likely to call

19. In African ungulates, degree of sociality is correlated with
    a. number of helpers at the nest
    b. horn size
    c. degree of polyandry
    d. size of home range
    e. diet

20. Tradition is associated with
    a. cultural evolution
    b. biological evolution
    c. both of the above
    d. none of the above

B. Provide the appropriate term to complete each statement.

    1. Male bees are called _____.

    2. For a male Mormon cricket, his largest parental investment is in the form of a(n) _____.

    3. _____ young are able to take care of themselves soon after birth and require little parental care.

    4. In _____, a single female mates with more than one male during the breeding season.

    5. The area utilized by an animal in the course of its daily activities is called the animal's _____.

    6. Animals such as goats that eat a wide variety of food items are called _____.

    7. The study of the influence of the environment on social organization is called _____.

    8. The _____ of a behavior refers to how the behavior increases the animal's survival and reproduction.

    9. The sex determination system of bees, wasps and ants is called _____.

    10. The proportion of genes shared through common descent between individuals is known as _____.

C. Briefly answer each of the following questions.

    1. Is altruism really "self-sacrificing" behavior?

    2. In a polyandrous mating system, which sex would you expect to exhibit mate choice and exaggerated secondary sexual characteristics?

CHAPTER 57 ANSWERS

TOPIC EXERCISES

1.   a. xiii   b. v   c. ix   d. x
        e. vi   f. viii   g. ii   h. vii
        i. iv   j. i   k. xi   l. iii
        m. xii

2.   a. polygyny   b. monogamy   c. polyandry

WHO'S WHO

    a. Tinbergen
    b. Trivers
    c. population geneticist who proposed idea of runaway sexual selection
    d. Wilson, Alexander, and Trivers
    e. Wynn-Edwards
    f. developed theories of kin selection and inclusive fitness
    g. has studied the reproductive ecology and behavior of burying beetles
    h. Sherman
    i. Wilson

LEARNING CHECKLIST

1. Studying its development, its physiological basis, and its evolution (p. 1199)

2. Specialists and generalists (p. 1200)

3. May need to eat lower energy foods that contain specific, needed nutrients; may lower energy intake to lower risk of predation to itself (p. 1200)

4. A home range is the area utilized by an animal during the course of its daily activities; home ranges may overlap in time or space; a territory is an area that is actively defended by an individual to exclude others from gaining access to some limited resource the territory contains (p. 1201)

5. Mate choice, number of mates during a breeding system, and parental care (p. 1202)

6. Acquire good genes or resources for offspring; leave more offspring (pp. 1202, 1205)

7. Intrasexual selection, intersexual selection (pp. 1203-1204)

8. Monogamy, polygyny, polyandry (p. 1205)

9. Ecology, needs of offspring, timing of female reproduction (p. 1206)

10. Advantages: decreased risk of predation, increased feeding rate; disadvantages: increased parasitism and diseases (p. 1207)

11. Personal and kin-selected (p. 1208)

12. Live in large colonies, have only one reproductive female, have division of labor or castes, have haplodiploidy sex determination (pp. 1209-1212)

13. African pied kingfisher and Florida scrubjay (pp. 1212-1213)

14. Biological evolution, cultural evolution (p. 1215)

MINI EXAM

A.

1. e	2. b	3. c	4. a	5. d	6. a
7. e	8. c	9. b	10. d	11. a	12. b
13. c	14. d	15. b	16. c	17. e	18. b
19. e	20. a				

B.

1. drones	2. spermatophore	3. Precocial
4. polyandry	5. home range	6. generalists
7. socioecology	8. adaptive significance	9. haplodiploidy
10. r, the coefficient of relatedness		

C. 1. Not really; in the long run the individual may very well benefit from their altruistic act if the altruism is reciprocated (increases personal fitness) or if the altruism leads to successful reproduction of kin (increases inclusive fitness). (pp. 1207-1208)

2. In a polyandrous mating system, one female mates with many males. You would expect the males to exhibit more mate choice and be selective about which female they allow to mate with them. At the same time, you would expect females to have more exaggerated secondary sexual characteristics to make them better able to obtain more mates - e.g., bigger body size or better weapons to outcompete other females or brighter coloration to be more attractive to males (pp. 1202-1206)